Revise

A2

Chemistry

Rob Ritchie

Contents

Chapter 4 Chemistry of organic functional groups

Chapter 5 Polymers, analysis and synthesis

Chapter 6 Synoptic assessment

Specification lists

AQA A2 Chemistry

MODULE	SPECIFICATION TOPIC	CHAPTER REFERENCE	STUDIED IN CLASS	REVISED	PRACTICE QUESTIONS
A2 Unit 1 (M4) Kinetics, equilibria and organic chemistry	Kinetics	1.1, 1.2			
	Equilibria	1.3			
	Acids and bases	1.5, 1.6, 1.7			
	Nomenclature and isomerism on organic chemistry	4.1			
	Compounds containing the carbonyl group	4.2, 4.3, 4.4, 4.5			
	Aromatic chemistry	4.6, 4.7			
	Amines	4.9			
	Amino acids	5.1, 5.3			
	Polymers	5.2			
	Organic synthesis and analysis	5.6			
	Structural determination	5.3, AS 4.7, 5.4, 5.5			
A2 Unit 2 (M5) Energetics, redox and inorganic chemistry	Thermodynamics	2.1, 2.2, AS 3.3			
	Periodicity	3.1			
	Redox equilibria	2.3, 2.4			
	Transition metals	3.3, 3.4, 3.6, 3.7			
	Reactions of inorganic compounds in aqueous solution	3.5, 3.8			

Examination analysis

A2 Chemistry comprises two unit tests. All questions are compulsory.
Synoptic assessment will form part of both units. Practical and investigative skills will also be assessed.

Units 1, 2 and 3 comprise AS Chemistry			50%
Unit 4	Structured questions: short and extended answers	1 hr 45 min test	20%
Unit 5	Structured questions: short and extended answers	1 hr 45 min test	20%
Unit 6	Internal assessment of practical and investigative skills		10%

The Sheffield College
Hillsborough LRC
Telephone: 0114 260 2254

OCR A2 Chemistry

MODULE	SPECIFICATION TOPIC	CHAPTER REFERENCE	STUDIED IN CLASS	REVISED	PRACTICE QUESTIONS
A2 Unit F324 (M4) Rings, polymers and analysis	Arenes	4.6, 4.7, 4.8			
	Carbonyl compounds	4.2			
	Carboxylic acids and esters	4.3, 4.4, 4.5			
	Amines	4.9			
	Amino acids and proteins	5.1, 5.2			
	Polyesters and polyamides	5.2			
	Synthesis	5.6			
	Chromatography	5.3			
	Spectroscopy	AS 4.7, 5.4, 5.5			
A2 Unit F325 (M5) Equilibria, energy and elements	How fast?	1.1, 1.2			
	How far?	1.3			
	Acids, bases and buffers	1.5, 1.6, 1.7			
	Lattice enthalpy	2.1			
	Enthalpy and entropy	2.2			
	Electrode potentials and fuel cells	2.3, 2.4			
	Transition elements	3.3, 3.4, 3.5, 3.6, 3.7, 3.8			

Examination analysis

A2 Chemistry comprises two unit tests. All questions are compulsory.
Synoptic assessment will form part of both units. Practical and investigative skills will also be assessed.

Units 1, 2 and 3 comprise AS Chemistry			50%
Unit F324 Structured questions: short and extended answers	1 hr test		15%
Unit F325 Structured questions: short and extended answers	1 hr 45 min test		25%
Unit F326 Internal assessment of practical and investigative skills			10%

Salters A2 Chemistry

MODULE	SPECIFICATION TOPIC	CHAPTER REFERENCE	STUDIED IN CLASS	REVISED	PRACTICE QUESTIONS
A2 Unit F334 (M4) *Chemistry of materials*	Equilibria	1.5			
	Organic functional groups	4.1, 4.2, 4.3, 4.4, 4.5, 4.6, 4.7, 4.8, 4.9, 5.1, 5.2			
	Organic reactions	4.2, 4.3, 4.8, 5.1, 5.2			
	Reaction mechanisms	4.2, 4.9			
	Applications of organic chemistry	5.6			
	Modern analytical techniques	5.3, AS 4.7, 5.4			
	Application	4.3, 4.4, 4.5, 4.9, 5.2			
	Kinetics	1.1, 1.2, 5.2			
	Isomerism	5.3			
	Formulae, equations and amount of substance	1.7, 3.6			
	Redox	2.3, 2.4, 3.4, 3.6			
	Inorganic chemistry and the Periodic Table	3.3, 3.5, 3.7, 3.8			
A2 Unit F335 (M5) *Chemistry by design*	Bonding and structure	4.9, 5.2, 5.6			
	Rates of reaction	1.1, 1.2			
	Equilibria	1.3, 1.5, 1.6, 1.7, 2.2, 2.4			
	Redox	2.4			
	Inorganic chemistry and the Periodic Table	2.4			
	Organic functional groups	4.4, 4.6			
	Organic reactions	4.7, 4.9, 5.6			
	Modern analytical techniques	3.4, 4.9, 5.3, 5.4, 5.5			
	Energetics	2.1, 2.2			
	Reaction mechanisms	4.2			
	Isomerism	4.1			
	Applications	5.6			

Examination analysis

A2 Chemistry comprises two unit tests. All questions are compulsory.
Synoptic assessment will form part of both units. Practical and investigative skills will also be assessed.

Units 1, 2 and 3 comprise AS Chemistry			50%
Unit F334 Structured questions: short and extended answers	1 hr 30 min test		15%
Unit F335 Structured questions: short and extended answers	2 hr test		20%
Unit F336 Individual investigation			15%

Edexcel A2 Chemistry

MODULE	SPECIFICATION TOPIC	CHAPTER REFERENCE	STUDIED IN CLASS	REVISED	PRACTICE QUESTIONS
A2 Unit 1 (M4) Rates, equilibria and further organic chemistry	How fast? – rates	1.1, 1.2			
	How far? – entropy	2.1, 2.2			
	Equilibria	1.3, 1.4, 2.2			
	Application of rates and equilibria	2.2			
	Acid/base equilibria	1.5, 1.6, 1.7			
	Further organic chemistry – chirality	4.1			
	Further organic chemistry – carbonyl compounds	4.2			
	Further organic chemistry – carboxylic acids	4.3, 4.4, 4.5			
	Further organic chemistry – carboxylic acid derivatives	4.4, 4.5, 5.2			
	Spectroscopy and chromatography	5.3, AS 4.7, 5.4, 5.5			
A2 Unit 2 (M5) Transition metals and organic nitrogen chemistry	Application of redox equilibria	2.3, 2.4, 3.6			
	Transition metals and their chemistry	3.3, 3.4, 3.5, 3.6 3.7, 3.8			
	Organic chemistry – arenes	4.6, 4.7, 4.8			
	Organic chemistry – nitrogen compounds	4.9, 5.1, 5.2			
	Organic chemistry – organic synthesis	5.5, 5.6			

Examination analysis

A2 Chemistry comprises two unit tests. All questions are compulsory.
Synoptic assessment will form part of both units. Practical and investigative skills will also be assessed.

Units 1, 2 and 3 comprise AS Chemistry			*50%*
Unit 4	*Objective questions; Structured questions: short and extended answers Data questions with use of a data booklet*	*1 hr 40 min test*	*20%*
Unit 5	*Objective questions; Structured questions: short and extended answers Contemporary context questions*	*1 hr 40 min test*	*20%*
Unit 6	*Internal assessment of practical and investigative skills*		*10%*

WJEC A2 Chemistry

MODULE	SPECIFICATION TOPIC	CHAPTER REFERENCE	STUDIED IN CLASS	REVISED	PRACTICE QUESTIONS
A2 Unit 1 (M4) Spectroscopy and organic chemistry	Spectroscopy	4.9, AS 4.7, 5.4, 5.5			
	Isomerism and aromaticity	4.6, 4.7			
	Alcohols and phenols	4.8			
	Aldehydes and ketones	4.2			
	Carboxylic acids and derivatives	4.3, 4.4, 4.5, 4.7, 4.8			
	Organic compounds containing nitrogen	4.9, 5.1, 5.2			
	Organic synthesis and analysis	5.2, 5.3, AS 4.7, 5.4, 5.5, 5.6			
	The process of how science works	5.5			
A2 Unit 2 (M5) Physical and inorganic chemistry	Redox and standard electrode potential	2.3, 2.4			
	Redox reactions	3.6			
	Applications of redox	2.3			
	Chemistry of the p-block – general	3.2			
	Chemistry of the p-block – Group 3 (13)	3.2			
	Chemistry of the p-block – Group 4 (14)	3.2			
	Chemistry of the p-block – Group 7 (17)	3.2			
	d-block transition elements	3.3, 3.4, 3.5, 3.7, 3.8			
	Chemical kinetics	1.1, 1.2			
	Enthalpy changes for solids and solutions	2.1			
	Entropy and feasibility of reactions	2.2			
	General equilibria	1.3, 1.4, 2.2			
	Acid-base equilibria	1.5, 1.6, 1.7			

Examination analysis

A2 Chemistry comprises two unit tests. All questions are compulsory.
Synoptic assessment will form part of both units. Practical and investigative skills will also be assessed.

Units 1, 2 and 3 comprise AS Chemistry			*50%*
Unit 4 Structured questions: short and extended answers		*1 hr 45 min test*	*20%*
Unit 5 Structured questions: short and extended answers		*1 hr 45 min test*	*20%*
Unit 6 Internal assessment of practical and investigative skills			*10%*

CCEA A2 Chemistry

MODULE	SPECIFICATION TOPIC	CHAPTER REFERENCE	STUDIED IN CLASS	REVISED	PRACTICE QUESTIONS
A2 Unit 1 (M4) *Periodic trends and further organic, physical and inorganic chemistry*	Lattice enthalpy	2.1			
	Enthalpy, entropy and free energy	2.1, 2.2			
	Kinetics	1.1, 1.2			
	Equilibrium	1.3, 1.4			
	Acid-base equilibria	1.5, 1.6, 1.7			
	Isomerism	4.1			
	Aldehydes and ketones	4.2			
	Carboxylic acids	4.3, 4.5			
	Esters, fats and oils	4.4			
	Periodic trends	3.1			
	Environmental chemistry	2.3, 2.4, 5.2			
A2 Unit 2 (M5) *Analytical, transition metals, electrochemistry and further organic chemistry*	Mass spectrometry	AS 4.7, 5.3, 5.4			
	Nuclear magnetic resonance spectroscopy	5.5			
	Volumetric analysis	3.5, 3.6			
	Colorimetry	3.4			
	Chromatography	5.3			
	Transition metals – general properties	3.3			
	Transition metals – complexes	3.4, 3.5, 3.6			
	Transition metals – catalytic behaviour	3.7			
	Transition metals – oxidation states	2.3, 2.4, 3.6, 3.8			
	Applications of transition metal complexes	3.4			
	Electrode potentials	2.3, 2.4			
	Arenes	4.6, 4.7			
	Amines	4.9			
	Amides	4.5, 4.9			
	Amino acids	5.1, 5.2			
	Polymer chemistry	5.2			

Examination analysis

A2 Chemistry comprises two unit tests. All questions are compulsory.
Synoptic assessment will form part of both units. Practical and investigative skills will also be assessed.

Units 1, 2 and 3 comprise AS Chemistry			*50%*
Unit 4	*Objective questions; structured questions: short and extended answers*	*2 hr test*	*20%*
Unit 5	*Objective questions; structured questions: short and extended answers*	*2 hr test*	*20%*
Unit 6	*Internal assessment of practical and investigative skills*		*10%*

AS/A2 Level Chemistry courses

AS and A2

All Chemistry A Level courses being studied from September 2008 are in two parts, with three separate modules in each part. Students first study the AS (Advanced Subsidiary) course. Some will then go on to study the second part of the A Level course, called A2. Advanced Subsidiary is assessed at the standard expected halfway through an A Level course: i.e., between GCSE and Advanced GCE. This means that new AS and A2 courses are designed so that difficulty steadily increases:

- AS Chemistry builds from GCSE science
- A2 Chemistry builds from AS Chemistry.

How will you be tested?

Assessment units

For AS Chemistry, you will be tested by three assessment units. For the full A Level in Chemistry, you will take a further three units. AS Chemistry forms 50% of the assessment weighting for the full A Level.

3 units for AS   3 units for A2

One of the units in AS and in A2 is practically based. You will take two theory units in each of AS and A2. Each theory unit can normally be taken in either January or June. Alternatively, you can study the whole course before taking any of the unit tests.

If you are disappointed with a module result, you can resit each module. The higher mark counts.

Coursework

Coursework forms part of your A Level Chemistry course in the form of the assessment of practical skills. More details are provided on page 11.

Key skills

It is important that you develop your key skills of Communication, Application of Number and Information Technology throughout your AS and A2 courses. These are important skills that you need whatever you do beyond AS and A Levels. To gain the key skills qualification, you will need to demonstrate your ability to put your ideas across to other people, collect data and use up-to-date technology in your work. You will have many opportunities during A2 Chemistry to develop your key skills.

What skills will I need?

For A2 Chemistry, you will be tested by *assessment objectives*: these are the skills and abilities that you should have acquired by studying the course. The assessment objectives for A2 Chemistry are shown below.

Knowledge and understanding of science and How Science Works

- recognising, recalling and showing understanding of scientific knowledge
- selection, organisation and communication of relevant information in a variety of forms.

Application of knowledge and understanding of science and How Science Works

- analysis and evaluation of scientific knowledge and processes
- applying scientific knowledge and processes to unfamiliar situations including those related to issues
- assessing the validity, reliability and credibility of scientific information.

How Science Works

- demonstrating and describing ethical, safe and skilful practical techniques and processes
- selecting appropriate qualitative and quantitative methods
- making, recording and communicating reliable and valid observations and measurements with appropriate precision and accuracy
- analysis, interpretation, explanation and evaluation of the methodology, results and impact of their own and others' experimental and investigative activities in a variety of ways.

Experimental and investigative skills

Chemistry is a practical subject and part of the assessment of A2 Chemistry will test your practical skills. This will be carried out during your lessons. You will be assessed on three main skills:

- implementing
- analysing evidence and drawing conclusions
- evaluating evidence and procedures.

The skills may be assessed in separate practical exercises. They may also be assessed all together in the context of a single 'whole investigation'.

You will receive guidance about how your practical skills will be assessed from your teacher. This Study Guide concentrates on preparing you for the written examinations testing the subject content of A2 Chemistry.

Synoptic assessment

- bringing together knowledge, principles and concepts from different areas of Chemistry and applying them in a particular context
- using chemical skills in contexts which bring together different areas of the subject.

More details of synoptic assessment in Chemistry are discussed in Chapter 6 of this Study Guide (pages 178–181).

Different types of questions in A2 examinations

In A2 Chemistry examinations, different types of question are used to assess your abilities and skills. Unit tests mainly use structured questions requiring both short answers and more extended answers.

Short-answer questions

A short-answer question may test recall or it may test understanding. Short answer questions normally have space for the answers printed on the question paper.

Here are some examples (the answers are shown in *italics*):

What is meant by isotopes?

Atoms of the same element with different masses.

Calculate the amount (in mol) of H_2O in 4.5 g of H_2O.

1 mol H_2O has a mass of 18 g. $\therefore$ 4.5 g of H_2O contains 4.5/18 = 0.25 mol H_2O.

Structured questions

Structured questions are in several parts. The parts usually have a common context and they often become progressively more difficult and more demanding as you work your way through the question. A structured question may start with simple recall, then test understanding of a familiar or an unfamiliar situation.

Here is an example of a structured question that becomes progressively more demanding.

(a) Write down the atomic structure of the two isotopes of potassium: ^{39}K and ^{41}K.

    (i) ^{39}K ...19... protons; ...20... neutrons; ...19... electrons. ✓

    (ii) ^{41}K ...19... protons; ...22... neutrons; ...19... electrons. ✓   [2]

(b) A sample of potassium has the following percentage composition by mass: ^{39}K: 92%; ^{41}K: 8% Calculate the relative atomic mass of the potassium sample.

    92 x 39/100 + 8 x 41/100 = 39.16 ✓   [1]

(c) What is the electronic configuration of a potassium atom?

    $1s^2 2s^2 2p^6 3s^2 3p^6 4s^1$ ✓   [1]

(d) The second ionisation energy of potassium is much larger than its first ionisation energy.

    (i) Explain what is meant by the *first ionisation energy* of potassium.

    The energy required to remove an electron ✓ *from each atom in 1 mole* ✓ *of gaseous atoms* ✓

    (ii) Why is there a large difference between the values for the first and the second ionisation energies of potassium?

    The 2nd electron removed is from a different shell ✓ *which is closer to the nucleus and experiences more attraction from the nucleus.* ✓ *This outermost electron experiences less shielding from the nucleus because there are fewer inner electron shells than for the 1st ionisation energy.* ✓   [6]

Extended answers

In A2 Level Chemistry, questions requiring more extended answers may form part of structured questions or may form separate questions. They may appear anywhere on the paper and will typically have between 5 and 15 marks allocated to the answers as well as several lines of answer space. These questions are also often used to assess your abilities to communicate ideas and put together a logical argument.

The correct answers to extended questions are often less well-defined than to those requiring short answers. Examiners may have a list of points for which credit is awarded up to the maximum for the question.

An example of a question requiring an extended answer is shown below.

The table below gives data on the oxides of Period 3 in the Periodic Table.

oxide	Na_2O	MgO	Al_2O_3	SiO_2	P_4O_{10}	SO_3
melting point /K	1548	3100	2290	1880	853	306
conductivity of molten compound	good	good	medium	poor	poor	poor

Describe and explain the trends in formula, structure and bonding shown by these data.   [11 marks]

Points that the examiners might look for include:

In the formula, the number of oxygen atoms bonded increases across the period. The oxidation number increases steadily by one for each successive element. ✔ This is because the number of electrons in the outer shell increases by one for each element in the period. ✔

The trend in structure is from giant to simple molecular ✔ with a changeover between silicon and phosphorus. ✔ Structure is related to the magnitude of the melting points. ✔

The high melting points (Na_2O ✔ SiO_2) result from strong forces between ions (for Na_2O – Al_2O_3) ✔ and between atoms (for SiO_2). ✔ The low melting points (P_4O_{10} ✔ SO_3) result from weak intermolecular forces or van der Waals' forces. ✔

The trend in bonding is from ionic to covalent ✔ with a changeover between Al_2O_3 and SiO_2. ✔ This is related to the conductivity of the molten oxide. ✔

Good conductivity results from mobile ions (Na_2O ✔ $Al2O_3$. ✔)

Poor conductivity shows that no mobile ions are present (SiO_2 ✔ SO_3. ✔)

13 marking points → 11 marks

In this type of response, there may be an additional mark for a clear, well-organised answer, using specialist terms. In addition, marks may be allocated for legible text with accurate spelling, punctuation and grammar.

Other types of questions

Free-response and open-ended questions allow you to choose the context and to develop your own ideas.

Multiple-choice or objective questions require you to select the correct response to the question from a number of given alternatives.

Stretch and Challenge

Stretch and Challenge is a concept that is applied to the structured questions in Units 4 and 5 of the exam papers for A2. In principle, it means that the sub-questions become progressively harder so as to challenge more able students and help differentiate between A and A* students.

Stretch and Challenge questions are designed to test a variety of different skills and your understanding of the material. They are likely to test your ability to make appropriate connections between different areas and apply your knowledge in unfamiliar contexts (as opposed to basic recall).

Exam technique

Links from AS

A2 Chemistry builds from the knowledge and understanding acquired after studying AS Chemistry. This Study Guide has been written so that you will be able to tackle A2 Chemistry from an AS Chemistry background.

You should not need to search for important chemistry from AS Chemistry because cross-references have been included as 'Key points from AS' to the AS Chemistry Study Guide: Revise AS.

What are examiners looking for?

Examiners use instructions to help you to decide the length and depth of your answer.

If a question does not seem to make sense, you may have misread it – read it again!

State, define or list

This requires a short, concise answer, often recall of material that can be learnt by rote.

Explain, describe or discuss

Some reasoning or some reference to theory is required, depending on the context.

Outline

This implies a short response, almost a list of sentences or bullet points.

Predict or deduce

You are not expected to answer by recall but by making a connection between pieces of information.

Suggest

You are expected to apply your general knowledge to a 'novel' situation, one which you have not directly studied during the A2 Chemistry course.

Calculate

This is used when a numerical answer is required. You should always use units in quantities and significant figures should be used with care.

Look to see how many significant figures have been used for quantities in the question and give your answer to this degree of accuracy.

If the question uses 3 sig figs, then give your answer to 3 sig figs also.

Some dos and don'ts

Dos

Do answer the question.

- No credit can be given for good Chemistry that is irrelevant to the question.

Do use the mark allocation to guide how much you write.

- Two marks are awarded for two valid points - writing more will rarely gain more credit and could mean wasted time or even contradicting earlier valid points.

Do use diagrams, equations and tables in your responses.

- Even in 'essay-type' questions, these offer an excellent way of communicating chemistry.

Do write legibly.

- An examiner cannot give marks if the answer cannot be read.

Do write using correct spelling and grammar. Structure longer essays carefully.

- Marks are now awarded for the quality of your language in exams.

Don'ts

Don't fill up any blank space on a paper.

- In structured questions, the number of dotted lines should guide the length of your answer.
- If you write too much, you waste time and may not finish the exam paper. You also risk contradicting yourself.

Don't write out the question again.

- This wastes time. The marks are for the answer!

Don't contradict yourself.

- The examiner cannot be expected to choose which answer is intended.

Don't spend too much time on a part that you find difficult.

- You may not have enough time to complete the exam. You can always return to a difficult calculation if you have time at the end of the exam.

What grade do you want?

Everyone would like to improve their grades but you will only manage this with a lot of hard work and determination. You should have a fair idea of your natural ability and likely grade in Chemistry and the hints below offer advice on improving that grade.

For a Grade A

You will need to be a very good all-rounder.

* You must go into every exam knowing the work extremely well.
* You must be able to apply your knowledge to new, unfamiliar situations.
* You need to have practised many, many exam questions so that you are ready for the type of question that will appear.

The exams test all areas of the specification and any weaknesses in your Chemistry will be found out. There must be no holes in your knowledge and understanding. For a Grade A, you must be competent in all areas.

For a Grade C

You must have a reasonable grasp of Chemistry but you may have weaknesses in several areas and you will be unsure of some of the reasons for the Chemistry.

* Many Grade C candidates are just as good at answering questions as Grade A students but holes and weaknesses often show up in just some topics.
* To improve, you will need to master your weaknesses and you must prepare thoroughly for the exam. You must become a better all-rounder.

For a Grade E

You cannot afford to miss the easy marks. Even if you find Chemistry difficult to understand and would be happy with a Grade E, there are plenty of questions in which you can gain marks.

* You must memorise all definitions.
* You must practise exam questions to give yourself confidence that you do know some Chemistry. In exams, answer the parts of questions that you know first. You must not waste time on the difficult parts. You can always go back to these later.
* The areas of Chemistry that you find most difficult are going to be hard to score on in exams. Even in the difficult questions, there are still marks to be gained. Show your working in calculations because credit is given for a sound method. You can always gain some marks if you get part of the way towards the solution.

What marks do you need?

The table below shows how your average mark is transferred into a grade.

average	80%	70%	60%	50%	40%
grade	A	B	C	D	E

The new A* grade

The Awarding bodies have now introduced an A* grade for A level. This follows on from the introduction of this grade at GCSE and is intended to be awarded to a relatively small number of the highest scoring candidates.

To achieve an A* grade you must score over 80% on all six units combined (grade A) but also 90% on the three A2 units combined. This is quite a difficult target!

Four steps to successful revision

Step 1: Understand

- Study the topic to be learned slowly. Make sure you understand the logic or important concepts.
- Mark up the text if necessary – underline, highlight and make notes.
- Re-read each paragraph slowly.

GO TO STEP 2

Step 2: Summarise

- Now make your own revision note summary:
  What is the main idea, theme or concept to be learned?
  What are the main points? How does the logic develop?
  Ask questions: Why? How? What next?
- Use bullet points, mind maps, patterned notes.
- Link ideas with mnemonics, mind maps, crazy stories.
- Note the title and date of the revision notes
  (e.g. Chemistry: Reaction rates, 3rd March).
- Organise your notes carefully and keep them in a file.

This is now in **short-term memory**. You will forget 80% of it if you do not go to Step 3.
GO TO STEP 3, but first take a 10 minute break.

Step 3: Memorise

- Take 25 minute learning 'bites' with 5 minute breaks.
- After each 5 minute break test yourself:
  Cover the original revision note summary
  Write down the main points
  Speak out loud (record on tape)
  Tell someone else
  Repeat many times.

The material is well on its way to **long-term memory**.
You will forget 40% if you do not do step 4. **GO TO STEP 4**

Step 4: Track/Review

- Create a Revision Diary (one A4 page per day).
- Make a revision plan for the topic, e.g. 1 day later, 1 week later, 1 month later.
- Record your revision in your Revision Diary, e.g.
  Chemistry: Reaction rates, 3rd March 25 minutes
  Chemistry: Reaction rates, 5th March 15 minutes
  Chemistry: Reaction rates, 3rd April 15 minutes
  ... and then at monthly intervals.

Chapter 1

Rates and equilibria

The following topics are covered in this chapter:

- *Orders and the rate equation*
- *Determination of reaction mechanisms*
- *The equilibrium constant, K_c*
- *The equilibrium constant, K_p*

- *Acids and bases*
- *The pH scale*
- *pH changes*

1.1 Orders and the rate equation

After studying this section you should be able to:

- *explain the terms 'rate of reaction', 'order', 'rate constant', 'rate equation'*
- *construct a rate equation and calculate its rate constant*
- *use the initial rates method to deduce orders*
- *use graphs to deduce reaction rates and orders*
- *understand that a temperature change increases the rate constant*
- *determine activation energy graphically*

LEARNING SUMMARY

Key points from AS

- **Reaction rates**
  Revise AS pages 104–107

During the study of reaction rates in AS Chemistry, reaction rates were described in terms of activation energy and the Boltzmann distribution. For A2 Chemistry, you will build upon this knowledge and understanding by measuring and calculating reaction rates using rate equations.

Orders and the rate equation

AQA	M4	SALTERS	M4
EDEXCEL	M4	WJEC	M5
OCR	M5	CCEA	M4

The rate of a reaction is determined from experimental results. Reaction rate **cannot** be determined from a chemical equation.

Suitable experimental techniques used to obtain rate data for a given reaction include:
- titration
- pH measurement
- colorimetry
- measuring volumes of gases evolved
- measuring mass changes.

The rate of a reaction is usually determined by the **change in concentration** of a reaction species **with time**.

- Units of rate = $\underbrace{mol\ dm^{-3}}_{concentration}\ \underbrace{s^{-1}}_{per\ time}$

Key points from AS

- **What is a reaction rate?**
  Revise AS pages 104–105

Orders of reaction

For a reaction: **A + B + C** ⟶ products,

- the **order** of the reaction shows how the reaction rate is affected by the concentrations of **A**, **B** and **C**.

If the order is 0 (zero order) with respect to reactant **A**,
- the rate is unaffected by changes in concentration of **A**:
  rate $\propto$ **[A]**^{0}

[A] means the concentration of reactant **A** in mol dm^{-3}.

If the order is 1 (first order) with respect to a reactant **B**,
- the rate is doubled by doubling of the concentration of reactant **B**:
  rate $\propto$ **[B]**^{1}

If the order is 2 (second order) with respect to a reactant **C**,

- the rate is quadrupled by doubling the concentration of reactant **C**:
  rate $\propto$ **[C]**^{2}

Combining the information above,

rate $\propto$ **[A]**^{0}**[B]**^{1}**[C]**^{2}

$\therefore$ *rate* = k**[B]**^{1}**[C]**^{2}

- This expression is called the **rate equation** for the reaction.
- k is the rate constant of the reaction.

> A number raised to the power of zero = 1 and zero order species can be omitted from the rate equation.

The rate equation

The rate equation of a reaction shows how the rate is affected by the concentration of reactants. A rate equation can only be determined from experiments.

> The rate of a reaction is determined from experimental results.
>
> It **cannot** be determined from the chemical equation.

In general, for a reaction: **A** + **B** $\longrightarrow$ **C**,
the reaction rate is given by: *rate* = k**[A]**^{m}**[B]**^{n}

- m and n are the **orders of reaction** with respect to **A** and **B** respectively.
- The **overall order** of reaction is $m + n$.
- The reaction rate is measured as the change in concentration of a reaction species with time.
- The units of rate are mol dm^{-3} s^{-1}.

The rate constant k indicates the rate of the reaction:

- a large value of $k \longrightarrow$ fast rate of reaction
- a small value of $k \longrightarrow$ slow rate of reaction.

Measuring rates using graphs

Concentration/time graphs

It is often possible to measure the concentration of a reactant or product continuously at various times during the course of an experiment.

- From the results, a concentration/time graph can be plotted.
- The shape of this graph can indicate the order of the reaction by measuring the **half-life** of a reactant.

> **Key points from AS**
>
> - **What is a reaction rate?**
>   *Revise AS pages 104–105*

> **KEY POINT**
>
> The half-life of a reactant is the time taken for its concentration to reduce by half.
>
> **A first-order reaction has a constant half-life.**

Example of a first order graph

The reaction between bromine and methanoic acid is shown below.

$Br_2(aq) + HCOOH(aq) \longrightarrow 2Br^-(aq) + 2H^+(aq) + CO_2(g)$

- During the course of the reaction, the orange bromine colour disappears as Br_2 reacts to form colourless Br^- ions. The order with respect to bromine can be determined by monitoring the rate of disappearance of bromine using a colorimeter.
- The concentration of the other reactant, methanoic acid, is kept virtually constant by using an excess of methanoic acid.

The concentration/time graph from this reaction is shown on the next page. Notice that the **half-life is constant** at 200 s, showing that this reaction is first order with respect to $Br_2(aq)$.

The half-life curve of a first-order reaction is concentration independent.

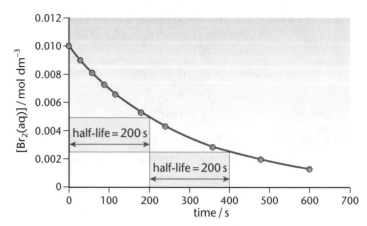

The shapes of concentration/time graphs for zero, first and second order reactions are shown below.

zero order

The concentration falls at a steady rate with time
• half-life **decreases** with time.

first order

The concentration halves in equal time intervals
• **constant** half-life.

second order

The half-life gets progressively longer as the reaction proceeds
• half-life **increases** with time.

• The first-order relationship can be confirmed by plotting a graph of log[**X**] against time, which gives a straight line.

Measuring rates from tangents

The gradient of the concentration/time graph is a measure of the rate of a reaction.

For the reaction: **A** ⟶ **B**, the graph below shows how the concentration of **A** changes during the course of the reaction.

> At any instant of time during the reaction, the rate can be measured by drawing a tangent to the curve.

KEY POINT

At the start of the reaction ($t = 0$):
• the tangent is steepest
• the concentration of **A** is greatest
• the reaction rate is fastest.

As the reaction proceeds:
• the tangent becomes less steep
• the concentration of **A** decreases
• the reaction rate slows down.

The initial rate of the reaction is the tangent of a concentration/time graph at time=0.

When the reaction is complete:
• the concentration of **A** is very small
• the gradient becomes zero
• the reaction stops.

At an instant of time, t, during the reaction:

• the rate of **change** in concentration of **A** $= -\dfrac{d[A]}{dt}$ *(the tangent)*

A reaction rate is expressed as a positive value.

For the reactant **A**, the **negative** sign shows a **decreasing** concentration with time.

For the product **B**, the **positive** sign shows **increasing** concentration.

The negative sign shows that the concentration of **A** decreases during the reaction. The rate could also be followed by measuring the rate of **increase** in concentration of the product **B**.

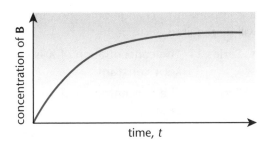

B is formed and its concentration increases during the reaction.

$$\text{rate of \textbf{change} in concentration of \textbf{B}} = + \frac{d[\mathbf{B}]}{dt}$$

Plotting a rate/concentration graph

- A concentration/time graph is first plotted.
- **Tangents** are drawn at several time values on the concentration/time graph, giving values of reaction rates.
- A second graph is plotted of **rate** against **concentration**.
- The shape of this graph confirms the order of the reaction.

zero order

Rate $\propto [\mathbf{A}]^0$ ∴ rate = constant
- Rate unaffected by changes in concentration.

first order

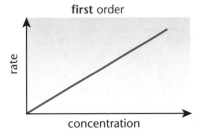

Rate $\propto [\mathbf{A}]^1$
- Rate doubles as concentration doubles.

second order

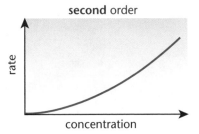

Rate $\propto [\mathbf{A}]^2$
- Rate quadruples as concentration doubles.

- The second-order relationship can be confirmed by plotting a graph of rate against $[\mathbf{A}]^2$, which gives a straight line.

Progress check

1 The data below shows how the concentration of reactant **A** changes during the course of a reaction.

Time / 10^4 s	0	0.36	0.72	1.08	1.44
[A] /mol dm^{-3}	0.240	0.156	0.104	0.068	0.045

(a) On graph paper, plot a concentration/time graph and, by drawing tangents, estimate:
   (i) the initial rate
   (ii) the rate 1×10^4 s after the reaction has started.
(b) Determine the half-life of the reaction and show that the reaction is first order with respect to **A**.

1 (a) (i) 2.5×10^{-5} mol dm^{-3} s^{-1} to 3.5×10^{-5} mol dm^{-3} s^{-1} (ii) 8.7×10^{-6} mol dm^{-3} s^{-1}
(b) Half-life = 5.8×10^3 s. Successive half-lives are constant.

Determination of a rate of equation using the initial rates method

AQA	M4	SALTERS	M4
EDEXCEL	M4	WJEC	M5
OCR	M5	CCEA	M4

For a reaction, **X + Y ⟶ Z**, a series of experiments can be carried out using different **initial** concentrations of the reactants **X** and **Y**.

It is important to change only one variable at a time, so two series of experiments will be required.

- **Series 1** – The concentration of **X** is changed whilst the concentration of **Y** is kept constant.

- **Series 2** – The concentration of **Y** is changed whilst the concentration of **X** is kept constant.

> Clock reactions give an approximation to the initial rates method.

Clock reactions are often used to obtain a value for the initial rate of a reaction. A clock reaction measures the **time**, *t*, from the start of the reaction until a visual change – usually a change in colour, appearance of a precipitate or a solid disappearing.

- The clock reaction is repeated several times whilst varying the concentration of one of the reactants. The concentration of any other reactant is kept constant.

- The **initial rate** of the reaction is approximately proportional to $1/t$.

- A **graph** is then plotted of **initial rate** ($1/t$) against **concentration**.

- The **order** with respect to the reactant of which the concentration has been varied, is found from the **shape of the graph**. (See page 21).

A series of clock reactions is repeated for different concentrations of each reactant. A rate/concentration graph is plotted for each reactant.

The results below show the initial rates using different concentrations of **X** and **Y**.

Experiment	[X(aq)] /mol dm^{-3}	[Y(aq)] /mol dm^{-3}	initial rate /mol dm^{-3} s^{-1}
1	1.0×10^{-2}	1.0×10^{-2}	0.5×10^{-3}
2	2.0×10^{-2}	1.0×10^{-2}	2.0×10^{-3}
3	2.0×10^{-2}	2.0×10^{-2}	4.0×10^{-3}

Determine the orders

Comparing experiments 1 and 2: [**Y**(aq)] has been kept constant

- [**X**(aq)] has been doubled,   rate × 4
  ∴ order with respect to **X**(aq) = 2.

Comparing experiments 2 and 3: [**X**(aq)] has been kept constant

- [**Y**(aq)] has been doubled,   rate doubles
  ∴ order with respect to **Y**(aq) = 1.

Use the orders to write the rate equation

- *rate* = k[**X**(aq)]^2[**Y**(aq)]

- The overall order of this reaction is (2 + 1) = third order

Calculate the rate constant for the reaction

> In this example, the results from Experiment 2 have been used.
>
> You will get the same value of k from the results of **any** of the experimental runs.
>
> Try calculating k from Experiment 1 and from Experiment 3. All give the same value.

Rearrange the rate equation:

$$\text{The rate constant, } k = \frac{rate}{[\textbf{X}(aq)]^2[\textbf{Y}(aq)]}$$

Calculate k using values from one of the experiments.

$$k = \frac{(2.0 \times 10^{-3})}{(2.0 \times 10^{-2})^2 \, (1.0 \times 10^{-2})} = 500 \text{ dm}^6 \text{ mol}^{-2} \text{ s}^{-1}$$

Units of rate constants

The units of a rate constant depend upon the rate equation for the reaction. We can determine units of k by substituting units for rate and concentration into the rearranged rate equation. The table below shows how units can be determined.

Notice how units need to be worked out afresh for reactions with different overall orders.

You do not need to memorise these but it is important that you are able to work these out when needed.

See also page 28 in which the units of the equilibrium constant K_c are discussed.

For a zero-order reaction:	For a first-order reaction:
$rate = k[A]^0 = k$ units of k = **mol dm^{-3} s^{-1}**	$rate = k[A] \qquad \therefore k = \dfrac{rate}{[A]}$ Units of $k = \dfrac{(\text{mol dm}^{-3}\text{ s}^{-1})}{(\text{mol dm}^{-3})} = \mathbf{s^{-1}}$
For a second-order reaction:	For a third-order reaction:
$rate = k[A]^2 \quad \therefore k = \dfrac{rate}{[A]^2}$ Units of $k = \dfrac{(\text{mol dm}^{-3}\text{ s}^{-1})}{(\text{mol dm}^{-3})^2}$ $= \mathbf{dm^3\ mol^{-1}\ s^{-1}}$	$rate = k[A]^2[B] \quad \therefore k = \dfrac{rate}{[A]^2[B]}$ Units of $k = \dfrac{(\text{mol dm}^{-3}\text{ s}^{-1})}{(\text{mol dm}^{-3})^2\,(\text{mol dm}^{-3})}$ $= \mathbf{dm^6\ mol^{-2}\ s^{-1}}$

Progress check

1 A chemical reaction is first order with respect to compound **P** and second order with respect to compound **Q**.
   (a) Write the rate equation for this reaction.
   (b) What is the overall order of this reaction?
   (c) By what factor will the rate increase if:
      (i) the concentration of **P only** is doubled
      (ii) the concentration of **Q only** is doubled
      (iii) the concentrations of **P** and **Q** are **both** doubled?
   (d) What are the units of the rate constant of this reaction?

2 The reaction of ethanoic anhydride, $(CH_3CO)_2O$, with ethanol, C_2H_5OH, can be represented by the equation:

$$(CH_3CO)_2O + C_2H_5OH \longrightarrow CH_3CO_2C_2H_5 + CH_3CO_2H$$

The table below shows the initial concentrations of the two reactants and the initial rates of reaction.

Experiment	$[(CH_3CO)_2O]$ /mol dm^{-3}	$[C_2H_5OH]$ /mol dm^{-3}	initial rate /mol dm^{-3} s^{-1}
1	0.400	0.200	6.60×10^{-4}
2	0.400	0.400	1.32×10^{-3}
3	0.800	0.400	2.64×10^{-3}

   (a) State and explain the order of reaction with respect to:
      (i) ethanoic anhydride   (ii) ethanol.
   (b) (i) Write an expression for the overall rate equation.
      (ii) What is the overall order of reaction?
   (c) Calculate the value, with units, for the rate constant, k.

(c) 8.25×10^{-3} dm^3 mol^{-1} s^{-1}.
(b) (i) $rate = k\ [(CH_3CO)_2O]\ [C_2H_5OH]$ (ii) second order.
   (ii) first order; concentration doubles; rate doubles.
2 (a) (i) first order; concentration doubles; rate doubles
(d) dm^6 mol^{-2} s^{-1}
(c) (i) rate doubles (ii) rate quadruples (iii) rate × 8
(b) third order
1 (a) $rate = k[P][Q]^2$;

23

How does the rate constant, k, vary with temperature?

AQA	M4	SALTERS	M4
EDEXCEL	M4	WJEC	M5
OCR	M5	CCEA	M4

Key points from AS

- **Boltzmann distribution**
- **Activation energy**
  Revise AS page 105

During AS Chemistry, you studied how the rate of reaction increases with temperature in terms of collisions, the activation energy of the reaction and the Boltzmann distribution of molecular energies.

The effect of temperature on rate constants

An increase in temperature speeds up the rate of most reactions by **increasing** the rate constant, k.

The table below shows the increase in the rate constant for the decomposition of hydrogen iodide with increasing temperature.

$$2HI(g) \longrightarrow H_2(g) + I_2(g)$$

For many reactions, the rate doubles for each 10°C increase in temperature.

temperature/K	556	629	700	781
rate constant, k /$dm^3\ mol^{-1}\ s^{-1}$	7.04×10^{-7}	6.04×10^{-5}	2.32×10^{-3}	7.90×10^{-2}

A reaction with a large activation energy has a small rate constant. Such a reaction may need a considerable temperature rise to increase the value of the rate constant sufficiently for a reaction to take place at all.

Why are catalysts so effective?

A catalyst is so effective because:

- it **reduces** the **activation energy**
- which **increases** the **rate constant, k**
- which **increases** the **rate of reaction.**

Measuring the activation energy experimentally

| EDEXCEL | M5 |

You do **not** need to remember the Arrhenius equation – it will always be provided in examination papers.

This is the key to use on your calculator.

'ln' is 'natural logarithm'.

If you take A level Maths, you will study ln and e^x.

The rate constant, k, and the temperature (in K), T, are linked mathematically by the Arrhenius equation:

$$\ln k = \text{constant} - \frac{E_a}{R}(1/T)$$

- E_a = activation energy
- R = gas constant, 8.31 J K^{-1} mol^{-1}

If the temperature, T, is changed, rate is proportional to k.

- A **graph** of **ln (rate)** against **1/T** will give a **straight line**.
- The **gradient** of the graph is $-\dfrac{E_a}{R}$ from which E_a can be determined.

Experimental procedure

Rate is also proportional to 1/time and a value for E_a can be determined by:

- measuring the initial rate for a reaction (as 1/time)
- repeating the experiment at different temperatures, T
- plotting a graph of ln (1/time) against 1/T
- measuring the gradient, which is $-\dfrac{E_a}{R}$.

1.2 Determination of reaction mechanisms

After studying this section you should be able to:

- understand what is meant by a rate-determining step
- predict a rate equation from a rate-determining step
- predict a rate-determining step from a rate equation
- use a rate equation and the overall equation for a reaction to predict a possible reaction mechanism

Predicting reaction mechanisms

EDEXCEL	M4	SALTERS	M4
OCR	M5	WJEC	M5
AQA	M4	CCEA	M4

Key points from AS

- **The hydrolysis of halogenoalkanes**
  Revise AS pages 139–140

You are **not** expected to remember these examples.

You **are** expected to interpret data to identify a rate-determining step and to suggest possible steps in the mechanism for the reaction.

This reaction proceeds via an S$_N$1 mechanism:

1 particle, (CH$_3$)$_3$CBr, is involved in the rate-determining step of a **N**ucleophilic **S**ubstitution mechanism.

The rate-determining step

Chemical reactions often take place in a series of steps. The detail of these steps is the **reaction mechanism**.

> **KEY POINT**
>
> The rate equation can provide clues about a likely reaction mechanism by identifying the **slowest** stage of a reaction sequence, called the **rate-determining step**.

The hydrolysis of tertiary halogenoalkanes

2-bromo-2-methylpropane, (CH$_3$)$_3$C–Br, is hydrolysed by aqueous alkali, OH⁻.

Experiments show that the rate equation for this reaction is:

$$rate = k[(CH_3)_3C–Br]$$

- The rate equation shows that a slow reaction step must involve **only** (CH$_3$)$_3$C–Br.
- OH⁻ has **no effect** on the reaction rate.

This supports the slow step below:

$$\underbrace{(CH_3)_3C–Br}_{\textbf{One} \text{ particle in rate-determining step}} \longrightarrow (CH_3)_3C^+ + Br^- \qquad \textbf{SLOW}$$

The overall equation for the hydrolyis of 1-bromobutane by aqueous alkali is shown below:

$$(CH_3)_3C–Br + OH^- \longrightarrow (CH_3)_3C–OH + Br^-$$

- This **does not** match the equation for the slow step above.
- The rate-determining step must be followed by further **fast** steps.
- OH⁻ must be involved as it is in the **overall equation**.

A possible second step is shown below:

$$(CH_3)_3C^+ + OH^- \longrightarrow (CH_3)_3C–OH \qquad \textbf{FAST}$$

The **overall equation** is the sum of the equations from each step in the mechanism.

Notice that (CH$_3$)$_3$C$^+$ does not feature in the overall equation. It is generated in one step and used up in another step.

In the hydrolysis of a tertiary halogenoalkane:

1st step	(CH$_3$)$_3$C–Br	$\longrightarrow$	(CH$_3$)$_3$C$^+$ + Br$^-$	**SLOW**
2nd step	(CH$_3$)$_3$C$^+$ + OH$^-$	$\longrightarrow$	(CH$_3$)$_3$C–OH	**FAST**
Overall equation	(CH$_3$)$_3$C–Br + OH$^-$	$\longrightarrow$	(CH$_3$)$_3$C–OH + Br$^-$	

The hydrolysis of primary halogenoalkanes

1-Bromobutane, $CH_3CH_2CH_2CH_2Br$, is hydrolysed by aqueous alkali, OH^-.

Experiments show that the rate equation for this reaction is:

$$rate = k[CH_3CH_2CH_2CH_2Br]\,[OH^-]$$

The **slow** reaction step must involve **both** $CH_3CH_2CH_2CH_2Br$ **and** OH^-.

This supports the slow step below:

$$\underbrace{CH_3CH_2CH_2CH_2Br + OH^-}_{\substack{\textbf{Two} \text{ particles in} \\ \text{rate-determining step}}} \longrightarrow CH_3CH_2CH_2CH_2OH + Br^- \quad \textbf{SLOW}$$

> This reaction proceeds via an S~N~2 mechanism:
>
> **2 particles,** $CH_3CH_2CH_2CH_2Br$ **and** OH^-, are involved in the rate-determining step of a ~nucleophilic~ Substitution mechanism.

The overall equation for the hydrolyis of 1-bromobutane by aqueous alkali is:

$$CH_3CH_2CH_2CH_2Br + OH^- \longrightarrow CH_3CH_2CH_2CH_2OH + Br^-$$

- This **does** match the equation for the slow step above.
- The reaction **mechanism** must have just a **single step**.

The reaction of iodine and propanone in acid

The reaction of iodine, I_2, and propanone, CH_3COCH_3, is catalysed by acid, H^+.

The overall equation for the acid-catalysed reaction of iodine and propanone is:

$$I_2 + CH_3COCH_3 \longrightarrow CH_3COCH_2I + H^+ + I^- \quad \textit{overall equation}$$

Experiments show that the rate equation for this reaction is:

$$rate = k[CH_3COCH_3]\,[H^+]$$

The **slow** rate-determining step must involve **both** CH_3COCH_3 and H^+.

A possible equation for the rate-determining step is shown below:

> The slow step is the **rate-determining step**.

$$\underbrace{CH_3COCH_3 + H^+}_{\substack{\textbf{Two} \text{ particles in} \\ \text{rate-determining step}}} \longrightarrow CH_3C(OH^+)CH_3 \quad \textbf{SLOW}$$

> If the species in the rate equation do not match those in the overall equation, the reaction mechanism must have more than one step.

- This does **not** match the overall equation.

Possible further steps are shown below:

$$CH_3C(OH^+)CH_3 \longrightarrow CH_2{=}C(OH)CH_3 + H^+ \quad \textbf{FAST}$$

$$CH_3C(OH){=}CH_2 + I_2 \longrightarrow CH_3(OH)CICH_2I \quad \textbf{FAST}$$

$$CH_3(OH)CICH_2I \longrightarrow CH_3COCH_2I + H^+ + I^- \quad \textbf{FAST}$$

> H^+ is a catalyst.
>
> It is needed for the first step but is regenerated in a further step.
>
> Overall, it is not consumed.

> **KEY POINT**
>
> The overall equation is the sum of the equations from each step in the mechanism.

- The rate of the reaction is controlled mainly by the slowest step of the mechanism – the **rate-determining step**.
- The rate equation only includes reacting species involved in the slow rate-determining step.
- The orders in the rate equation match the number of species involved in the rate-determining step.

Progress check

1 CH_3CH_2Br and cyanide ions, CN^- react as follows:
$$CH_3CH_2Br + CN^- \longrightarrow CH_3CH_2CN + Br^-$$
Show two different possible reaction routes for this reaction and write down the expected rate equation for each route.

Using chirality as evidence for mechanisms

EDEXCEL   M4

By studying the optical activity of reactants and products, we can gain further insights into the actual mode of attack during this mechanism.

If we hydrolyse an **optically active** tertiary halogenoalkane that has a **chiral** carbon atom,

- the organic product has **no** optical activity
- a 50:50 racemic mixture of optical isomers is obtained.

This supported the S_N1 mechanism as shown below.

S_N1: no optical activity in organic product

The alternative mechanism would involve an S_N2 mechanism.

S_N2: alternative for tertiary halogenoalkanes

For primary halogenoalkanes, the situation is the other way around:

The S_N2 mechanism does takes place.

The S_N1 mechanism does not take place.

attack on opposite side of molecule to leaving group

organic product would be optically active but with the chiralty swapped over

- In the actual hydrolysis, a single optical isomer product is **not** produced.
- Therefore, mechanism **cannot** take place.

Addition of carbonyl compounds

A similar situation arises during nucleophilic addition to carbonyl compounds.

For details of nucleophilic addition to carbonyl compounds, see page 115.

- The organic product has **no** optical activity.
- A 50:50 racemic mixture of optical isomers is obtained.

1.3 The equilibrium constant, K_c

After studying this section you should be able to:

- deduce, for homogeneous reactions, K_c in terms of concentrations
- calculate values of K_c given appropriate data
- understand that K_c is changed only by changes in temperature
- understand how the magnitude of K_c relates to the equilibrium position
- calculate, from data, the concentrations present at equilibrium

LEARNING SUMMARY

Key points from AS

- **Chemical equilibrium**
  Revise AS pages 110–115

During the study of equilibrium in AS Chemistry, the concept of dynamic equilibrium is introduced and le Chatelier's principle is used to predict how a change in conditions may alter the equilibrium position. For A2 Chemistry, you will build upon this knowledge and understanding to find out the exact position of equilibrium using the Equilibrium Law.

The equilibrium law

AQA	M4	SALTERS	M5
EDEXCEL	M4	WJEC	M5
OCR	M5	CCEA	M4

The equilibrium law states that, for an equation:

$$a\,\mathbf{A} + b\,\mathbf{B} \rightleftharpoons c\,\mathbf{C} + d\,\mathbf{D},$$

$$K_c = \frac{[\mathbf{C}]^c\,[\mathbf{D}]^d}{[\mathbf{A}]^a\,[\mathbf{B}]^b}$$

- $[\mathbf{A}]^a$, etc., are the **equilibrium** concentrations of the reactants and products of the reaction.

> The overall equation for the reaction is used to write K_c.

- Each product and reactant has its equilibrium concentration raised to the **power** of its **balancing number** in the equation.

- The equilibrium concentrations of the **products** are multiplied together on **top** of the fraction.

- The equilibrium concentrations of the **reactants** are multiplied together on the **bottom** of the fraction.

Working out K_c

For the equilibrium: $H_2(g) + I_2(g) \rightleftharpoons 2HI(g)$

> For A2 Chemistry, most courses only use **homogeneous equilibria** – all species are in the same phase:
>
> all gaseous (g)
>
> or
>
> all aqueous (aq)
>
> or
>
> all liquid (l).

applying the equilibrium law above: $K_c = \dfrac{[HI(g)]^2}{[H_2(g)]\,[I_2(g)]}$

Equilibrium concentrations of $H_2(g)$, $I_2(g)$ and $HI(g)$ are shown below:

$[H_2(g)]$ /mol dm^{-3}	$[I_2(g)]$ /mol dm^{-3}	$[HI(g)]$ /mol dm^{-3}
0.0114	0.00120	0.0252

$$K_c = \frac{[HI(g)]^2}{[H_2(g)]\,[I_2(g)]} = \frac{0.0252^2}{0.0114 \times 0.00120} = 46.4$$

Units of K_c

> The units must be worked out afresh for each equilibrium.
>
> See also page 23 in which the units of the rate constant are discussed.

- In the K_c expression, each concentration value is replaced by its units:

$$K_c = \frac{[HI(g)]^2}{[H_2(g)]\,[I_2(g)]} = \frac{(\text{mol dm}^{-3})^2}{(\text{mol dm}^{-3})\,(\text{mol dm}^{-3})}$$

- For this equilibrium, the units cancel.

∴ in the equilibrium: $H_2(g) + I_2(g) \rightleftharpoons 2HI(g)$, K_c has no units.

Properties of K_c

The magnitude of K_c indicates the extent of a chemical equilibrium.

- $K_c = 1$ indicates an equilibrium halfway between reactants and products.
- $K_c = 100$ indicates an equilibrium well in favour of the products.
- $K_c = 1 \times 10^{-2}$ indicates an equilibrium well in favour of the reactants.

K_c indicates how FAR a reaction proceeds; **not** how FAST.
K_c is unaffected by changes in concentration or pressure.
K_c can **only** be changed by altering the temperature.

How does K_c vary with temperature?

It cannot be stressed too strongly that K_c can be changed only by altering the temperature. How K_c changes depends upon whether the reaction gives out or takes in heat energy.

If the forward reaction is **exothermic**, K_c **decreases** with increasing temperature. Raising the temperature reduces the equilibrium yield of products.

$$H_2(g) + I_2(g) \rightleftharpoons 2HI(g): \qquad \Delta H^{\ominus}_{298} = -9.6 \text{ kJ mol}^{-1}$$

temperature /K	500	700	1100
K_c	160	54	25

If the forward reaction is **endothermic**, K_c **increases** with increasing temperature. Raising the temperature increases the equilibrium yield of products.

$$N_2(g) + O_2(g) \rightleftharpoons 2NO(g): \qquad \Delta H^{\ominus}_{298} = +180 \text{ kJ mol}^{-1}$$

temperature /K	500	700	1100
K_c	5×10^{-13}	4×10^{-8}	1×10^{-5}

Although changes in K_c affect the equilibrium yield, the actual conditions used may be different.

If the forward reaction is **exothermic**, K_c increases and the equilibrium yield increases as temperature decreases.

However, a decrease in temperature may slow down the reaction so much that the reaction is stopped.

In practice, a compromise will be needed where equilibrium and rate are considered together – a reasonable equilibrium yield must be obtained in a reasonable length of time.

Progress check

1   For each of the following equilibria, write down the expression for K_c. State the units for K_c for each reaction.
(a) $N_2O_4(g) \rightleftharpoons 2NO_2(g)$ (c) $H_2(g) + Br_2(g) \rightleftharpoons 2HBr(g)$
(b) $CO(g) + 2H_2(g) \rightleftharpoons CH_3OH(g)$ (d) $2SO_2(g) + O_2(g) \rightleftharpoons 2SO_3(g)$

2   Explain whether the two reactions, **A** and **B**, are exothermic or endothermic.

| temperature /K | numerical value of K_c | |
	reaction **A**	reaction **B**
200	5.51×10^{-8}	4.39×10^{4}
400	1.46	4.03
600	3.62×10^{2}	3.00×10^{-2}

2   Reaction **A**: endothermic; K_c increases with increasing temperature.
Reaction **B**: exothermic; K_c decreases with increasing temperature.

1   (a) $K_c = \dfrac{[NO_2(g)]^2}{[N_2O_4(g)]}$ (b) $K_c = \dfrac{[CH_3OH(g)]}{[CO(g)][H_2(g)]^2}$ (c) $K_c = \dfrac{[HBr(g)]^2}{[H_2(g)][Br_2(g)]}$ (d) $K_c = \dfrac{[SO_3(g)]^2}{[SO_2(g)]^2[O_2(g)]}$

Determination of K_c from experiment

AQA M4	SALTERS M5
EDEXCEL M4	WJEC M5
OCR M5	CCEA M4

The equilibrium constant K_c can be calculated using experimental results. The example below shows how to:

- determine the equilibrium concentrations of the components in an equilibrium mixture
- calculate K_c.

The ethyl ethanoate esterification equilibrium

> The most important stage in this calculation is to find the **change** in the number of moles of each species in the equilibrium.

0.200 mol CH_3COOH and 0.100 mol C_2H_5OH were mixed together with a trace of acid catalyst in a total volume of 250 cm^3. The mixture was allowed to reach equilibrium:

$$CH_3COOH + C_2H_5OH \rightleftharpoons CH_3COOC_2H_5 + H_2O.$$

Analysis of the mixture showed that 0.115 mol of CH_3COOH were present at equilibrium.

First summarise the results

It is useful to summarise the results as an 'I.C.E.' table: 'Initial/Change/Equilibrium'.

	CH_3COOH	C_2H_5OH	$CH_3COOC_2H_5$	H_2O
Initial no. of moles	0.200	0.100	0	0
Change in moles				
Equilibrium no. of moles	0.115			

From the CH_3COOH values:

- moles of CH_3COOH that reacted = 0.200 − 0.115 = **0.085** mol

Find the change in moles of each component in the equilibrium

The amount of each component can be determined from the balanced equation. The change in moles of CH_3COOH is already known.

> In this experiment, 0.085 mol CH_3COOH has **reacted** with 0.085 mol C_2H_5OH to form 0.085 mol $CH_3COOC_2H_5$ and 0.085 mol H_2O.

	CH_3COOH	+	C_2H_5OH	$\rightleftharpoons$	$CH_3COOC_2H_5$	+	H_2O
equation:							
molar quantities:	1 mol		1 mol $\longrightarrow$		1 mol		1 mol
change/mol:	−0.085		−0.085		+0.085		+0.085

Equilibrium concentrations are determined for each component

> Note that the total volume is 250 cm^3 (0.250 dm^3). The concentration must be expressed as mol dm^{-3}.

	CH_3COOH	+	C_2H_5OH	$\rightleftharpoons$	$CH_3COOC_2H_5$	+	H_2O
Initial amount/mol	0.200		0.100		0		0
Change in moles	−0.085		−0.085		+0.085		+0.085
Equilibrium amount/mol	0.115		0.015		0.085		0.085
Equilibrium conc. /mol dm^{-3}	$\dfrac{0.115}{0.250}$		$\dfrac{0.015}{0.250}$		$\dfrac{0.085}{0.250}$		$\dfrac{0.085}{0.250}$

Write the expression for K_c and substitute values

$$K_c = \frac{[CH_3COOC_2H_5]\,[H_2O]}{[CH_3COOH]\,[C_2H_5OH]} = \frac{\dfrac{0.085}{0.250} \times \dfrac{0.085}{0.250}}{\dfrac{0.115}{0.250} \times \dfrac{0.015}{0.250}}$$

Calculate K_c

$\therefore K_c = 4.19$ (no units: all units cancel)

Partition coefficients (CCEA only)

When a solute is distributed between two immiscible solvents (usually an organic solvent and water), different amounts of solute dissolve in each layer.

The **partition coefficient**, K_d, is a measure of the relative solubility of a solute between these two solvents.

$$K_d = \frac{\text{concentration in organic solvent}}{\text{concentration in water}}$$

Non-polar organic compounds are more soluble in an organic solvent than in water and have a K_d value >1. By carrying out multiple extractions, virtually all of the organic compound can be extracted from an aqueous layer.

A solvent extraction is a common technique used in organic chemistry to extract an organic solute from water into an organic solvent.

This is used during purification of an organic compound. The impurities remain dissolved in the water, whilst the required organic compound is transferred into the organic solvent.

Progress check

1 Several experiments were set up for the $H_2(g)$, $I_2(g)$ and $HI(g)$ equilibrium. The equilibrium concentrations are shown below.

$[H_2(g)]$ /mol dm^{-3}	$[I_2(g)]$ /mol dm^{-3}	$[HI(g)]$ /mol dm^{-3}
0.0092	0.0020	0.0296
0.0077	0.0031	0.0334
0.0092	0.0022	0.0308
0.0035	0.0035	0.0235

Calculate the value for K_c for each experiment. Hence, show that each experiment has the same value for K_c (allowing for experimental error). Work out an average value for K_c.

2 2 moles of ethanoic acid, CH_3COOH were mixed with 3 moles of ethanol and the mixture was allowed to reach equilibrium.

$$CH_3COOH + C_2H_5OH \rightleftharpoons CH_3COOC_2H_5 + H_2O$$

At equilibrium, 0.5 moles of ethanoic acid remained.
(a) Work out the equilibrium concentrations of each component in the mixture. (You will need to use V to represent the volume but this will cancel out in your calculation.)
(b) Use these values to calculate K_c.

3 When 0.50 moles of $H_2(g)$ and 0.18 moles of $I_2(g)$ were heated at 500°C, the equilibrium mixture contained 0.01 moles of $I_2(g)$.
The equation is:
$H_2(g) + I_2(g) \rightleftharpoons 2HI(g)$
(a) How many moles of $I_2(g)$ reacted?
(b) How many moles of $H_2(g)$ were present at equilibrium?
(c) How many moles of $HI(g)$ were present at equilibrium?
(d) Calculate the equilibrium constant, K_c for this reaction.

3 (a) 0.17 mol (b) 0.33 mol (c) 0.34 mol (d) 35.
(b) K = 3.
2 (a) CH_3COOH, 0.5/V mol dm^{-3}; C_2H_5OH, 1.5/V mol dm^{-3}; $CH_3COOC_2H_5$, 1.5/V mol dm^{-3}; H_2O, 1.5/V mol dm^{-3}.
1 values: 47.6; 46.7; 46.9; 45.1. average = 46.6

1.4 The equilibrium constant, K_p

After studying this section you should be able to:

- *understand and use the terms mole fraction and partial pressure*
- *calculate from data the partial pressures present at equilibrium*
- *deduce, for homogeneous reactions, K_p in terms of partial pressures*
- *calculate from data the value of K_p, including determination of units*

Partial pressure

Equilibria involving gases are usually expressed in terms of K_p, the equilibrium constant in terms of partial pressures.

> **KEY POINT**
>
> In a gas mixture, the *partial pressure* of a gas, p, is the contribution that a gas makes towards the total pressure, P.

The air is a gas mixture with approximate molar proportions of 80% $N_2(g)$ and 20% $O_2(g)$.

> The mole fraction of a gas is the same as its proportion by volume.

- The partial pressure of $N_2(g)$ is 80% of the total pressure.
- The partial pressure of $O_2(g)$ is 20% of the total pressure.

> As with all fractions, the sum of the mole fractions in a mixture must equal ONE.

> **KEY POINT**
>
> For a gas **A** in a gas mixture:
>
> the mole fraction of **A**, $x_A = \dfrac{\text{number of moles of } \textbf{A}}{\text{total number of moles in gas mixture}}$
>
> partial pressure of **A**, p_A = mole fraction of **A** × total pressure = $x_A \times P$

> The sum of the partial pressures in a mixture must equal the total pressure.

The mole fractions in air are: $\quad x_{N_2} = \dfrac{80}{100} = 0.8; \quad x_{O_2} = \dfrac{20}{100} = 0.2$

At normal atmospheric pressure, 100 kPa,

$p_{N_2} = 0.8 \times 100 = 80$ kPa; $\qquad p_{O_2} = 0.2 \times 100 = 20$ kPa

Progress check

1 A gas mixture at a total pressure of 300 kPa contains 3 moles of $N_2(g)$ and 1 mole of $O_2(g)$.
   (a) What is the mole fraction of each gas?
   (b) What is the partial pressure of each gas?

1 (a) N_2, 0.75; O_2, 0.25.   (b) N_2, 225 kPa; O_2, 75 kPa.

The equilibrium constant, K_p

K_p is written in a similar way to K_c but with partial pressures replacing concentration terms.

For the equilibrium: $\quad H_2(g) + I_2(g) \rightleftharpoons 2HI(g)$

the equilibrium constant in terms of partial pressures, K_p, is given by:

$$K_p = \frac{p_{HI}^{\,2}}{p_{H_2} \times p_{I_2}}$$

> Don't use [ ] in K_p.
> This is a common exam mistake.

- p means the equilibrium partial pressure

> K_p only includes gases.
> Ignore any other species.

- suitable units for partial pressures are kilopascals (kPa) or pascals (Pa) – but the same unit must be used for all gases

- the power to which the partial pressures is raised is the *balancing number* in the chemical equation.

Working out K_p

An equilibrium mixture contains 13.5 mol $N_2(g)$, 3.6 mol $H_2(g)$, and 1.0 mol $NH_3(g)$. The total equilibrium pressure is 200 kPa. Calculate K_p.

Find the mole fractions and partial pressures

Total number of gas moles = 13.5 + 3.6 + 1.0 = 18.1 mol

> Check that the partial pressures add up to give the total pressure:
> 149 + 40 + 11 = 200 kPa

$$p_{N_2} = \frac{13.5}{18.1} \times 200 = 149 \text{ kPa} \qquad p_{H_2} = \frac{3.6}{18.1} \times 200 = 40 \text{ kPa}$$

$$p_{NH_3} = \frac{1.0}{18.1} \times 200 = 11 \text{ kPa}$$

Calculate K_p

For the reaction: $N_2(g) + 3H_2(g) \rightleftharpoons 2NH_3(g)$,

$$K_p = \frac{p_{NH_3}^2}{p_{N_2} \times p_{H_2}^3}$$

$$\therefore K_p = \frac{11^2}{149 \times 40^3} = 1.27 \times 10^{-5} \text{ kPa}^{-2}$$

The units for K_p are found by replacing each partial pressure value in the K_p expression by its units:

substituting units: $K_p = \dfrac{(kPa)^2}{(kPa)\,(kPa)^3}$ $\quad\therefore$ units of K_p are: kPa^{-2}

Progress check

1 For the following equilibria, write an expression for K_p and work out the value for K_p including units.
   (a) $2HI(g) \rightleftharpoons H_2(g) + I_2(g)$
       partial pressures: $HI(g)$, 56 kPa; $H_2(g)$, 22 kPa; $I_2(g)$, 22 kPa
   (b) $2NO_2(g) \rightleftharpoons 2NO(g) + O_2(g)$
       partial pressures: $NO_2(g)$, 45 kPa; $NO(g)$, 60 kPa; $O_2(g)$, 30kPa

2 In the equilibrium: $2SO_2(g) + O_2(g) \rightleftharpoons 2SO_3(g)$
   2.0 mol of $SO_2(g)$ were mixed with 1.0 mol $O_2(g)$. The mixture was allowed to reach equilibrium at constant temperature and a constant pressure of 900 kPa in the presence of a catalyst. At equilibrium, 0.5 mol of the $SO_2(g)$ had reacted.
   (a) How many moles of SO_2, O_2 and SO_3 were in the equilibrium mixture?
   (b) What were the mole fractions and partial pressures of SO_2, O_2 and SO_3 in the equilibrium mixture?
   (c) Calculate K_p

1 (a) 0.15 (b) 53 kPa.
2 (a) 1.5 mol SO_2; 0.75 mol O_2; 0.5 mol SO_3.
   (b) $x(SO_2) = 0.55$; $x(O_2) = 0.27$; $x(SO_3) = 0.18$.
   $p(SO_2) = 495$ kPa; $p(O_2) = 243$ kPa; $p(SO_3) = 162$ kPa.
   (c) 4.4×10^{-4} kPa^{-1}

1.5 Acids and bases

After studying this section you should be able to:

- describe what is meant by Brønsted–Lowry acids and bases
- understand conjugate acid–base pairs
- understand the difference between a strong and a weak acid
- define the acid dissociation constant, K_a

LEARNING SUMMARY

Key points from AS

- **Calculations in acid–base titrations**
  Revise AS page 40
- **Acids and bases**
  Revise AS pages 45–47

During the study of acids and bases at GCSE, you learnt that the pH scale can be used to measure the strength of acids and bases. You also learnt the reactions of acids with metals, carbonates and alkalis. During AS Chemistry, you revisited these reactions and found out how titrations can be used to measure the concentration of an unknown acid or base. For A2 Chemistry, you will study acids in terms of proton transfer, strength, pH and buffers.

Brønsted–Lowry acids and bases

AQA	M4	SALTERS	M4, M5
EDEXCEL	M4	WJEC	M5
OCR	M5	CCEA	M4

A molecule of an acid contains a hydrogen atom that can be released as a positive hydrogen ion or proton, H^+.

- An acid is a substance producing an excess of hydrogen ions in solution – the Arrhenius theory.
- An acid is a proton donor – the Brønsted–Lowry theory.

At A level, we use the Brønsted–Lowry model of acids and bases in terms of proton transfer.

> An acid is a proton donor.
>
> A base is a proton acceptor.

> **KEY POINT**
>
> - A Brønsted–Lowry **acid** is a proton donor.
> - A Brønsted–Lowry **base** is a proton acceptor.
> - An **alkali** is a base that dissolves in water forming $OH^-(aq)$ ions.

Key points from AS

- **Acids, bases and alkalis**
  Revise AS pages 45–46

Salts are always formed in solution from these typical acid reactions. The salt can be isolated by evaporation of water.

H_2SO_4 forms sulfates

HCl forms chlorides

HNO_3 forms nitrates

With most metals, nitric acid reacts in a different way. If you are asked for the reaction of an acid with a metal, choose a different acid!

The role of $H^+(aq)$ in acid reactions (OCR only)

The H^+ ion is the active part in typical acid reactions. The ionic equations below emphasise this role. The reaction is essentially the same, irrespective of the acid involved.

Acids react with carbonates, forming carbon dioxide:

solid carbonate:

$$2H^+(aq) + CaCO_3(s) \longrightarrow Ca^{2+}(aq) + H_2O(l) + CO_2(g)$$

aqueous carbonate:

$$2H^+(aq) + CO_3^{2-}(aq) \longrightarrow H_2O(l) + CO_2(g)$$

Acids react with bases (metal oxides), forming water:

$$2H^+(aq) + CaO(s) \longrightarrow Ca^{2+}(aq) + H_2O(l)$$

Acids react with alkalis, forming water:

$$H^+(aq) + OH^-(aq) \longrightarrow H_2O(l)$$

Acids react with many metals, forming hydrogen:

$$2H^+(aq) + Mg(s) \longrightarrow Mg^{2+}(aq) + H_2(g)$$

Acid–base pairs

Acids and bases are linked by H^+ as **conjugate pairs**:

- the **conjugate acid** donates H^+
- the **conjugate base** accepts H^+.

$$HCl \rightleftharpoons H^+ + Cl^-$$
conjugate acid   conjugate base

Examples of some conjugate acid–base pairs are shown below.

		acid		base
hydrochloric acid	HCl	$\rightleftharpoons$	H^+ +	Cl^-
sulfuric acid	H_2SO_4	$\rightleftharpoons$	H^+ +	HSO_4^-
ethanoic acid	CH_3COOH	$\rightleftharpoons$	H^+ +	CH_3COO^-

An acid needs a base

An acid can only donate a proton if there is a base to accept it. Most reactions of acids take place in aqueous conditions with water acting as the base. By mixing an acid with a base, an equilibrium is set up comprising **two acid–base conjugate pairs**.

The equilibrium system in aqueous ethanoic acid is shown below.

> You should be able to identify acid–base pairs in equations such as this.

proton donor H^+ proton acceptor

| ACID 1 | | | BASE 1 |

$$H_2O(l) + CH_3COOH(aq) \rightleftharpoons H_3O^+(aq) + CH_3COO^-(aq)$$

BASE 2   ACID 2

proton acceptor H^+ proton donor

> In equations, the oxonium ion H_3O^+ is usually shown as $H^+(aq)$.

- In a reaction involving an aqueous acid such as hydrochloric acid, the 'active' species is the **oxonium** ion, H_3O^+ (ACID 2 above).
- Formation of the oxonium ion requires **both** an acid **and** water.

Progress check

1 Identify the acid–base pairs in the acid–base equilibria below.
(a) $HNO_3 + H_2O \rightleftharpoons H_3O^+ + NO_3^-$
(b) $NH_3 + H_2O \rightleftharpoons NH_4^+ + OH^-$
(c) $H_2SO_4 + H_2O \rightleftharpoons HSO_4^- + H_3O^+$

2 Write equations for the following acid–base equilibria:
(a) hydrochloric acid and hydroxide ions
(b) ethanoic acid, CH_3COOH, and water.

(b) $CH_3COOH + H_2O \rightleftharpoons H_3O^+ + CH_3COO^-$
2 (a) $HCl + OH^- \rightleftharpoons H_2O + Cl^-$
(c) acid 1: H_2SO_4, base 1: HSO_4^-, acid 2: H_3O^+, base 2: H_2O
(b) acid 1: H_2O, base 1: OH^-, acid 2: NH_4^+, base 2: NH_3
1 (a) acid 1: HNO_3, base 1: NO_3^-, acid 2: H_3O^+, base 2: H_2O

Strength of acids and bases

AQA	M4	SALTERS	M5
EDEXCEL	M4	WJEC	M5
OCR	M5	CCEA	M4

The acid–base equilibrium of an acid, HA, in water is shown below.

$$HA(aq) + H_2O(l) \rightleftharpoons H_3O^+(aq) + A^-(aq)$$

To emphasise the loss of H^+, this can be shown more simply as **dissociation** of the acid HA:

$$HA(aq) \rightleftharpoons H^+(aq) + A^-(aq).$$

The **strength** of an acid shows the extent of dissociation into H^+ and A^-.

> A strong acid is completely dissociated.

Strong acids

A **strong** acid, such as nitric acid, HNO_3, is a **good** proton donor.
- There is almost **complete** dissociation.

$$\overset{\text{equilibrium}}{HNO_3(aq) \rightleftharpoons H^+(aq) + NO_3^-(aq)}$$

- Virtually all of the potential acidic power has been released as $H^+(aq)$.
- At equilibrium, $[H^+(aq)]$ is much greater than $[HNO_3(aq)]$.

> A weak acid only partially dissociates.

Weak acids

A **weak** acid, such as ethanoic acid, CH_3COOH, is a **poor** proton donor.
- There is only **partial** dissociation.

$$\overset{\text{equilibrium}}{CH_3COOH(aq) \rightleftharpoons H^+(aq) + CH_3COO^-(aq)}$$

Only a small proportion of the potential acidic power has been released as $H^+(aq)$.
At equilibrium, $[CH_3COOH(aq)]$ is much greater than $[H^+(aq)]$.

> K_a is just a special equilibrium constant K_c for equilibria showing the dissociation of acids.

The acid dissociation constant, K_a

The extent of acid dissociation is shown by the **acid dissociation constant**, K_a.
For the reaction: $HA(aq) \rightleftharpoons H^+(aq) + A^-(aq)$,

> $[HA(aq)]$, $[H^+(aq)]$ and $[A^-(aq)]$ are equilibrium concentrations.

$$K_a = \frac{[H^+(aq)][A^-(aq)]}{[HA(aq)]}$$

units: $K_a = \dfrac{(mol\ dm^{-3})^2}{(mol\ dm^{-3})} = mol\ dm^{-3}$.

> K_a is sometimes called the acidity constant.

- A **large** K_a value shows that the extent of **dissociation is large** – the acid is strong.
- A **small** K_a value shows that the extent of **dissociation is small** – the acid is weak.

Acid strength and concentration

> *Concentrated* and *dilute* are terms used to describe the **amount** of dissolved acid in a solution.
>
> *Strong* and *weak* are terms used to describe the degree of **dissociation** of an acid.

The distinction between the strength and concentration of an acid is important.

Progress check

1. For each of the following acid–base equilibria, write down the expression for K_a. State the units of K_a for each reaction.
   (a) $HCOOH(aq) \rightleftharpoons H^+(aq) + HCOO^-(aq)$
   (b) $C_6H_5COOH(aq) \rightleftharpoons H^+(aq) + C_6H_5COO^-(aq)$

2. Samples of two acids, hydrochloric acid and ethanoic acid, have the same concentration: $0.1\ mol\ dm^{-3}$. Explain why one 'dilute acid' is *strong* whereas the other 'dilute acid' is *weak*.

2 Concentration applies to the amount, in mol, in 1 dm^3 of solution. Both solutions have 0.1 mol dissolved in 1 dm^3 of solution and are dilute. Hydrochloric acid is strong because its dissociation is near to complete. However, ethanoic acid only donates a small proportion of its potential protons, its dissociation is incomplete and it is a weak acid.

1 (a) $K_a = \dfrac{[H^+(aq)][HCOO^-(aq)]}{[HCOOH(aq)]}$ units: mol dm^{-3}

(b) $K_a = \dfrac{[H^+(aq)][C_6H_5COO^-(aq)]}{[C_6H_5COOH(aq)]}$ units: mol dm^{-3}

1.6 The pH scale

After studying this section you should be able to:

- *define the terms pH, pK_a and K_w*
- *calculate pH from [H$^+$(aq)]*
- *calculate [H$^+$(aq)] from pH*
- *understand the meaning of the ionisation product of water, K_w*
- *calculate pH for strong bases*

pH and [H$^+$(aq)]

The concentrations of H$^+$(aq) ions in aqueous solutions vary widely between about 10 mol dm^{-3} and about 1×10^{-15} mol dm^{-3}.

The **pH scale** is a logarithmic scale used to overcome the problem of using this large range of numbers and to ease the use of negative powers.

The pH scale	
pH	[H$^+$] / mol dm^{-3}
0	1
1	1×10^{-1}
2	1×10^{-2}
3	1×10^{-3}
4	1×10^{-4}
5	1×10^{-5}
6	1×10^{-6}
7	1×10^{-7}
8	1×10^{-8}
9	1×10^{-9}
10	1×10^{-10}
11	1×10^{-11}
12	1×10^{-12}
13	1×10^{-13}
14	1×10^{-14}

> **KEY POINT**
>
> pH is defined as: $\quad$ pH $= -\log_{10}$ [H$^+$(aq)]
> - where [H$^+$(aq)] is the concentration of hydrogen ions in aqueous solution.
> - [H$^+$(aq)] can be calculated from pH using:
> $$[H^+(aq)] = 10^{-pH}$$

Notice how the value of pH is linked to the power of 10.

pH	2	9	3.6	10.3
[H$^+$(aq)]/mol dm^{-3}	10^{-2}	10^{-9}	$10^{-3.6}$	$10^{-10.3}$

What does a pH value mean?

- A **low** value of [H$^+$(aq)] matches a **high** value of pH.
- A **high** value of [H$^+$(aq)] matches a **low** value of pH.
- A change of pH by 1 changes [H$^+$(aq)] by 10 times.
- An acid of pH 4 contains 10 times the concentration of H$^+$(aq) ions as an acid of pH 5.

Calculating the pH of strong acids

For a strong acid, HA:

- we can assume complete dissociation
- the concentration of H$^+$(aq) can be found directly from the acid concentration: [H$^+$] = [HA].

HA is **monoprotic**: each HA molecule can donate **one** H$^+$ ion.

10^x

log

This is the key to use on your calculator when doing pH and [H$^+$] calculations.

For 10^x, press the **SHIFT** or **INV** key first.

You should be able to convert pH into [H$^+$(aq)] and *vice versa*.

Example 1

A strong acid, HA, has a concentration of 0.010 mol dm^{-3}. What is the pH?

Complete dissociation. $\quad \therefore$ [H$^+$(aq)] = 0.010 mol dm^{-3}

$$pH = -\log_{10} [H^+(aq)] = -\log_{10} (0.010) = \mathbf{2.0}$$

Example 2

A strong acid, HA, has a pH of 3.4. What is the concentration of H$^+$(aq)?

Complete dissociation. $\quad \therefore$ [H$^+$(aq)] $= 10^{-pH} = 10^{-3.4}$ mol dm^{-3}

$$\therefore [H^+(aq)] = \mathbf{3.98 \times 10^{-4}} \text{ mol dm}^{-3}$$

Hints for pH calculations

Calculations involving pH are easy once you have learnt how to use your calculator properly.

- Try the examples on the previous page until you can remember the order to press the keys.
- Try reversing each calculation to go back to the original value. Repeat several times until you have mastered how to use **your** calculator for pH calculations.
- **Don't** borrow a calculator or you will get confused. Different calculators may need the keys to be pressed in a different order!
- Look at your answer and decide whether it looks sensible.

> Learn: $pH = -\log_{10} [H^+(aq)]$
>
> $[H^+(aq)] = 10^{-pH}$.

KEY POINT

Progress check

1 Calculate the pH of solutions with the following $[H^+(aq)]$ values.
   (a) 0.01 mol dm^{-3}
   (b) 0.0001 mol dm^{-3}
   (c) 1.0×10^{-13} mol dm^{-3}
   (d) 2.50×10^{-3} mol dm^{-3}
   (e) 8.10×10^{-6} mol dm^{-3}
   (f) 4.42×10^{-11} mol dm^{-3}

2 Calculate $[H^+(aq)]$ of solutions with the following pH values.
   (a) pH 3   (c) pH 2.8   (e) pH 12.2
   (b) pH 10   (d) pH 7.9   (f) pH 9.6

3 How many times more hydrogen ions are in an acid of pH 1 than an acid of pH 5?

4 How can a solution have a pH with a negative value?

4 A solution with $[H^+(aq)] > 1$ mol dm^{-3} has a negative pH value.

3 pH 1 has 10 000 times more H$^+$ ions than pH 5.

2 (a) 1×10^{-3} mol dm^{-3} (c) 1.58×10^{-3} mol dm^{-3} (e) 6.31×10^{-13} mol dm^{-3}
   (b) 1×10^{-10} mol dm^{-3} (d) 1.26×10^{-8} mol dm^{-3} (f) 2.51×10^{-10} mol dm^{-3}

1 (a) 2 (b) 4 (c) 13 (d) 2.60 (e) 5.09 (f) 10.4

Calculating the pH of weak acids

AQA	M4	SALTERS	M5
EDEXCEL	M4	WJEC	M5
OCR	M5	CCEA	M4

The pH of a weak acid HA can be calculated from:

- the **concentration** of the acid and
- the value of the acid dissociation constant, K_a.

Assumptions and approximations

Consider the equilibrium of a weak aqueous acid HA(aq):

$$HA(aq) \rightleftharpoons H^+(aq) + A^-(aq)$$

- Assuming that only a very small proportion of HA dissociates, the equilibrium concentration of HA(aq) will be very nearly the same as the concentration of undissociated HA(aq).

$$\therefore [HA(aq)]_{equilibrium} \approx [HA(aq)]_{start}$$

- Assuming that there is a negligible proportion of H$^+$(aq) from ionisation of water:

$$[H^+(aq)] \approx [A^-(aq)]$$

- Using these approximations

$$K_a = \frac{[H^+(aq)] [A^-(aq)]}{[HA(aq)]} \qquad \therefore K_a \approx \frac{[H^+(aq)]^2}{[HA(aq)]}$$

For calculations, use

$$K_a \approx \frac{[H^+(aq)]^2}{[HA(aq)]}$$

Take care to learn this method.

Many marks are dropped on exam papers by students who have not done so!

Example

For a weak acid $[HA(aq)] = 0.100$ mol dm^{-3}, $K_a = 1.70 \times 10^{-5}$ mol dm^{-3} at 25°C. Calculate the pH.

$$K_a = \frac{[H^+(aq)]\,[A^-(aq)]}{[HA(aq)]} \approx \frac{[H^+(aq)]^2}{[HA(aq)]}$$

$$\therefore\ 1.70 \times 10^{-5} = \frac{[H^+(aq)]^2}{0.100}$$

$$\therefore\ [H^+(aq)] = \sqrt{0.100 \times 1.70 \times 10^{-5}} = 0.00130 \text{ mol dm}^{-3}$$

$$pH = -\log_{10}[H^+(aq)] = -\log_{10}(0.00130) = \mathbf{2.89}$$

K_a and pK_a

AQA M4   SALTERS M5
EDEXCEL M4   WJEC M5
OCR M5   CCEA M4

Values of K_a can be made more manageable if expressed in a logarithmic form, pK_a (see also page 37: pH and $[H^+(aq)]$).

$$pK_a = -\log_{10}K_a$$
$$K_a = 10^{-pKa}$$

K_a and pK_a conversions are just like those between pH and H^+.

- A **low** value of K_a matches a **high** value of pK_a
- A **high** value of K_a matches a **low** value of pK_a

Comparison of K_a and pK_a

The smaller the pK_a value, the stronger the acid.

acid		K_a / mol dm^{-3}	pK_a
methanoic acid	HCOOH	1.6×10^{-4}	$-\log_{10}(1.6 \times 10^{-4}) = \mathbf{3.8}$
benzoic acid	C_6H_5COOH	6.3×10^{-5}	$-\log_{10}(6.3 \times 10^{-5}) = \mathbf{4.2}$

Progress check

1 Find the pH of solutions of a weak acid HA ($K_a = 1.70 \times 10^{-5}$ mol dm^{-3}), with the following concentrations:
   (a) 1.00 mol dm^{-3}; (b) 0.250 mol dm^{-3}; (c) 3.50×10^{-2} mol dm^{-3}

2 Find values of K_a and pK_a for the following weak acids.
   (a) 1.0 mol dm^{-3} solution with a pH of 4.5
   (b) 0.1 mol dm^{-3} solution with a pH of 2.2
   (c) 2.0 mol dm^{-3} solution with a pH of 3.8.

2 (a) $K_a = 1 \times 10^{-9}$ mol dm^{-3}, $pK_a = 9$
   (b) $K_a = 3.98 \times 10^{-4}$ mol dm^{-3}, $pK_a = 3.4$
   (c) $K_a = 1.26 \times 10^{-8}$ mol dm^{-3}, $pK_a = 7.9$

1 (a) 2.38 (b) 2.69 (c) 3.11

The ionisation of water and K_w

AQA M4   SALTERS M5
EDEXCEL M4   WJEC M5
OCR M5   CCEA M4

In water, a very small proportion of molecules dissociates into $H^+(aq)$ and $OH^-(aq)$ ions. The position of equilibrium lies well to the left of the equation below, representing this dissociation.

$$\overleftarrow{\text{equilibrium}}$$
$$H_2O(l) \rightleftharpoons H^+(aq) + OH^-(aq)$$

Treating water as a weak acid: $K_a = \dfrac{[H^+(aq)]\,[OH^-(aq)]}{[H_2O(l)]}$

Rearranging gives:

$$\underbrace{K_a \times [H_2O(l)]}_{\text{constant, } K_w} = [H^+(aq)]\,[OH^-(aq)]$$

$[H_2O(l)]$ is constant and is included within K_w

> **KEY POINT**
>
> The constant K_w is called the **ionic product of water**
> - $K_w = [H^+(aq)]\,[OH^-(aq)]$
> - At 25°C, $K_w = 1.0 \times 10^{-14}$ mol^2 dm^{-6}.

In water, the concentrations of $H^+(aq)$ and $OH^-(aq)$ ions are the same.

- $[H^+(aq)] = [OH^-(aq)] = 10^{-7}$ mol dm^{-3} $(10^{-14} = 10^{-7} \times 10^{-7})$

Hydrogen ion and hydroxide ion concentrations

Linking [H⁺] and [OH⁻]

$10^{-14} = [H^+][OH^-]$

Water: pH = 7,
$[H^+] = 10^{-7}$ mol dm^{-3}
$10^{-14} = 10^{-7} \times 10^{-7}$

An acid: pH = 3
$[H^+] = 10^{-3}$ mol dm^{-3}
$10^{-14} = 10^{-3} \times 10^{-11}$

An alkali: pH = 10
$[H^+] = 10^{-10}$ mol dm^{-3}
$10^{-14} = 10^{-10} \times 10^{-4}$

All aqueous solutions contain $H^+(aq)$ and $OH^-(aq)$ ions. The proportions of these ions in a solution are determined by the pH.

In water	$[H^+(aq)] = [OH^-(aq)]$
In **acidic** solutions	$[H^+(aq)] > [OH^-(aq)]$
In **alkaline** solutions	$[H^+(aq)] < [OH^-(aq)]$

The concentrations of $H^+(aq)$ and $OH^-(aq)$ are linked by K_w.

- At 25°C $1.0 \times 10^{-14} = [H^+(aq)] [OH^-(aq)]$
- The indices of $[H^+(aq)]$ and $[OH^-(aq)]$ add up to –14.

Calculating the pH of strong alkalis

The pH of a strong alkali can be found using K_w.

For a strong alkali, BOH:

- we can assume complete dissociation
- the concentration of $OH^-(aq)$ can be found directly from the alkali concentration: $[BOH] = [OH^-]$.

To find the pH of an alkali, first find [H⁺] using K_w and [OH⁻].

Example

A strong alkali, BOH, has a concentration of 0.50 mol dm^{-3}.

What is the pH?

Complete dissociation. $\therefore [OH^-(aq)] = 0.50$ mol dm^{-3}

$$K_w = [H^+(aq)] [OH^-(aq)] = 1 \times 10^{-14} \text{ mol}^2 \text{ dm}^{-6}$$

$$\therefore [H^+(aq)] = \frac{K_w}{[OH^-(aq)]} = \frac{1 \times 10^{-14}}{0.50} = 2 \times 10^{-13} \text{ mol dm}^{-3}$$

$$pH = -\log_{10} [H^+(aq)] = -\log_{10} (2 \times 10^{-13}) = \mathbf{12.7}$$

Progress check

1 Find the $[H^+(aq)]$ and pH of the following alkalis at 25°C:
   (a) 1×10^{-3} mol dm^{-3} $OH^-(aq)$
   (b) 3.5×10^{-2} mol dm^{-3} $OH^-(aq)$.

2 Find the pH of the following solutions of strong bases at 25°C:
   (a) 0.01 mol dm^{-3} KOH (aq)
   (b) 0.20 mol dm^{-3} NaOH (aq).

2 (a) pH = 12; (b) pH = 13.3.
1 (a) $[H^+(aq)] = 1 \times 10^{-11}$ mol dm^{-3}; pH = 11
   (b) $[H^+(aq)] = 2.86 \times 10^{-13}$ mol dm^{-3}; pH = 12.5.

1.7 pH changes

After studying this section you should be able to:

- *recognise the shapes of titration curves for acids and bases with different strengths*
- *explain the choice of suitable indicators for acid–base titrations*
- *determine K_a from a titration curve*
- *carry out unstructured titration calculations*
- *state what is meant by a buffer solution*
- *explain how pH is controlled by each component in a buffer solution*
- *calculate the pH of a buffer solution*

LEARNING SUMMARY

Titration curves

AQA	M4	WJEC	M5
EDEXCEL	M4	CCEA	M4
OCR	M5		

Choosing an indicator using titration curves

A titration curve shows the changes in pH during a titration.

In the titration curves below, different combinations of strong and weak acids and alkalis have been used.

- The end point of a titration is identified by the colour change of the indicator.
- Different indicators change colour at different pH values.
- The pH values at which the indicators methyl orange (**MO**) and phenolphthalein (**P**) change colour are shown on each diagram.

strong acid/strong alkali

both indicators suitable

strong acid/weak alkali

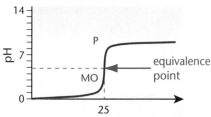

*methyl orange (**MO**) suitable*
*phenolphthalein (**P**) unsuitable*

Choose the correct indicator

Strong acid/strong alkali
phenolphthalein ✓
methyl orange ✓

Strong acid/weak alkali
phenolphthalein ✗
methyl orange ✓

Weak acid/strong alkali
phenolphthalein ✓
methyl orange ✗

Weak acid/weak alkali
phenolphthalein ✗
methyl orange ✗

weak acid/strong alkali

*phenolphthalein (**P**) suitable*
*methyl orange (**MO**) unsuitable*

weak acid/weak alkali

neither indicator suitable

Key features of titration curves

- The pH changes rapidly at the near vertical portion of the titration curve. The mid-point of the vertical portion is the **equivalence point** of the titration.
- The sharp change in pH is brought about by a very small addition of alkali, typically the addition of one drop.
- The indicator is only suitable if its pK_{ind} value is within the pH range of the near vertical portion of the titration curve.

Determination of K_a from a titration curve

EDEXCEL M4

Titration curves can be used to determine a value for K_a using the procedure below.

- A pH titration curve is plotted and the volume of alkali for neutralisation is read off from the curve (see diagram below).

- The pH at half-neutralisation (i.e. half the alkali required for neutralisation) is read off from the titration curve.

Determination of K_a

The acid dissociation constant, $K_a = \dfrac{[H^+(aq)]\,[A^-(aq)]}{[HA(aq)]}$

At half-neutralisation, **[HA(aq)] = [A⁻(aq)]**, so $K_a = [H^+(aq)]$

$\therefore K_a = \mathbf{10^{-pH}}$, which is easily calculated from the value obtained from the titration curve.

Buffering region of the titration curve

At the start of the titration curve, there is a relatively rapid rise in pH.

As the alkali is added, the salt of the weak acid starts to form. This gives a mixture of a **weak acid** and its **salt** – a **buffer** solution.

The increase in pH in the titration curve slows down in the buffering region.

Enthalpy changes during neutralisation

OCR M5

The *standard enthalpy change of neutralisation* $\Delta H^\ominus_{neut}$ is the energy change that accompanies the neutralisation of an acid by a base to form 1 mole of $H_2O(l)$, under standard conditions.

$$HCl(aq) \; + \; NaOH(aq) \; \rightleftharpoons \; NaCl(aq) \; + \; H_2O(l) \quad \Delta H^\ominus_{neut} = -57.9 \text{ kJ mol}^{-1}$$

acid   base   1 mol

The ionic equation for this reaction is simply:

$$H^+(aq) + OH^-(aq) \longrightarrow H_2O(l).$$

- In aqueous solution, strong acids and bases are completely dissociated and $\Delta H^\ominus_{neut}$ is approximately equal to the value above.

- For weak acids, this enthalpy change is less exothermic because some input of energy is required to dissociate the acid (see also pages 35–36).

Unstructured titration calculations

In AS chemistry examinations, titration problems are usually highly structured. You are helped through calculations with each step being asked in a sequence that leads to the final solution.

In A2 chemistry examinations:

- problems will be set in which you are only provided with a summary of the experimental results
- you will be expected to navigate your own way through the problem; you will have no hints about how to solve the problem.

The key to success is a good understanding of the stages required to solve a titration problem. Most problems follow a common framework.

Acid–base titrations are always likely to be carried out in chemical analysis. In A2, you will also come across redox titrations (see pages 96-98). Although these are different types of titration, the principles for solving any calculations are the same.

AS exam questions would help you through titration calculations by asking each step as a question.

But at A2 you are really on your own! You should now know more chemistry than at AS and also be able to tackle chemistry problems independently.

At least that is what the setters of examination questions expect!

Stage 1

All titrations use a standard solution – one whose concentration is known. In the titration, you measure the volume of this solution that exactly reacts with a second solution.

- You first find the amount, in moles, of the compound in the standard solution.

E.g.   In a titration 25.0 cm^3 of 0.100 mol dm^{-3} NaOH reacted exactly with a solution of H_2SO_4.

$$n = c \times \frac{V}{1000} = 0.100 \times \frac{25.0}{1000} = 0.00250 \text{ mol}$$

Remember that the steps shown here are key to solving most titration calculations.

See also redox titrations, pages 96-98.

Stage 2

- The equation is then usually used to find the number of moles of the other substance dissolved in the second solution:

E.g. $2NaOH(aq) + H_2SO_4(aq) \longrightarrow$ *products*

	2 mol	1 mol
amounts:	0.00250	0.00125 mol

Stage 3

- Finally, this value is processed in some way to find out some further information about the second substance. This is the hardest stage and it may contain several steps. This stage may also vary between different problems.

Worked example

Compound **A** is a straight-chain carboxylic acid. A student analysed a sample of acid **A** by the procedure below.

The student dissolved 5.437 g of **A** in water and made the solution up to 250 cm^3.

In a titration, 25.0 cm^3 of 0.200 mol dm^{-3} NaOH were neutralised by exactly 23.45 cm^3 of solution **A**.

Use the results to calculate the molar mass of acid **A** and suggest its identity.

The amount of NaOH used can be calculated from the titration results:

The concentration and volume of NaOH are known. So we work out the amount of NaOH first.

$$\text{amount of NaOH} = 0.200 \times \frac{25.0}{1000} = 0.00500 \text{ mol}$$

The amount of carboxylic acid that reacts with the NaOH can be determined from the balanced equation for the reaction:

Carboxylic acid **A** must have the formula: RCOOH

The equation and molar reacting quantities are:

$$NaOH(aq) + RCOOH(aq) \longrightarrow RCOONa(aq) + H_2O(l)$$
$$\textbf{1 mol} \qquad \textbf{1 mol}$$

∴ in the titration: 0.00500 mol NaOH reacts with **0.00500 mol RCOOH**

> In this titration there is the same number of moles of each reactant. We work this out from the balanced equation.

You must now look at what the question is asking. You need to think about how you are going to solve the rest of the problem.

- Here, we must first find out the amount, in moles, of **A** that was used to prepare the original 250 cm³ solution.
- In the titration, 23.45 cm³ of this solution of **A** was used – we know the number of moles of **A** dissolved in this volume.
- We need to scale up these quantities to find the number of moles of **A** dissolved in 250 cm³ of solution:

> This step is important but many candidates forget to do this (or don't understand that it must be done!)

23.45 cm³ of RCOOH(aq) in the titration contains 0.00500 mol RCOOH

1 cm³ of RCOOH(aq) in the titration contains $\dfrac{0.00500}{23.45}$ mol RCOOH

250 cm³ of RCOOH(aq) contains $\dfrac{0.00500}{23.45} \times 250 = 0.0533$ mol RCOOH

> This step is easy, provided that you have remembered the following:
>
> $n = \dfrac{\text{mass } m}{\text{Molar mass } M}$

The molar mass of RCOOH can now be determined and we have solved the first part of the problem:

$$n = \frac{m}{M} \quad \therefore \text{ Molar mass, } M = \frac{m}{n} = \frac{5.437}{0.0533} = \textbf{102.0 g mol}^{-1}$$

Finally, we need to suggest a possible structure for straight-chain carboxylic acid A.

The formula of the straight-chain carboxylic acid is RCOOH.

COOH has a relative mass of $12.0 + 16.0 \times 2 + 1.0 = 45.0$.

> These problems may mix together chemistry from different parts of your synoptic assessment. See pages 178–180.

∴ the alkyl group R has a relative mass of $102.0 - 45.0 = 57.0$

∴ the alkyl group must be $CH_3CH_2CH_2CH_2$ $(15.0 + 14.0 + 14.0 + 14.0)$

and carboxylic acid **A** is $\textbf{CH}_3\textbf{CH}_2\textbf{CH}_2\textbf{CH}_2\textbf{COOH}$ (pentanoic acid).

Buffer solutions

AQA	M4	SALTERS	M5
EDEXCEL	M4	WJEC	M5
OCR	M5	CCEA	M4

A buffer solution minimises changes in pH during the addition of an acid or an alkali to a solution. The buffer solution maintains a near-constant pH by removing most of any added acid or alkali.

A **buffer solution** is a mixture of:

- a **weak acid, HA**, and
- its **conjugate base, A⁻**:

$$HA(aq) \rightleftharpoons H^+(aq) + A^-(aq)$$
$$\text{weak acid} \qquad\qquad\qquad\qquad \text{conjugate base}$$

> Buffers are added to foods to prevent deterioration due to pH change (caused by bacterial or fungal activity).

In a buffer solution, the concentration of hydrogen ions, $[H^+(aq)]$, is very small compared with the concentrations of the weak acid $[HA(aq)]$ or the conjugate base $[A^-(aq)]$.

$$[H^+(aq)] \ll [HA(aq)] \quad \text{and} \quad [H^+(aq)] \ll [A^-(aq)].$$

How does a buffer act?

Addition of an acid, H⁺(aq), to a buffer

We can explain how a buffer minimises pH changes by using le Chatelier's principle.

On addition of an acid:

- $[H^+(aq)]$ is increased
- the pH change is opposed and the **equilibrium moves to the left, removing** $[H^+(aq)]$ and forming $HA(aq)$
- the **conjugate base** $A^-(aq)$ removes **most** of any added $[H^+(aq)]$.

A⁻ removes most of any added acid.

add acid, H⁺(aq)

$$HA(aq) \rightleftharpoons H^+(aq) + A^-(aq)$$
weak acid   conjugate base

most added H⁺(aq) is removed

Addition of an alkali, OH⁻(aq), to a buffer

On addition of an alkali:

- the added $OH^-(aq)$ reacts with the small concentration of $H^+(aq)$:

$$H^+(aq) + OH^-(aq) \longrightarrow H_2O(l)$$

- the pH change is opposed – the **equilibrium moves to the right, restoring** $[H^+(aq)]$ as $HA(aq)$ dissociates
- the **weak acid** HA restores **most** of any $[H^+(aq)]$ that has been removed.

add alkali, OH⁻(aq)

$$HA(aq) \rightleftharpoons H^+(aq) + A^-(aq)$$
weak acid   conjugate base

most H⁺(aq) is restored

HA removes added alkali.

> **KEY POINT**
>
> Although the two components in a buffer solution react with added acid and alkali, they **cannot stop** the pH from changing. They do however **minimise** pH changes.

Common buffer solutions

An acidic buffer

Remember these buffers:
CH_3COOH/CH_3COONa
and
NH_4Cl/NH_3

A common acidic buffer is an aqueous solution containing a mixture of ethanoic acid, CH_3COOH, and the ethanoate ion, CH_3COO^-.

- Ethanoic acid acts as the weak acid, CH_3COOH.
- Sodium ethanoate, $CH_3COO^-Na^+$, acts as a source of the **conjugate base**, CH_3COO^-.

An alkaline buffer

The pH of healthy blood is maintained at between 7.35 and 7.40 by the carbonic acid–hydrogencarbonate buffer system.

H_2CO_3 is the **weak acid**,
HCO_3^- is the **conjugate base**.
$H_2CO_3(aq) \rightleftharpoons H^+(aq) + HCO_3^-(aq)$

Blood cannot sustain life if its pH lies much outside of this narrow range.

A common alkaline buffer is an aqueous solution containing a mixture of the ammonium ion, NH_4^+, and ammonia, NH_3.

- Ammonium chloride, $NH_4^+Cl^-$, acts as source of the **weak acid**, NH_4^+.
- Ammonia acts as the **conjugate base**, NH_3.

Calculations involving buffer solutions

AQA	M4	SALTERS	M5
EDEXCEL	M4	WJEC	M5
OCR	M5	CCEA	M4

The pH of a buffer solution depends upon:
- the acid dissociation constant, K_a, of the buffer system
- the **ratio** of the weak **acid** and its conjugate **base**.

For a buffer comprising the weak acid, HA, and its conjugate base, A^-,

For buffer calculations, learn:

$$[H^+(aq)] = K_a \times \frac{[HA(aq)]}{[A^-(aq)]}$$

The pH of a buffer can be controlled by the acid/base ratio.

$$K_a = \frac{[H^+(aq)]\,[A^-(aq)]}{[HA(aq)]}$$

$$\therefore [H^+(aq)] = K_a \times \frac{[HA(aq)]}{[A^-(aq)]}$$

acid dissociation constant

ratio of the weak acid and its conjugate base

Example
Calculate the pH of a buffer comprising 0.30 mol dm^{-3} $CH_3COOH(aq)$ ($K_a = 1.7 \times 10^{-5}$ mol dm^{-3}) and 0.10 mol dm^{-3} $CH_3COO^-(aq)$.

$$[H^+(aq)] = K_a \times \frac{[HA(aq)]}{[A^-(aq)]}$$

$$\therefore [H^+(aq)] = 1.7 \times 10^{-5} \times \frac{0.30}{0.10} = 5.1 \times 10^{-5} \text{ mol dm}^{-3}$$

$$\therefore pH = -\log_{10}[H^+(aq)] = -\log_{10}(5.1 \times 10^{-5})$$

$$\therefore pH \text{ of the buffer solution} = \mathbf{4.3}$$

Progress check

1 Three buffer solutions are made from benzoic acid, C_6H_5COOH and sodium benzoate, C_6H_5COONa with the following compositions:

> Buffer A: 0.10 mol dm^{-3} C_6H_5COOH and 0.10 mol dm^{-3} C_6H_5COONa
> Buffer B: 0.75 mol dm^{-3} C_6H_5COOH and 0.25 mol dm^{-3} C_6H_5COONa
> Buffer C: 0.20 mol dm^{-3} C_6H_5COOH and 0.80 mol dm^{-3} C_6H_5COONa

(a) Write the equation for the equilibrium in these buffers.
(b) Write an expression for K_a of benzoic acid.
(c) Calculate the pH of each of the buffer solutions
   (K_a for $C_6H_5COOH = 6.3 \times 10^{-5}$ mol dm^{-3}.)

(c) Buffer A: 4.2 Buffer B: 3.7 Buffer C: 4.8
(b) $K_a = \frac{[H^+(aq)]\,[C_6H_5COO^-(aq)]}{[C_6H_5COOH(aq)]}$
(a) $C_6H_5COOH \rightleftharpoons H^+(aq) + C_6H_5COO^-(aq)$ 1

Sample question and model answer

Many cosmetics contain buffers. Human skin is slightly acidic and has a pH of approximately 5.50. Skin-care products often buffer at a pH 5.50 or below.

(a) What do you understand by the term *buffer*?

Don't use the phrases 'keeps the pH constant' or 'stops the pH from changing'.

The pH will change but the buffer keeps the change small.

A solution that minimises a change in pH. ✓ [1]

(b) Lactic acid, $CH_3CH(OH)COOH$, is used in many cosmetics. Lactic acid is a weak acid with an acid dissociation constant, K_a, of 8.40×10^{-4} mol dm^{-3}.

(i) Write an equation to show the dissociation of lactic acid into its ions.

$CH_3CH(OH)COOH \rightleftharpoons CH_3CH(OH)COO^- + H^+$ ✓ (equilibrium sign essential)

(ii) Write an expression for the acid dissociation constant, K_a, of lactic acid.

$$K_a = \frac{[CH_3CH(OH)COO^-(aq)] \, [H^+(aq)]}{[CH_3CH(OH)COOH(aq)]} \checkmark$$

(iii) Calculate the pH of a 1.25×10^{-2} mol dm^{-3} solution of lactic acid.

These approximations simplify the K_a expression to:

$$K_a \approx \frac{[H^+]^2}{[HA]}$$

$CH_3CH(OH)COO^- \approx H^+$.

equilibrium conc. of weak acid ≈ undissociated concentration of weak acid.

$$\therefore K_a \approx \frac{[H^+(aq)]^2}{[CH_3CH(OH)COOH(aq)]} \qquad 8.4 \times 10^{-4} = \frac{[H^+(aq)]^2}{1.25 \times 10^{-2}} \checkmark$$

Make sure that your calculator skills are good and show your working. A correct method will secure most available marks.

Notice the use throughout of 3 significant figures (in the question and in the answers).

$[H^+(aq)] = \sqrt{(1.25 \times 10^{-2} \times 8.40 \times 10^{-4})} = 3.24 \times 10^{-3}$ ✓ mol dm^{-3}

$\therefore$ pH $= -\log(3.24 \times 10^{-3}) = 2.49.$ ✓ [5]

(c) A buffer solution can be made based on lactic acid and a salt of lactic acid. Explain how this buffer solution acts as a buffer.

Practise explaining how a buffer works. This is often asked in exams and it is harder to answer than it appears.

You need to discuss shifts in the equilibrium between the weak acid and its conjugate base.

In the equilibrium $CH_3CH(OH)COOH \rightleftharpoons CH_3CH(OH)COO^- + H^+$, there are large excesses of $CH_3CH(OH)COOH$ and $CH_3CH(OH)COO^-$. ✓

The equilibrium above shifts in response to added acid and alkali. ✓

On addition of an alkali, OH^- ions react with the small concentration of H^+ present:

$H^+(aq) + OH^-(aq) \longrightarrow H_2O(l)$

The equilibrium shifts to the right, restoring most of any H^+ ions removed: ✓

$CH_3CH(OH)COOH \longrightarrow CH_3CH(OH)COO^- + H^+$ ✓

Lactate ions from sodium lactate remove most of any added acid, shifting the equilibrium to the left: ✓

$CH_3CH(OH)COO^- + H^+ \longrightarrow CH_3CH(OH)COOH$ ✓ [6]

(d) A buffer solution based on lactic acid is required to buffer at a pH 3.80. Calculate the ratio of lactic acid : sodium lactate that will be needed to give this pH.

The calculated ratio is 0.189.

To get $\frac{1}{5.30}$ you need to press the x^{-1} key.

The answer means that you need 5.3 times the concentration of sodium lactate to lactic acid.

In the buffer, $[H^+(aq)] = 10^{-3.80} = 1.58 \times 10^{-4}$ ✓ mol dm^{-3}

In the buffer, $[H^+(aq)] = K_a \times \dfrac{[CH_3CH(OH)COOH(aq)]}{[CH_3CH(OH)COO^-(aq)]}$ ✓

$\therefore$ ratio $\dfrac{[CH_3CH(OH)COOH(aq)]}{[CH_3CH(OH)COO^-(aq)]} = \dfrac{[H^+(aq)]}{K_a} = \dfrac{1.58 \times 10^{-4}}{8.4 \times 10^{-4}}$ ✓

ratio lactic acid : sodium lactate $= 0.189 = \dfrac{1}{5.30}$ ✓ [4]

[Total: 16]

Practice examination questions

1 The reaction between hydrogen peroxide and iodide ions in an acid solution can be written as follows.

$$H_2O_2(aq) + 2I^-(aq) + 2H^+(aq) \longrightarrow I_2(aq) + 2H_2O(l)$$

(a) The table below shows initial rates from different initial concentrations of $H_2O_2(aq)$, $I^-(aq)$ and $H^+(aq)$ at constant temperature.

$[H_2O_2(aq)]$ /mol dm^{-3}	$[I^-(aq)]$ /mol dm^{-3}	$[H^+(aq)]$ /mol dm^{-3}	initial rate /10^{-6} mol dm^{-3} s^{-1}
0.00075	0.10	0.10	2.1
0.00150	0.10	0.10	4.2
0.00150	0.10	0.20	4.2
0.00075	0.70	0.10	14.7

(i) Determine, with reasoning, the order with respect to each reactant.

(ii) Write the rate equation and calculate the value of the rate constant, k, for this reaction.   [9]

(b) (i) What is meant by the term *rate-determining step*?

(ii) Using the rate equation in (a)(ii), suggest an equation for the rate-determining step of this reaction.   [2]

[Total: 11]

2 (a) A chemical reaction is second order with respect to compound **A** and first order with respect to compound **B**.

(i) Write the rate equation for this reaction.

(ii) What is the overall order of this reaction?

(iii) By what factor will the rate increase if the concentrations of **A** and **B** are both tripled?

(iv) When $[A] = 0.40$ mol dm^{-3} and $B = 0.35$ mol dm^{-3}, the rate = 1.76×10^{-4} mol dm^{-3} s^{-1}. Calculate the value of the rate constant, stating its units.   [5]

(b) Propanone and iodine react together in acidic solution to give iodopropanone according to the overall equation below.

$$CH_3COCH_3(aq) + I_2(aq) \longrightarrow CH_3COCH_2I(aq) + HI(aq)$$

The rate equation is: *rate* = $k[CH_3COCH_3(aq)]\,[H^+(aq)]$

(i) State, with an explanation, the role of the $H^+(aq)$ ions in this reaction.

(ii) Suggest a possible equation for the rate-determining step.   [3]

[Total: 8]

3 The equilibrium below was set up.

$$CH_3COOCH_2CH_3 + H_2O \rightleftharpoons CH_3COOH + CH_3CH_2OH$$

The equilibrium mixture contains 1.35 mol of ethyl ethanoate, 1.35 mol of water, 0.15 mol of ethanoic acid, and 3.15 mol of ethanol. It has a volume of 353 cm^3.

(a) Calculate K_c for this equilibrium to 2 significant figures. State the units, if any.   [3]

(b) More ethanol was to be added to the equilibrium mixture.

(i) What would happen to the equilibrium? Explain your reasoning.

(ii) What would be the effect of this change on the value of K_c? Explain your reasoning.   [4]

[Total: 7]

Practice examination questions *(continued)*

4 When 0.60 moles of $H_2(g)$ and 0.18 moles of $I_2(g)$ were heated to constant temperature in a sealed container with a volume of 1 dm^3, an equilibrium was set up:

$$H_2(g) + I_2(g) \rightleftharpoons 2HI(g)$$

At equilibrium, 0.16 mol $I_2(g)$ had reacted.

(a) (i) Determine the equilibrium concentrations of H_2, I_2, and HI.

   (ii) Calculate the equilibrium constant, K_c, for this reaction.   [6]

(b) When the equilibrium mixture was heated by 100°C the value of K_c decreased. What additional information is provided by this observation?   [2]

[Total: 8]

5 Nitric acid, HNO_3 is a strong acid and methanoic acid, HCOOH, is a weak acid ($K_a = 1.6 \times 10^{-4}$ mol dm^{-3}).

(a) Define the term *Brønsted–Lowry acid*.   [1]

(b) Write the acid–base equilibrium that would be set up between methanoic acid and nitric acid. State the role of methanoic acid in this equilibrium.   [2]

(c) Calculate the pH of the following solutions:

   (i) 0.176 mol dm^{-3} nitric acid

   (ii) 0.372 mol dm^{-3} potassium hydroxide

   (iii) 0.263 mol dm^{-3} methanoic acid.

   (iv) a solution containing 0.255 mol dm^{-3} methanoic acid and 0.325 sodium methanoate.   [10]

[Total: 13]

6 (a) (i) What is meant by the terms *strong acid* and *weak acid*?

   (ii) Define the term *Brønsted–Lowry base*.   [2]

(b) 25.0 cm^3 of a solution of sodium hydroxide contained 1.50×10^{-3} mol of NaOH.

   (i) Calculate the pH of this solution at 298 K.

   (ii) A student added 50.0 cm^3 of 0.250 mol dm^{-3} HCl to the 25.0 cm^3 solution of sodium hydroxide.

   Calculate the pH of the solution formed.   [8]

(c) A sample of hydrochloric acid had a pH of 1.52. 25 cm^3 of this acid was diluted with 15 cm^3 of water.

   Calculate the pH of the resulting solution.   [4]

[Total: 14]

Chapter 2

Energy changes in chemistry

The following topics are covered in this chapter:

- *Enthalpy changes*
- *Entropy changes*

- *Electrochemical cells*
- *Predicting redox reactions*

2.1 Enthalpy changes

After studying this section you should be able to:

- *explain and use the term 'lattice enthalpy'*
- *construct Born–Haber cycles to calculate the lattice enthalpy of simple ionic compounds*
- *explain the effect of ionic charge and ionic radius on the numerical magnitude of a lattice enthalpy*
- *calculate enthalpy changes of solution for ionic compounds from enthalpy changes of hydration and lattice enthalpies*

LEARNING SUMMARY

Key points from AS

- **Enthalpy changes**
  Revise AS pages 95–103

During the study of enthalpy changes in AS Chemistry, you learnt how to:

- calculate enthalpy changes directly from experiments using the relationship $Q = mc\Delta T$
- calculate enthalpy changes indirectly using Hess' law.

These key principles are built upon by considering the enthalpy changes that bond together an ionic lattice.

Lattice enthalpy

Ionic bonding is the electrostatic attraction between oppositely charged ions. Lattice enthalpy indicates the strength of the ionic bonds in an ionic lattice.

Key points from AS

- **Ionic bonding**
  Revise AS pages 52–59

> **The lattice enthalpy ($\Delta H^\ominus_{L.E.}$) of an ionic compound is the enthalpy change that accompanies the formation of 1 mole of an ionic compound from its constituent gaseous ions. ($\Delta H^\ominus_{L.E.}$ is exothermic.)**

KEY POINT

Each ion is surrounded by oppositely-charged ions, forming a giant ionic lattice.

$$Na^+(g) + Cl^-(g) \longrightarrow Na^+Cl^-(s)$$

Lattice enthalpy is also sometimes called the **enthalpy change of lattice formation**.

The opposite change, to break up the lattice, is called the **enthalpy change of lattice dissociation**.

$$Na^+Cl^-(s) \longrightarrow Na^+(g) + Cl^-(g)$$

Determination of lattice enthalpies

Lattice enthalpies cannot be determined directly and must be calculated indirectly using Hess' Law from other enthalpy changes that can be found experimentally. The energy cycle used to calculate a lattice enthalpy is the **Born–Haber cycle**.

The basis of the Born–Haber cycle is the formation of an ionic lattice from its element by two routes.

The Born–Haber cycle for sodium chloride is shown below.

Definitions for these enthalpy changes are shown below.

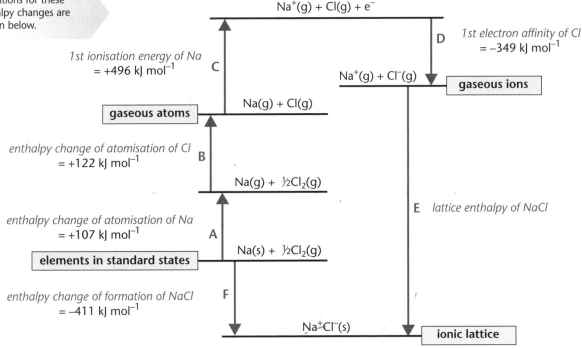

1st ionisation energy of Na = +496 kJ mol⁻¹

1st electron affinity of Cl = −349 kJ mol⁻¹

enthalpy change of atomisation of Cl = +122 kJ mol⁻¹

enthalpy change of atomisation of Na = +107 kJ mol⁻¹

enthalpy change of formation of NaCl = −411 kJ mol⁻¹

E lattice enthalpy of NaCl

- the 1st ionisation energy of Na is **endothermic**
- the 1st electron affinity of Cl is **exothermic**.

Route 1: A + B + C + D + E   *Route 2:* F

Using Hess' Law: A + B + C + D + E = F

$\Delta H^{\ominus}_{at}$ Na(g) + $\Delta H^{\ominus}_{at}$ Cl(g) + $\Delta H^{\ominus}_{I.E.}$Na(g) + $\Delta H^{\ominus}_{E.A.}$Cl(g) + E = $\Delta H^{\ominus}_{f}$ Na⁺Cl⁻(s)

∴ +107 + 122 + 496 + (−349) + E = −411

Hence, the lattice energy of Na⁺Cl⁻(s), **E** = **−787** kJ mol⁻¹

Definitions for enthalpy changes

The enthalpy changes involved in these two routes are shown below.

The standard enthalpy change of formation ($\Delta H^{\ominus}_{f}$) is the enthalpy change that takes place when one mole of a compound in its standard state is formed from its constituent elements in their standard states under standard conditions.

$$Na(s) + ½Cl_2(g) \longrightarrow Na^+Cl^-(s) \qquad \Delta H^{\ominus}_{f} = -411 \text{ kJ mol}^{-1}$$

KEY POINT

Be careful when using $\Delta H^{\ominus}_{at}$ involving diatomic elements.

$\Delta H^{\ominus}_{at}$ relates to the formation of 1 mole of atoms. For chlorine, this involves ½Cl₂ only.

The standard enthalpy change of atomisation ($\Delta H^{\ominus}_{at}$) of an element is the enthalpy change that accompanies the formation of 1 mole of gaseous atoms from the element in its standard state.

$$Na(s) \longrightarrow Na(g) \qquad \Delta H^{\ominus}_{at} = +107 \text{ kJ mol}^{-1}$$
$$½Cl_2(g) \longrightarrow Cl(g) \qquad \Delta H^{\ominus}_{at} = +122 \text{ kJ mol}^{-1}$$

KEY POINT

For gaseous molecules $\Delta H^{\ominus}_{at}$ can be determined from the **bond enthalpy** (B.E.).

Cl–Cl(g) $\longrightarrow$ 2Cl(g)

$\Delta H^{\ominus}_{B.E.}$ = +244 kJ mol⁻¹

½Cl–Cl(g) $\longrightarrow$ Cl(g)

$\Delta H^{\ominus}_{at}$ = +122 kJ mol⁻¹

The first ionisation energy ($\Delta H^{\ominus}_{I.E.}$) of an element is the enthalpy change that accompanies the removal of 1 electron from each atom in 1 mole of gaseous atoms to form 1 mole of gaseous 1+ ions.

$$Na(g) \longrightarrow Na^+(g) + e^- \qquad \Delta H^{\ominus}_{I.E.} = +496 \text{ kJ mol}^{-1}$$

KEY POINT

Be careful when using electron affinities. $\Delta H^{\ominus}_{E.A.}$ relates to the formation of 1 mole of 1− ions. For chlorine, this involves Cl(g) only.

The first electron affinity ($\Delta H^{\ominus}_{E.A.}$) of an element is the enthalpy change that accompanies the addition of 1 electron to each atom in 1 mole of gaseous atoms to form 1 mole of gaseous 1− ions.

$$Cl(g) + e^- \longrightarrow Cl^-(g) \qquad \Delta H^{\ominus}_{E.A.} = -349 \text{ kJ mol}^{-1}$$

KEY POINT

Key points from AS

- **Polarisation**
  Revise AS pages 58–59

Factors affecting the size of lattice enthalpies

The strength of an ionic lattice and the value of its lattice enthalpy depend upon:

- ionic size
- ionic charge.

Effect of ionic size

The effect of increasing ionic size can be seen by comparing the lattice enthalpies of sodium halides as shown below.

Lattice energy has a negative value. You should use the term *'becomes less/more negative'* instead of *'becomes bigger/smaller'* to describe any trend in lattice energy.

compound	lattice enthalpy / kJ mol⁻¹	ions	effect of size of halide ion
NaCl	–787	(+)(−)	ionic size increases:
NaBr	–751	(+)(−)	• charge density decreases • attraction between ions decreases
NaI	–705	(+)(−)	• lattice energy becomes less negative.

Effect of ionic charge

The strongest ionic lattices with the most negative lattice enthalpies contain **small, highly charged ions**.

The diagram below compares the change in ionic size and ionic charge across Period 3 in the Periodic Table.

With increased charge on cation, two factors increase the magnitude of lattice energy:

- increased charge produces **more** attraction
- decreasing size produces **more** attraction.

With increased charge on anion, there are two competing factors:

- from Cl⁻ to P³⁻, the increasing ionic charge produces **more** attraction
- however, the ionic size also increases producing **less** attraction.

Key points from AS

- **Polarisation**
  Revise AS pages 58–59
- **The thermal stability of s-block compounds**
  Revise AS pages 78–79

Limitations of lattice enthalpies

Theoretical lattice enthalpies can be calculated by considering each ion as a perfect sphere. Any difference between this theoretical lattice enthalpy and lattice enthalpy calculated using a Born–Haber cycle indicates a degree of covalent bonding caused by polarisation. Polarisation is greatest between:

- a small densely charged cation and
- a large anion.

From the ions shown in the diagram above, we would expect the largest degree of covalency between Al³⁺ and P³⁻.

Enthalpy change of solution

AQA	M5	SALTERS	M5
EDEXCEL	M4	WJEC	M5
OCR	M5	CCEA	M4

Key points from AS

- **Indirect determination of enthalpy changes**
  Revise AS pages 99–100

An ionic lattice dissolves in **polar** solvents (e.g. water). In this process, the giant ionic lattice is broken up by polar water molecules which surround each ion in solution.

When sodium chloride is dissolved in water, the enthalpy change of this process can be measured directly as the enthalpy change of solution.

The energy cycle

The complete energy cycle for dissolving sodium chloride in water is shown below. Definitions of these enthalpy changes are shown below.

Lattice enthalpy **forms** the ionic lattice. Notice that the energy change to break 1 mole of the ionic lattice = – (lattice enthalpy).

Route 1: **A + B + C**

Route 2: **D**

Using Hess' Law: **A + B + C = D**

The production of hydrated ions comprises two changes:
- hydration of $Na^+(g)$
- hydration of $Cl^-(g)$.

To determine the enthalpy change of hydration of $Cl^-(aq)$, **C**,

$$-\Delta H^{\ominus}_{L.E.} NaCl(s) + \Delta H^{\ominus}_{hyd} Na^+(g) + \mathbf{C} = \Delta H^{\ominus}_{solution} NaCl(s)$$

$$\therefore\; -(-787) + (-390) + \mathbf{C} = +13$$

Hence, the enthalpy change of hydration of $Cl^-(aq)$, **C = –384 kJ mol^{-1}**

Definitions for enthalpy changes

The enthalpy changes involved in these two routes are shown below.

> The **standard enthalpy change of solution** ($\Delta H^{\ominus}_{solution}$) is the enthalpy change that accompanies the dissolving of 1 mole of a solute in a solvent to form an infinitely dilute solution under standard conditions.
>
> $$Na^+Cl^-(s) + aq \longrightarrow Na^+(aq) + Cl^-(aq) \qquad \Delta H^{\ominus}_{solution} = +13 \text{ kJmol}^{-1}$$

KEY POINT

> The **standard enthalpy change of hydration** ($\Delta H^{\ominus}_{hyd}$) of an ion is the enthalpy change that accompanies the hydration of 1 mole of gaseous ions to form 1 mole of hydrated ions in an infinitely dilute solution under standard conditions.
>
> $$Na^+(g) + aq \longrightarrow Na^+(aq) \qquad \Delta H^{\ominus}_{hyd} = -390 \text{ kJmol}^{-1}$$
> $$Cl^-(g) + aq \longrightarrow Cl^-(aq) \qquad \Delta H^{\ominus}_{hyd} = -384 \text{ kJmol}^{-1}$$

KEY POINT

Factors affecting the magnitude of hydration enthalpy

The values obtained for each ion depend upon the size of the charge and the size of the ion.

ion	Na^+	Mg^{2+}	Al^{3+}	Cl^-	Br^-	I^-
$\Delta H^{\ominus}_{hyd}$/kJ mol^{-1}	–390	–1891	–4613	–384	–351	–307
effect of charge	• increasing ionic charge • greater attraction for water					
ionic radius/nm	0.102	0.072	0.053	0.180	0.195	0.215
effect of size	• decreasing ionic size • greater attraction for water			• increasing ionic size • less attraction for water		

Bond enthalpies

 M5

Key points from AS

• **Bond enthalpy**
  Revise AS pages 102–103

For AQA,

• you should be able to use mean bond enthalpies to calculate an approximate value of ΔH for other reactions.

> $\Delta H = \Sigma$(bond enthalpies in reactants) – Σ(bond enthalpies in products).
>
> **KEY POINT**

• you should be able to explain why values from mean bond enthalpy calculations differ from those determined from enthalpy cycles.

> A **mean bond enthalpy** gives the typical value of a particular bond, having taken into account the same bond in different environments.
>
> In particular environments a bond may have a different value for the bond enthalpy than the mean value.
>
> **KEY POINT**

For full details, you will need to refer to *Revise AS Chemistry*, Chapter 3.3.

Progress check

1 Using the information below:
   (a) name each enthalpy change **A** to **E**
   (b) construct a Born–Haber cycle for sodium bromide and calculate the lattice enthalpy (enthalpy change of lattice formation) of sodium bromide.

enthalpy change	equation	$\Delta H^{\ominus}$/kJ mol^{-1}
A	$Na(s) + \frac{1}{2}Br_2(l) \longrightarrow NaBr(s)$	–361
B	$Br(g) + e^- \longrightarrow Br^-(g)$	–325
C	$Na(s) \longrightarrow Na(g)$	+107
D	$Na(g) \longrightarrow Na^+(g) + e^-$	+496
E	$\frac{1}{2}Br_2(l) \longrightarrow Br(g)$	+112

2 You are provided with the following enthalpy changes.
   $$Na^+(g) + F^-(g) \longrightarrow NaF(s) \qquad \Delta H = -918 \text{ kJ mol}^{-1}$$
   $$Na^+(g) + aq \longrightarrow Na^+(aq) \qquad \Delta H = -390 \text{ kJ mol}^{-1}$$
   $$F^-(g) + aq \longrightarrow F^-(aq) \qquad \Delta H = -457 \text{ kJ mol}^{-1}$$
   (a) Name each of these three enthalpy changes.
   (b) Write an equation, including state symbols, for which the enthalpy change is the enthalpy change of solution of NaF.
   (c) Calculate the enthalpy change of solution of NaF.

Special properties of water arising from hydrogen bonding

SALTERS   M5

Hydrogen bonding is strong enough to have significant effects on physical properties, resulting in some unusual properties for water.

Water has an unexpectedly high boiling point

The boiling points of the Group 6 hydrides are shown below.

> When water changes state, the covalent bonds between the H and O atoms in an H$_2$O molecule are strong and do not break.
>
> It is the intermolecular forces that break.

hydride	H$_2$O	H$_2$S	H$_2$Se	H$_2$Te
boiling point/K	373	212	232	271

The boiling points increase from H$_2$S $\longrightarrow$ H$_2$Te:

- the number of electrons in molecules increase
- van der Waals' forces increase
- more energy is required to break the intermolecular bonds to vaporise the hydrides.

But the **boiling point** of H$_2$O is **higher** than expected. This provides evidence that there are some extra forces acting between the molecules that must be broken to boil each hydride. These extra forces are hydrogen bonds.

> Without hydrogen bonding, H$_2$O would be a gas at room temperature and pressure.

This difference is also evident in the unusually high **enthalpy change of vaporisation** of water.

> Enthalpy change of vaporisation is a measure of the energy required to convert water from a liquid to a gas.

This has consequences for the Earth's climate.

- Energy is **required** to **vaporise** water molecules from the oceans into water vapour but this energy is **released** when water molecules **condense** as rain.
- Heat is transferred from the oceans to the land, stabilising the Earth's temperature across different climate zones.

Water has a relatively large specific heat capacity

Compared with similar compounds, water has an unusually high value specific heat capacity. Hydrogen bonds have to be overcome before energy can be transferred to water molecules to increase the kinetic energy of the molecules.

> Specific heat capacity, *c*, is a measure of the energy required to heat a substance.

This has consequences for the Earth's climate.

- Because extra energy is needed to change the temperature of water, the vast stores of water in the oceans help to stabilise the Earth's temperature especially via ocean currents from one region to another.

Water is more dense than ice

- Solids are *usually* denser than liquids – but ice is less dense than water.
- Particles in solids are usually packed closer together than in liquids.
- Hydrogen bonds hold water molecules apart in an open lattice structure.

> Solids are usually denser than liquids – but ice is less dense than water.

∴ ice is less dense than water.

The diagram below shows how the open lattice of ice collapses on melting.

hydrogen bonds break

MELTING OF ICE

tetrahedral open lattice in ice

ice lattice collapses: molecules move closer together

2.2 Entropy changes

After studying this section you should be able to:

- explain that entropy is a measure of disorder
- calculate entropy changes from standard entropies
- understand that entropy, enthalpy and temperature determine the feasibility of a reaction
- apply rates and equilibrium to industrial applications

LEARNING SUMMARY

Entropy

AQA	M5	SALTERS	M5
EDEXCEL	M4	WJEC	M5
OCR	M5	CCEA	M4

What is entropy?

Entropy, S, is a measure of disorder.

Entropy increases whenever particles become more disordered, e.g.

- when a gas spreads spontaneously through a room
- with increasing temperature
- during changes in state: solid $\longrightarrow$ liquid $\longrightarrow$ gas
- when a solid lattice dissolves
    $$NaCl(aq) + aq \longrightarrow Na^+(aq) + Cl^-(aq)$$

> At 0 K, perfect crystals have zero entropy.

- in a reaction in which there is an increase in the number of gaseous molecules (i.e. when a gas is evolved)
    $$NaHCO_3(s) + HCl(aq) \longrightarrow NaCl(aq) + H_2O(l) + CO_2(g)$$
    $$MgCO_3(s) \longrightarrow MgO(s) + CO_2(g)$$

Calculating entropy changes

The standard entropy, $S^\ominus$, of a substance is the entropy content of one mole of a substance, under standard conditions.

The entropy change of a reaction can be calculated using standard entropies of the reactants and products.

> $$\Delta S = \Sigma S^\ominus \text{ (products)} - \Sigma S^\ominus \text{ (reactants)}$$

KEY POINT

Example

> Notice that standard entropies have units of J K⁻¹ mol⁻¹.

The equation below is for the carbon reduction of chromium oxide, Cr_2O_3.
$$Cr_2O_3(s) + 3C(s) \longrightarrow 2Cr(s) + 3CO(g)$$

	$Cr_2O_3(s)$	$C(s)$	$Cr(s)$	$CO(g)$
$S^\ominus$/J K⁻¹ mol⁻¹	+81	+6	+24	+198

$\Delta S = \Sigma S^\ominus$ (products) $- \Sigma S^\ominus$ (reactants)

$= [(2 \times 24) + (3 \times 198)] - [(+81) + (3 \times 6)] = 543$ J K⁻¹ mol⁻¹

Spontaneous processes

A **spontaneous** process is one that proceeds of its **own accord**.

Processes lead to **increased stability** if they lead to a **lower energy** state.

This is obviously the situation in an exothermic reaction in which the enthalpy (heat energy) decreases during a reaction. It therefore seems surprising that **some** reactions are **endothermic** and that these can **occur spontaneously** at room temperature.

Enthalpy changes alone cannot explain whether a reaction takes place.

For this, we must consider both the ΔH and ΔS.

Different exam boards have taken different approaches to this and these are discussed below. Select the correct approach for your specification.

Free energy

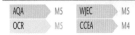

| AQA | M5 | WJEC | M5 |
| OCR | M5 | CCEA | M4 |

Whether a chemical or physical process takes place is dependent on

- the temperature, T,
- the entropy change in the system, ΔS,
- the enthalpy change, ΔH, with the surroundings.

The change in *Free Energy*, ΔG, automatically determines the balance between enthalpy change, entropy change and temperature:

$$\Delta G = \Delta H - T\Delta S$$

> The balance between entropy and enthalpy is the feasibility of a reaction.

Feasibility of a reaction

Processes are spontaneous (feasible) when ΔG is negative. The sign of ΔG depends upon ΔH and ΔS, as shown below.

ΔH	ΔS	ΔG
–ve	+ve	always –ve: reaction feasible
+ve	–ve	always +ve: reaction never feasible
–ve	–ve	–ve at low temperatures
+ve	+ve	–ve at high temperatures

> ΔG varies with temperature:
> when ΔH and ΔS have the same sign, the feasibility of the process depends on the temperature, T.

- $\Delta G = \Delta H - T\Delta S$
- The reaction is feasible when $\Delta G < 0$.

Example

The equation below is for the carbon reduction of chromium oxide, Cr_2O_3.

$$Cr_2O_3(s) + 3C(s) \longrightarrow 2Cr(s) + 3CO(g)$$

$\Delta H = +807$ kJ mol^{-1}; $\Delta S = 543$ J K^{-1} mol^{-1}

What is the minimum temperature that this reaction takes place spontaneously?

$\Delta S = 543$ J K^{-1} mol^{-1} = 0.543 kJ K^{-1} mol^{-1}

$\Delta G = \Delta H - T\Delta S$;

Minimum temperature when $\Delta G = 0$.

> Be careful with units:
> ΔH: kJ mol^{-1}
> ΔS: J K^{-1} mol^{-1}

$$\therefore 0 = \Delta H - T\Delta S; \quad T = \frac{\Delta H}{\Delta S} = \frac{807}{0.543} = 1486 \text{ K}$$

ΔG and equilibrium constants (WJEC only)

For a reaction with ΔG negative:

- equilibrium constants will have large values as the products predominate.

For a reaction with ΔG positive:

- equilibrium constants will have small values as the reactants predominate.

Total entropy

EDEXCEL ▸ M4   SALTERS ▸ M5

For a chemical process to take place, there are two types of entropy (disorder) that need to be considered:

- the entropy change of the chemical system, ΔS_{system}
- the entropy change of the surroundings, $\Delta S_{surroundings}$

ΔS_{system}

This is the disorder of the particles making up the chemicals – the chemical 'system'. ΔS_{system} measures the number of ways that the particles can be arranged. It also measures the number of ways that energy can be distributed between the particles.

> Entropy is a measure of the number of ways that molecules and their associated energy quanta can be arranged.

ΔS_{system} can be calculated using:

$$\Delta S_{system} = \Sigma S^{\ominus} \text{ (products)} - \Sigma S^{\ominus} \text{ (reactants)}$$

A system becomes more stable when ΔS_{system} is positive.

$\Delta S_{surroundings}$

This is the disorder of energy in the surroundings.

In terms of energy, the surroundings become more stable when $\Delta S_{surroundings}$ increases and energy spreads from the chemicals into the surroundings in an exothermic process.

$\Delta S_{surroundings}$ is related to the enthalpy change and temperature, in K:

$$\Delta S_{surroundings} = -\frac{\Delta H}{T}$$

The surrounding system becomes more stable during an exothermic reaction when $\Delta S_{surroundings}$ is positive.

Feasibility of a reaction

> ΔS_{total} only tells us the 'thermodynamic stability'. Even if a reaction is thermodynamically stable, it may not seem to take place if the activation energy is great and the rate of reaction is slow ('kinetic stability').

The total entropy, ΔS_{total}, is the overall balance of entropy from the system and from the surroundings:

$$\Delta S_{total} = \Delta S_{system} + \Delta S_{surroundings}$$

or
$$\Delta S_{total} = \Delta S_{system} - \frac{\Delta H}{T}$$

For a process to take place, the natural direction of change is towards increasing total entropy when ΔS_{total} is positive, i.e. $\Delta S_{total} > 0$.

The process is then feasible and takes place 'spontaneously'.

Example

The equation below is for the carbon reduction of chromium oxide, Cr_2O_3.

$$Cr_2O_3(s) + 3C(s) \longrightarrow 2Cr(s) + 3CO(g)$$

$\Delta H = +807 \text{ kJ mol}^{-1}$; $\Delta S = 543 \text{ J K}^{-1} \text{ mol}^{-1}$

What is the minimum temperature that this reaction takes place at spontaneously?

$$\Delta S_{system} = 543 \text{ J K}^{-1} \text{ mol}^{-1} = 0.543 \text{ kJ K}^{-1} \text{ mol}^{-1}$$

$$\Delta S_{total} = \Delta S_{system} - \frac{\Delta H}{T}$$

Minimum temperature when $\Delta S_{total} = 0$.

> Be careful with units:
> ΔH: kJ mol^{-1}
> ΔS: J K^{-1} mol^{-1}

$$\therefore \Delta S_{system} - \frac{\Delta H}{T} = 0; \ \Delta S_{system} = \frac{\Delta H}{T}; \ T = \frac{\Delta H}{\Delta S_{system}} = \frac{807}{0.543} = 1486 \text{ K}$$

ΔS and equilibrium constants (Edexcel only)

For a reaction in which ΔS_{total} increases, the magnitude of the equilibrium constant also increases:

- $\Delta S = R\ln K$

Progress check (all specifications)

1 State whether the equations below have a positive or negative entropy change.
(a) $H_2O(g) \longrightarrow H_2O(l)$
(b) $N_2(g) + 3H_2(g) \longrightarrow 2NH_3(g)$
(c) $CaCl_2(s) + aq \longrightarrow Ca^{2+}(aq) + 2Cl^-(aq)$

2 The equation below is for the thermal decomposition of calcium carbonate.
$$CaCO_3(s) \longrightarrow CaO(s) + CO_2(g) \qquad \Delta H = +178 \text{ kJ mol}^{-1}$$

	$CaCO_3(s)$	$CaO(s)$	$CO_2(g)$
$S^{\ominus}/$ J K^{-1} mol^{-1}	+93	+40	+214

(a) What is ΔS?
(b) What is the minimum temperature for decomposition to take place?

2 (a) 161 J K⁻¹ mol⁻¹; (b) 1106 K
1 (a) –ve; (b) –ve; (c) +ve.

Applying rates and equilibrium to industrial processes

AQA	M4	SALTERS	M5
EDEXCEL	M4	WJEC	M5
OCR	M5	CCEA	M4

Industrial processes need to obtain economic yields of the product being manufactured. In the section above, we discussed the importance of the balance between **enthalpy, entropy and temperature**.

Equilibrium

You do not need to know the actual industrial conditions used in the Haber process.

In the Haber process for the production of ammonia
$$N_2(g) + 3H_2(g) \rightleftharpoons 2NH_3(g) \qquad \Delta H^{\ominus} = -92 \text{ kJ mol}^{-1}$$

- the right-hand side has **fewer moles of gas** than the left-hand side (reactants), favoured by a **high** pressure
- the forward reaction is **exothermic**, favoured by a **low** temperature.

We can arrive at these conclusions by using le Chatelier's principle from AS Chemistry.

The optimum equilibrium conditions for maximum equilibrium yield are: **high pressure and low temperature**.

The need for compromise

In reality it may not be feasible to use optimum equilibrium conditions.

The rate of a reaction increases with higher temperatures and pressures – but temperature has a much larger effect.

- Compressing gases to **high pressures** has a high **energy cost**. There are also considerable **safety** implications of using very high pressures.
- At **low temperatures**, the rate of reaction is **slow** as few molecules possess the necessary activation energy of the reaction.

There needs to be a compromise.

Compromising

Optimum conditions, reaction rate, feasibility, reality, safety and economics must be considered.

- Use of a **high enough pressure** to **increase** the **equilibrium yield** without increasing **energy costs** in generating the pressure or compromising **safety**.
- Increase the temperature just enough to increase the rate of reaction so that the reaction takes place in a realistic time frame, whilst still producing an **adequate equilibrium yield**.

Equilibrium in never reached

Another factor is that industrial processes do not operate at equilibrium:

- products are removed – we never have a closed system
- there is insufficient time for equilibrium to be reached.

But it is still important to consider the conditions needed to secure a high equilibrium yield.

The search for better processes

The chemical industry takes steps to maximise the **atom economy** of the process. Many factors need to be considered, including:

Hazards can be reduced by developing processes that reduce risks from toxic reactants, explosions, acidic or flammable gases, toxic emissions, etc.

- **recycling** unreacted reagents
- developing **alternative reactions** and processes
- using **more available** raw materials, preferably **renewable**
- using **catalysts** to allow processes to occur at **lower temperatures**, cutting energy needs
- developing **simpler processes** requiring less costly chemical plants
- using **co-products** and **by-products**, rather than disposing of them.

Global warming from energy production

SALTERS ▷ M5   CCEA ▷ M4

Key points from AS

- **Global warming**
  Revise AS pages 147–148

Much of the CO_2 released into the atmosphere dissolves in the oceans.

The concentration of carbon dioxide in the atmosphere depends on natural processes including:

- photosynthesis
- respiration
- the solubility of the gas in surface waters.

Combustion of non-renewable hydrocarbon fuels for energy is causing an increase in the atmospheric concentration of carbon dioxide. Carbon dioxide is a greenhouse gas, implicated as a likely cause for global warming.

The **greenhouse effect** of a gas (e.g. CO_2) depends on:

- its atmospheric concentration
- its ability to absorb infra-red radiation.

Reducing atmospheric CO_2 levels

Various approaches are being considered to reduce atmospheric CO_2 levels. These include:

- more economical use of fuels
- the use of alternative fuels (including hydrogen, see pages 65–66)
- capture and storage of CO_2
- increased photosynthesis.

2.3 Electrochemical cells

After studying this section you should be able to:

- *understand the principles of an electrochemical cell*
- *define the term 'standard electrode (redox) potential', $E^{\ominus}$*
- *describe how to measure standard electrode potentials*
- *calculate a standard cell potential from standard electrode potentials*
- *write cell diagrams*
- *describe applications of electrochemical cells, including fuel cells*
- *understand that rusting is an electrochemical process*

LEARNING SUMMARY

Key points from AS

- **Redox reactions**
  Revise AS pages 42–44

During the study of redox in AS Chemistry you learnt:

- that oxidation and reduction involve transfer of electrons in a redox reaction
- the rules for assigning oxidation states
- how to construct an overall redox equation from two half-equations.

These key principles are built upon by considering electrochemical cells in which redox reactions provide electrical energy.

Electricity from chemical reactions

AQA	M5	SALTERS	M4
EDEXCEL	M5	WJEC	M5
OCR	M5	CCEA	M5

In a redox reaction, electrons are transferred between the reacting chemicals.

For example, zinc reacts with aqueous copper(II) ions in a redox reaction.

$$Zn(s) + Cu^{2+}(aq) \longrightarrow Zn^{2+}(aq) + Cu(s)$$

oxidation: $Zn(s) \longrightarrow Zn^{2+}(aq) + 2e^-$
reduction: $Cu^{2+}(aq) + 2e^- \longrightarrow Cu(s)$

If this reaction is carried out simply by mixing zinc with aqueous copper(II) ions:

- heat energy is produced and, unless used as useful heat, is often wasted.

An electrochemical cell controls the transfer of electrons:

- electrical energy is produced and can be used for electricity.

Electrochemical cells are the basis of all batteries. Their true value is as a portable form of electricity.

The zinc-copper electrochemical cell

An electrochemical cell comprises two **half-cells**. In each half-cell, the **oxidation** and **reduction** processes take place **separately**.

A zinc-copper cell has two half-cells:

- an oxidation half-cell containing reactants and products from the oxidation half-reaction: $Zn^{2+}(aq)$ and $Zn(s)$
- a reduction half-cell containing reactants and products from the reduction half-reaction: $Cu^{2+}(aq)$ and $Cu(s)$.

A half-cell contains the oxidised and reduced species from a half-equation.

The species can be converted into one another by addition or removal of electrons.

The circuit is completed using:

- a connecting **wire** which transfers **electrons** between the half-cells
- a **salt bridge** which transfers **ions** between the half-cells.

The salt bridge consists of filter paper soaked in aqueous KNO_3 or NH_4NO_3.

salt bridge

OXIDATION   REDUCTION

Remember these charge carriers:

ELECTRONS through the wire;

IONS through the salt bridge.

oxidation half-cell: $Zn^{2+}(aq)$ and $Zn(s)$
- **Zn is oxidised to Zn^{2+}:** $Zn(s) \longrightarrow Zn^{2+}(aq) + 2e^-$
- electrons are **supplied** to the external circuit
- the polarity is **negative**.

reduction half-cell: $Cu^{2+}(aq)$ and $Cu(s)$
- **Cu^{2+} is reduced to Cu:** $Cu^{2+}(aq) + 2e^- \longrightarrow Cu(s)$
- electrons are **taken** from the external circuit
- the polarity is **positive**.

The measured cell e.m.f. of 1.10 V indicates that there is a potential difference of 1.10 V between the copper and zinc half-cells.

Standard electrode potentials

AQA	M5	SALTERS	M4
EDEXCEL	M5	WJEC	M5
OCR	M5	CCEA	M5

A **hydrogen half-cell** is used as the standard for the measurement of standard electrode potentials.

The standard hydrogen half-cell is based upon the half-reaction below.

$$H^+(aq) + e^- \rightleftharpoons \tfrac{1}{2}H_2(g)$$

A hydrogen half-cell typically comprises

- 1 mol dm^{-3} hydrochloric acid as the source of $H^+(aq)$

- a supply of hydrogen gas, $H_2(g)$ at 100 kPa

- an inert platinum electrode on which the half-reaction above takes place.

> **KEY POINT**
>
> The **standard electrode potential** of a half-cell, $E^\ominus$, is the e.m.f. of a half-cell compared with a standard hydrogen half-cell.
> All measurements are at **298 K** with solution **concentrations of 1 mol dm^{-3}** and gas **pressures of 100 kPa.**

Measuring standard electrode potentials

Half-cells comprising a metal and a metal ion

The diagram below shows how a hydrogen half-cell can be used to measure the standard electrode potential of a copper half-cell.

A high-resistance voltmeter is used to minimise the current that flows.

Hydrogen half-cell

> **KEY POINT**
>
> - The standard electrode potential of a half-cell represents its contribution to the cell e.m.f.
> - The contribution made by the hydrogen half-cell to the cell e.m.f. is defined as 0 V.
> - The **sign** of the standard electrode potential of a half-cell indicates its **polarity** compared with the hydrogen half-cell.

As with the hydrogen half-cell, the platinum electrode provides a surface on which the half-reaction can take place.

Half-cells comprising ions of different oxidation states

The half-reaction in a half-cell can be between aqueous ions of the same element with different oxidation states. To allow electrons to pass into the half-cell, an inert electrode of platinum is used.

A half-cell can contain $Fe^{3+}(aq)$ and $Fe^{2+}(aq)$ ions:

$$Fe^{3+}(aq) \rightleftharpoons Fe^{2+}(aq) + e^-$$

A standard $Fe^{3+}(aq)/Fe^{2+}(aq)$ half-cell requires:

Pt (inert electrode)

$Fe^{2+}(aq)$, 1 mol dm^{-3}
$Fe^{3+}(aq)$, 1 mol dm^{-3}

Alternatively the solution can contain **equal** concentrations of Fe^{2+} and Fe^{3+}.

- a solution containing **both**
  - 1 mol dm^{-3} $Fe^{3+}(aq)$ **and**
  - 1 mol dm^{-3} $Fe^{2+}(aq)$
- an inert platinum electrode with a connecting wire.

The electrochemical series

AQA	M5
EDEXCEL	M5
OCR	M5
SALTERS	M4
WJEC	M5
CCEA	M5

A standard electrode potential indicates the availability of electrons from a half-reaction.

Metals are reducing agents.

- Metals typically react by donating electrons in a redox reaction.
- Reactive metals have the greatest tendency to donate electrons and their half-cells have the most negative electrode potentials.

Non-metals are oxidising agents.

Key points from AS

- **Reactivity of s-block elements**
  Revise AS page 77
- **The relative reactivity of the halogens as oxidising agents**
  Revise AS page 81

- Non-metals typically react by accepting electrons in a redox reaction.
- Reactive non-metals have the greatest tendency to accept electrons and their half-cells have the most positive electrode potentials.

The **electrochemical series** shows electrode reactions listed in order of their $E^\ominus$ values. The electrochemical series below lists with the **most positive $E^\ominus$** value at the top. This enables oxidising and reducing agents to be easily compared. The reduced form is shown on the right-hand side of the electrode equilibrium.

This version of the electrochemical series shows standard electrode potentials listed with the **most positive $E^\ominus$** value at the top.

You will find versions of the electrochemical series listed with the **most negative $E^\ominus$** value at the top.

This does not matter. The important point is that the potentials are listed **in order** and **can be compared.**

strongest oxidising agent	*electrode reaction*					$E^\ominus$/ V	
	$F_2(g)$	+	$2e^-$	$\rightleftharpoons$	$2F^-(aq)$	+2.87	
	$Cl_2(g)$	+	$2e^-$	$\rightleftharpoons$	$2Cl^-(aq)$	+1.36	
	$Br_2(l)$	+	$2e^-$	$\rightleftharpoons$	$2Br^-(aq)$	+1.09	
	$Ag^+(aq)$	+	e^-	$\rightleftharpoons$	$Ag(s)$	+0.80	
	$Cu^{2+}(aq)$	+	$2e^-$	$\rightleftharpoons$	$Cu(s)$	+0.34	
	$H^+(aq)$	+	e^-	$\rightleftharpoons$	$\frac{1}{2}H_2(g)$	0	
	$Fe^{2+}(aq)$	+	$2e^-$	$\rightleftharpoons$	$Fe(s)$	−0.44	
	$Zn^{2+}(aq)$	+	$2e^-$	$\rightleftharpoons$	$Zn(s)$	−0.76	
	$Cr^{3+}(aq)$	+	$3e^-$	$\rightleftharpoons$	$Cr(s)$	−0.77	*strongest reducing agent*
	$K^+(aq)$	+	e^-	$\rightleftharpoons$	$K(s)$	−2.92	

In the electrochemical series:
- the **oxidised** form is on the **left-hand side** of the half-equation
- the **reduced** form is on the **right-hand side** of the half-equation.

KEY POINT

Standard cell potentials and cell reactions

AQA	M5
EDEXCEL	M5
OCR	M5
SALTERS	M4
WJEC	M5
CCEA	M5

The **standard cell potential** of a cell is the e.m.f. acting between the two half-cells making up the cell under standard conditions.

The **cell reaction** is:

Key points from AS

- **Combining half-equations**
  Revise AS page 44

- the overall process taking place in the cell
- the sum of the reduction and oxidation half-reactions taking place in each half-cell.

Calculating the standard cell potential of a silver-iron(II) cell

Identify the two relevant half-reactions and the polarity of each electrode.

The more positive of the two systems is the positive terminal of the cell.

$Ag^+(aq)$ + e^- ⇌ $Ag(s)$ $E^\ominus$ = + 0.80 V   *positive terminal*
$Fe^{2+}(aq)$ + $2e^-$ ⇌ $Fe(s)$ $E^\ominus$ = –0.44 V   *negative terminal*

The standard electrode potential is the difference between the $E^\ominus$ values:

> $E^\ominus_{cell}$ is the difference between the standard electrode potentials.

Simply subtract the $E^\ominus$ of the negative terminal from the $E^\ominus$ of the positive terminal:

$$E^\ominus_{cell} = E^\ominus \; (positive \; terminal) - E^\ominus \; (negative \; terminal)$$
$$\therefore \; E^\ominus_{cell} = 0.080 - (-0.44) = \mathbf{1.24 \; V}$$

Determination of the cell reaction in a silver-iron(II) cell

Work out the actual direction of the half-equations.

> The more negative half-equation is reversed. The negative terminal is then on the left-hand side.

The **half-equation** with the **more negative $E^\ominus$** value provides the electrons and proceeds to the left. This half-equation is reversed so that the two half-reactions taking place can be clearly seen and compared.

$Ag^+(aq)$ + e^- ⟶ $Ag(s)$ *reaction at positive terminal*
$Fe(s)$ ⟶ $Fe(aq)$ + $2e^-$ *reaction at negative terminal*

The overall cell reaction can be found by adding the half-equations.

> This is discussed in detail in the AS Chemistry Study Guide, page 44.

The silver half-equation must first be multiplied by '2' to balance the electrons.
The two half-equations are then added.

$2Ag^+(aq)$ + $Fe(s)$ ⟶ $2Ag(s)$ + $Fe^{2+}(aq)$

Cell diagrams

AQA ▶ M5   EDEXCEL ▶ M5

A simple metal electrode comprises a metal in contact with a solution of its ions, e.g. $Cu(s)|Cu^{2+}(aq)$. This is the half-cell.

- The solid vertical line shows a boundary between a solid and a solution.

A cell diagram is a convenient way of representing a cell.

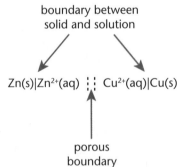

Two dotted vertical lines show a porous boundary between two half-cells. This is the salt bridge in simple cells.

Notice that the ions in solution are shown in contact with the salt bridge. The metals taking the electric current in and out of the cell are shown at either end of the cell diagram.

The standard cell potential of the cell, as shown in the cell diagram, is defined as:

$$E^\ominus(cell) = E^\ominus(right\text{-}hand \; side) - E^\ominus(left\text{-}hand \; side)$$

The sign of the cell gives the polarity of the right-hand half-cell.

For the cell shown above,

- $E^\ominus(cell) = 0.34 - (-0.76) = +1.10 \; V$
- the $Cu(s)|Cu^{2+}(aq)$ half-cell (shown on the right) is positive.

Electrochemical cells

Electrochemical cells can be used as a commercial source of electrical energy.

Cells can be divided into three main types:

- non-rechargeable cells – the cell is used until the chemicals are used up to such a point at which the voltage falls
- rechargeable cells – the cell reaction can readily be reversed when recharging, allowing the cell to be used again
- fuel cells – the cell reaction requires external supplies of a fuel and an oxidant, which are consumed and need to be replenished.

An electrochemical cell comprises two half-cells with different electrode potentials. For example, a simple cell can be set up based on zinc and copper.

The redox systems are shown below.

$$Zn^{2+}(aq) + 2e^- \rightleftharpoons Zn(s) \qquad E^\ominus = -0.74 \text{ V}$$
$$Cu^{2+}(aq) + 2e^- \rightleftharpoons Cu(s) \qquad E^\ominus = +0.34 \text{ V}$$

The more negative zinc system provides the electrons:

Overall: $Zn(s) + Cu^{2+}(aq) \longrightarrow Cu(s) + Zn^{2+}(aq)$

Chargeable and non-rechargeable cells are used as our modern-day cells and batteries.

Other common examples include:
- nickel and cadmium (NiCad) batteries used in rechargeable batteries
- lithium 'button' cells used in watches
- lithium-ion batteries used in laptops.

All these cells work on the same principle, using two redox systems.

Fuel cells for energy

In a fuel cell, energy from the reaction of a fuel with oxygen is used to create a voltage.

- The reactants flow in and products flow out, while the electrolyte remains in the cell.
- Fuel cells can operate virtually continuously as long as the fuel and oxygen continue to flow into the cell. Fuel cells do not have to be recharged.

In the future, a 'hydrogen economy' based on hydrogen fuel cells may well contribute greatly to energy needs.

The diagram below shows a simple hydrogen–oxygen fuel cell.

- At the negative electrode (cathode),
    $$H_2(g) \longrightarrow 2H^+(aq) + 2e^-$$
- At the positive electrode (anode),
    $$\tfrac{1}{2}O_2(g) + 2H^+(aq) + 2e^- \longrightarrow H_2O(l)$$
- Overall: $H_2(g) + \tfrac{1}{2}O_2(g) \longrightarrow H_2O(l)$

In exams, you are unlikely to have to recall a specific storage cell.

But do take care! Your specification **may** expect you to know the hydrogen fuel cell.

You might also be expected to make predictions on a supplied electrochemical cell. All relevant electrode potentials and other data would be supplied though.

Other hydrogen fuel cells operate with an alkaline electrolyte.

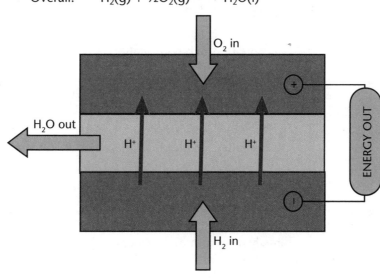

Development of fuel cell vehicles (FCVs)

Fuel cells are being developed as an alternative to finite oil-based fuels in cars.

Scientists in the car industry are developing fuel cell vehicles (FCVs), fuelled by:

- hydrogen gas
- hydrogen-rich fuels.

Hydrogen-rich fuels include methanol, natural gas, or petrol. These are converted into hydrogen gas by an onboard 'reformer'. These fuels are easier to transport and deliver into an FCV than hydrogen gas.

FCVs have advantages over conventional petrol or diesel-powered vehicles.

- Pure hydrogen emits only water.
- Hydrogen-rich fuels produce only small amounts of air pollutants and CO_2.
- Efficiency can be more than twice that of similarly-sized conventional vehicles. Other advanced technologies are being investigated to further increase efficiency.

Hydrogen might be stored in FCVs:

- as a liquid under pressure
- adsorbed on the surface of a solid material
- absorbed within a solid material.

> Advantages of hydrogen fuel cells:
> less pollution and less CO_2,
> greater efficiency.

Limitations of hydrogen fuel cells

There are logistical problems in the development of hydrogen fuel cells:

- storing and transporting hydrogen, in terms of safety, feasibility of a pressurised liquid and a limited life cycle of a solid 'adsorber' or 'absorber'
- limited lifetime (requiring regular replacement and disposal) and high production costs
- use of toxic chemicals in their production
- initial manufacture of hydrogen requires energy
- public and political acceptance of hydrogen as a fuel.

> Liquefying hydrogen is costly in terms of energy use.
>
> Safety is a major concern: Hydrogen is very flammable.

Future energy needs

Political and social desire to move to a hydrogen economy has many obstacles including ignorance that energy is needed to produce hydrogen and that fuel cells have a finite life.

> Hydrogen is an 'energy carrier' and not an 'energy source'. Hydrogen is first made either by electrolysis of water or by reacting methanol (a finite fuel) with steam.

Fuel cells as breathalysers

EDEXCEL   M5

Ethanol fuel cells are being used in some modern breathalysers to measure the concentration of blood alcohol.

- A platinum catalyst in the fuel cell oxidises ethanol to ethanoic acid, releasing electrons. The electrons increase the current in the fuel cell – the greater the current, the more ethanol in the breath and the greater the concentration of blood alcohol.

Other modern methods are based on IR absorption.

- A particular IR absorption identifies the presence of ethanol in the breath and the intensity of this absorption peak is directly related to the ethanol level.

For IR absorption, see AS pages 143–144.

The oldest method used a chemical reaction based on the reduction of orange chromium(VI) to green chromium(III) by ethanol. The degree of colour change is directly related to the level of alcohol in the expired air.

For reduction of chromium compounds, see page 98.

Progress check

1 Use the standard electrode potentials on page 63, to answer the questions that follow.
   (a) Calculate the standard cell potential for the following cells.
      (i) F_2/F^- and Ag^+/Ag
      (ii) Ag^+/Ag and Cr^{3+}/Cr
      (iii) Cu^{2+}/Cu and Cr^{3+}/Cr.
   (b) For each cell in (a) determine which half-reactions proceed, and hence construct, the cell reaction.

Corrosion as an electrochemical process

SALTERS ▷ M5

Rusting

Rusting is an electrochemical process involving **iron**, **oxygen** and **water**.

The key redox systems involved are shown below:

$$Fe^{2+} + 2e^- \rightleftharpoons Fe \qquad E^\ominus = -0.44 \text{ V}$$
$$\tfrac{1}{2}O_2 + H_2O + 2e^- \rightleftharpoons 2OH^- \qquad E^\ominus = +0.44 \text{ V}$$

- The Fe^{2+}/Fe system has the **more negative** $E^\ominus$ value and its half-reaction will **supply electrons**.
- This equation is therefore reversed.

oxidation:	Fe	$\longrightarrow Fe^{2+} + 2e^-$
reduction:	$\tfrac{1}{2}O_2 + H_2O + 2e^-$	$\longrightarrow 2OH^-$
overall:	$Fe + \tfrac{1}{2}O_2 + H_2O$	$\longrightarrow Fe^{2+} + 2OH^-$

- The Fe^{2+} and OH^- ions now combine to form iron(II) hydroxide.
- Finally $Fe(OH)_2$ is **oxidised** by **oxygen** in the presence of **water**, forming **rust**:

$$Fe(OH)_2 \xrightarrow{O_2/H_2O} Fe_2O_3 \bullet xH_2O$$
$$\text{RUST}$$

Corrosion prevention

The main methods for protecting iron and steel from corrosion are:
- sacrificial protection by galvanising and use of zinc blocks
- barrier protection using oil, grease, paint or a polymer coating.

In **sacrificial protection**,
- the iron is in contact with a metal with a more negative $E^\ominus$ value
- Mg or Zn are usually used.

> Sacrificial protection is used to protect cars (a zinc coating) and North Sea oil platforms (zinc blocks).

$$Mg^{2+} + 2e^- \rightleftharpoons Mg \qquad E^\ominus = -2.36 \text{ V}$$
$$Zn^{2+} + 2e^- \rightleftharpoons Zn \qquad E^\ominus = -0.76 \text{ V}$$
$$Fe^{2+} + 2e^- \rightleftharpoons Fe \qquad E^\ominus = -0.44 \text{ V}$$

more negative $E^\ominus$

When an electrochemical cell is set up the iron is protected:
- the **metal** with a **more negative** $E^\ominus$ value **supplies the electrons** and is sacrificed.

Once reacted, the Zn or Mg can be replaced but the iron is still there.

Recycling of scrap iron and steel

All steel packaging except aerosols can be recycled.
- Incineration is used to clean the metal.
- Iron and steel are separated using magnets.
- The composition of new steel is easily adjusted.
- Scrap is used to adjust the temperature of the furnace.

2.4 Predicting redox reactions

LEARNING SUMMARY

After studying this section you should be able to:

- *use standard cell potentials to predict the feasibility of a reaction*
- *recognise the limitations of such predictions*
- *understand redox processes in the nitrogen cycle*

Key points from AS	

- **Redox reactions**
  Revise AS pages 42–44

During AS Chemistry, you learnt how to combine two half-equations to construct a full redox equation.

Standard electrode potentials can be used to predict the direction of any aqueous redox reaction from the relevant half-reactions.

Using standard electrode potentials to make predictions

AQA	M5	SALTERS	M4
EDEXCEL	M5	WJEC	M5
OCR	M5	CCEA	M5

By studying standard electrode potentials, predictions can be made about the likely feasibility of a reaction.

The table below shows three redox systems.

	redox system	$E^{\ominus}$ /V
A	$H_2O_2(aq) + 2H^+ + 2e^- \rightleftharpoons 2H_2O(l)$	+1.77
B	$I_2(aq) + 2e^- \rightleftharpoons 2I^-(aq)$	+0.54
C	$Fe^{3+}(aq) + 3e^- \rightleftharpoons Fe(s)$	−0.04

We can predict the redox reactions that may take place between these species by treating the redox systems as if they are half-cells.

Comparing the redox systems A and B

- The I_2/I^- system has the less positive $E^{\ominus}$ value and its half-reaction will proceed to the left, donating electrons:

$$H_2O_2(aq) + 2H^+(aq) + 2e^- \longrightarrow 2H_2O(l) \qquad E^{\ominus} = +1.77 \text{ V}$$
$$I_2(aq) + 2e^- \longleftarrow 2I^-(aq) \qquad E^{\ominus} = +0.54 \text{ V}$$

> Notice that a reaction takes place between reactants from different sides of each half equation.

We would therefore predict that **H_2O_2 and H^+** would react with **I^-**.

Comparing the redox systems B and C

- The Fe^{3+}/Fe system has the more negative $E^{\ominus}$ value and its half-reaction will proceed to the left, donating electrons:

$$I_2(aq) + 2e^- \longrightarrow 2I^-(aq) \qquad E^{\ominus} = +0.54 \text{ V}$$
$$Fe^{3+}(aq) + 3e^- \longleftarrow Fe(s) \qquad E^{\ominus} = -0.04 \text{ V}$$

We would therefore predict that **I_2** would react with **Fe**.

Comparing the redox systems A and C

- The Fe^{3+}/Fe system has the more negative $E^{\ominus}$ value and its half-reaction will proceed to the left, donating electrons:

$$H_2O_2(aq) + 2H^+(aq) + 2e^- \longrightarrow 2H_2O(l) \qquad E^{\ominus} = +1.77 \text{ V}$$
$$Fe^{3+}(aq) + 3e^- \longleftarrow Fe(s) \qquad E^{\ominus} = -0.04 \text{ V}$$

We would therefore predict that **H_2O_2 and H^+** would react with **Fe**.

> **KEY POINT**
>
> When comparing two redox systems, we can predict that a reaction may take place between:
> - the stronger reducing agent with the more negative $E^{\ominus}$, on the right-hand side of the redox system
> - the stronger oxidising agent with the more positive $E^{\ominus}$, on the left-hand side of the redox system.

Limitations of standard electrode potentials

AQA	M5	SALTERS	M4
EDEXCEL	M5	WJEC	M5
OCR	M5	CCEA	M4

Electrode potentials and ionic concentration

Non-standard conditions alter the value of an electrode potential.

The half-equation for the copper half-cell is shown below.

$$Cu^{2+}(aq) + 2e^- \rightleftharpoons Cu(s)$$

Using le Chatelier's principle, by increasing the concentration of $Cu^{2+}(aq)$:

A change in electrode potential resulting from concentration changes means that predictions made on the basis of the **standard** value may not be valid.

- the equilibrium opposes the change by moving to the right
- electrons are removed from the equilibrium system
- the electrode potential becomes more positive.

Will a reaction actually take place?

Remember that these are equilibrium processes.

- Predictions can be made but these give no indication of the reaction rate which may be extremely slow, caused by a large activation energy.
- The actual conditions used may be different from the standard conditions used to record $E^\ominus$ values. This will affect the value of the electrode potential (see above).
- Standard electrode potentials apply to aqueous equilibria. Many reactions take place that are not aqueous.

As a general working rule:

- the larger the difference between $E^\ominus$ values, the more likely that a reaction will take place
- if the difference between $E^\ominus$ values is less than 0.4 V, then a reaction is unlikely to go to completion.

E(cell), ΔS and equilibrium constants

| EDEXCEL | M5 |

For the zinc-copper electrochemical cell, we would predict the overall cell reaction as:

$$Zn(s) + Cu^{2+}(aq) \longrightarrow Cu(s) + Zn^{2+}(aq) \qquad E^\ominus(cell) = +1.10 \text{ V}$$

For redox reactions, E(cell), entropy and equilibrium are linked.

A reaction is likely to proceed if:

For the link between ΔS and K, see page 59.

- E(cell) is positive or
- ΔS_{total} is positive or
- $K > 1$

Remember that these predictions are based upon just the starting and finishing points. There may be a large energy barrier (activation energy) between these extremes and the rate of reaction may be very slow.

> **KEY POINT**
>
> For an overall cell reaction as written above with a positive E(cell),
>
> $$E(cell) \quad \propto \quad \Delta S_{total} \quad \propto \quad \ln K$$

Progress check

1 For each of the three predicted reactions on page 68, construct full redox equations.

2 Use the standard electrode potentials below to answer the questions that follow.

$$Fe^{3+}(aq) + e^- \rightleftharpoons Fe^{2+}(aq) \qquad E^\ominus = +0.77 \text{ V}$$
$$Br_2(l) + 2e^- \rightleftharpoons 2Br^-(aq) \qquad E^\ominus = +1.07 \text{ V}$$
$$Ni^{2+}(aq) + 2e^- \rightleftharpoons Ni(s) \qquad E^\ominus = -0.25 \text{ V}$$
$$O_2(g) + 4H^+(aq) + 4e^- \rightleftharpoons 2H_2O(l) \qquad E^\ominus = +1.23 \text{ V}$$

(a) Arrange the reducing agents in order with the most powerful first.

(b) Predict the reactions that could take place.

1 A and B: $H_2O_2(aq) + 2H^+(aq) + 2I^-(aq) \longrightarrow I_2(aq) + 2H_2O(l)$; B and C: $2Fe(s) + 3I_2(aq) \longrightarrow 2Fe^{3+}(aq) + 6I^-(aq)$;
A and C: $3H_2O_2(aq) + 6H^+(aq) + 2Fe(s) \longrightarrow 2Fe^{3+}(aq) + 6H_2O(l)$.
2 a) $Ni(s)$, $Fe^{2+}(aq)$, $Br^-(l)$, $H_2O(l)$.
b) Br_2 with Fe^{2+}; Fe^{3+} with Ni; O_2 and H^+ with Fe^{2+}; Br_2 with Ni; O_2 and H^+ with Br^-; O_2 and H^+ with Ni.

Redox processes in the nitrogen cycle

SALTERS   M5

In the nitrogen cycle, nitrogen is present in many forms and oxidation states, e.g.

gases:			aqueous ions:		
nitrogen	N_2	0	ammonium	NH_4^+	−3
ammonia	NH_3	−3	nitrate(III)	NO_2^-	+3
nitrogen(I) oxide	N_2O	+1	nitrate(V)	NO_3^-	+5
nitrogen(II) oxide	NO	+2			
nitrogen(IV) oxide	NO_2	+4			

Chemists benefit agriculture by developing chemicals to:

• provide extra nutrients (fertilisers)
• control soil pH
• control pests (insecticides and pesticides).

In the environment, many redox processes involve nitrogen.

Fixation and nitrification

Conversion of nitrogen gas into soluble nitrogen-containing ions:

$$N_2 \quad \rightarrow \quad NH_4^+ \quad \rightarrow \quad NO_2^- \quad \rightarrow \quad NO_3^-$$
$$0 \qquad\quad -3 \qquad\quad +3 \qquad\quad +5$$

Denitrification

Conversion of soluble nitrogen-containing ions into nitrogen gas:

$$NO_3^- \rightarrow NO_2^- \rightarrow NO \rightarrow N_2O \rightarrow N_2$$
$$+5 \qquad +3 \qquad +2 \qquad +1 \qquad 0$$

Advantages and disadvantages of fertilisers (Salters and CCEA only)

Advantages

The soluble nitrogen content of the soil can be enhanced by adding 'artificial' fertilisers containing ammonium and nitrate ions.

• Extra nitrogen nutrients are provided, improving food production.
• Large quantities of fertilisers are produced by the chemical industry.
• Natural fertilisers, based on manure, or crop rotation, can improve soil structure.

Disadvantages

Nitrate fertilisers are soluble and can be leached out of the soil.

• Excessive use of artificial fertilisers can reduce the quality of soil structure.
• Nitrates can run off fields into rivers and ponds – a source of water pollution. Strategies, such as preventing the run off, can be put into place to reduce and manage water pollution.
• Excess nitrogen in watercourses can lead to eutrophication – excessive plant growth and decay causing depletion of dissolved oxygen needed for the survival of other aquatic life, such as fish.

Sample question and model answer

Take care to include correct state symbols – essential when showing the equations representing these enthalpy changes.

(a) The lattice enthalpy of magnesium oxide can be found using a Born–Haber cycle. Write equations, including state symbols, for the process that takes place during each enthalpy change.

(i) The enthalpy change of formation of magnesium oxide.

$Mg(s) + \frac{1}{2}O_2(g) \longrightarrow MgO(s)$ formulae ✓ state symbols ✓

(ii) The lattice enthalpy of magnesium oxide.

$Mg^{2+}(g) + O^{2-}(g) \longrightarrow MgO(s)$ formulae ✓ state symbols ✓

(iii) The first ionisation energy of magnesium.

$Mg(g) \longrightarrow Mg^{+}(g) + e^{-}$ formulae ✓ state symbols ✓ [6]

(b) Use the data below to construct a Born–Haber cycle and hence calculate a value for the lattice enthalpy of magnesium oxide.

enthalpy change	/ kJ mol^{-1}
atomisation of magnesium	+148
1st ionisation energy of magnesium	+738
2nd ionisation energy of magnesium	+1451
atomisation of oxygen	+248
1st electron affinity of oxygen	−141
2nd electron affinity of oxygen	+791
formation of magnesium oxide	−602

This Born–Haber cycle includes all the enthalpy changes that you may encounter in a Born–Haber cycle.

Most cycles in exams are simpler.

Note the different signs for the 1st and 2nd electron affinities.

magnesium part of cycle ✓
oxygen part of cycle ✓
MgO part of cycle ✓

By Hess' Law.

$\Delta H_{at}(Mg) + \Delta H_{at}(O) + \Delta H_{1st\ i.e.}(Mg) + \Delta H_{2nd\ i.e.}(Mg) + \Delta H_{1st\ e.a.}(O) + \Delta H_{2nd\ e.a.}(O) + L.E.(MgO) = \Delta H_f(MgO)$

∴ $(+148) + (+248) + (+738) + (+1451) + (−141) + (+791) + L.E.(MgO)$
    $= (−602)$

∴ Lattice energy MgO $= −3837$ kJ mol^{-1} correct value ✓ correct sign ✓

                                         [5]

                                [Total: 11]

Practice examination questions

1 The Born–Haber cycle for the formation of potassium bromide from potassium and bromine may be represented by a series of stages labelled **A** to **F** as shown.

(a) (i) Write the letters **A** to **F** next to the corresponding definition in the table below.

definition	letter	$\Delta H/kJ\ mol^{-1}$
1st ionisation energy of potassium		+419
1st electron affinity of bromine		−325
the enthalpy of atomisation of potassium		+89
the enthalpy of atomisation of bromine		+112
the lattice enthalpy of potassium bromide		
the enthalpy of formation of potassium bromide		−394

(ii) Calculate the lattice enthalpy of potassium bromide from the data given. [5]

(b) Explain whether you would expect the lattice enthalpies of the following compounds to be more or less exothermic than that of potassium bromide.

(i) KI; (ii) $CaBr_2$ [4]

[Total: 9]

2 (a) Write equations, including state symbols, for the following:

(i) the lattice enthalpy of magnesium chloride

(ii) the enthalpy change of hydration of a Mg^{2+} ion

(iii) the enthalpy change of solution of magnesium chloride. [3]

(b) The lattice enthalpy of $MgCl_2$ is −2526 kJ mol^{-1}.

The enthalpy change of hydration of Mg^{2+} is −1891 kJ mol−1.

The enthalpy change of hydration of Cl$^-$ is −384 kJ mol−1.

Calculate the enthalpy change of solution of magnesium chloride. [3]

[Total: 6]

3 Chromium can be prepared by the reduction of chromium(III) oxide with aluminium.

$$Cr_2O_3(s) + 2Al(s) \longrightarrow 2Cr(s) + Al_2O_3(s)$$

The table below gives information about the reactants and products.

substance	$Cr_2O_3(s)$	$Al(s)$	$Cr(s)$	$Al_2O_3(s)$
$\Delta H_f/kJ\ mol^{-1}$	−602	0	0	−1676
$S/J\ K^{-1}\ mol^{-1}$	27	28	81	51

Calculate the free energy change for this reaction at 298 K and comment on its feasibility at this temperature.

[Total: 8]

Practice examination questions *(continued)*

4 A standard cell was set up as shown below.

(a) What conditions are necessary for this cell to be a standard cell? [2]

(b) What is the purpose of the salt bridge? [1]

(c) The standard electrode potentials for the half-cells above are:

$$Ni^{2+} + 2e^- \rightleftharpoons Ni \qquad E^{\ominus} = -0.25 \text{ V}$$
$$Fe^{3+} + e^- \rightleftharpoons Fe^{2+} \qquad E^{\ominus} = +0.77 \text{ V}$$

(i) Calculate the standard cell potential of the complete cell.

(ii) Draw an arrow on the diagram above to show the direction of electron flow in the external circuit.

(iii) What is the polarity of each electrode? [3]

(d) (i) Write equations for the reaction at each electrode.

(ii) Hence write an equation to show the overall reaction. [3]

(e) The solution in the nickel half-cell was replaced by a solution that had a higher concentration of Ni^{2+}(aq) ions. Predict the effect on the cell potential. Explain your reasoning. [2]

[Total: 11]

5 (a) Use the standard electrode potentials given below to answer the questions that follow.

			$E^{\ominus}$/ V
Mg^{2+}(aq) + 2e$^-$	$\rightleftharpoons$	Mg(s)	−2.37
I_2(aq) + 2e$^-$	$\rightleftharpoons$	2I$^-$(aq)	+0.54
Mn^{3+}(aq) + e$^-$	$\rightleftharpoons$	Mn^{2+}(aq)	+1.49

(i) Which of the six species above is the strongest oxidising agent?

(ii) Predict, with an equation and a reason, which species above would react with I$^-$(aq) ions to form iodine, I_2(aq). [4]

(b) The standard electrode potentials for two redox equilibria are given below.

$$O_2(g) + 2H_2O(l) + 4e^- \rightleftharpoons 4OH^-(aq) \qquad E^{\ominus} = +0.40 \text{ V}$$
$$V^{3+}(aq) + e^- \rightleftharpoons V^{2+}(aq) \qquad E^{\ominus} = -0.26 \text{ V}$$

Two half-cells based on these redox equilibria are connected to make a cell. Determine the cell potential, $E^{\ominus}$, for this cell and write an equation for the cell reaction. [3]

[Total: 7]

Chapter 3

The Periodic Table

The following topics are covered in this chapter:

- Oxides and chlorides of the Period 3 elements
- Chemistry of the p-block elements
- The transition elements
- Transition element complexes

- Ligand substitution of complex ions
- Redox reactions of transition metal ions
- Catalysis
- Reactions of metal aqua-ions

Key points from AS

- **Bonding and structure**
  Revise AS pages 51–71

During AS Chemistry, you learnt about physical trends in properties of **elements** across Period 3. Across Period 3, **compounds** of the elements also show characteristic trends. For A2 Chemistry, physical and chemical trends in the properties of Period 3 oxides and chlorides are explained in terms of bonding and structure.

3.1 Oxides and chlorides of the Period 3 elements

After studying this section you should be able to:

- describe and explain the periodic variation of the formulae and boiling points of the main oxides and chlorides of Period 3
- describe the reactions of Period 3 elements with oxygen
- describe the action of water on Period 3 oxides and chlorides
- describe these reactions in terms of structure and bonding
- describe the reaction of Period 3 oxides with acids and bases

LEARNING SUMMARY

The formulae of the Period 3 oxides

AQA M5 CCEA M4

Across Period 3, the formulae of compounds show a regular pattern which depends upon the **number of electrons** in the outer shell.

The **oxidation state** of an element indicates the **number of electrons** involved in **bonding**. The relationship of the formulae of the Period 3 oxides with electronic structure and oxidation state is shown below.

Key points from AS

- **The modern Periodic Table**
  Revise AS pages 72–75
- **Redox reactions**
  Revise AS pages 42–44

The highest oxidation state of an element is usually the group number.

Chlorine forms several oxides. The highest is Cl_2O_7.

element	Na	Mg	Al	Si	P	S	Cl
electrons in outer shell	1	2	3	4	5	6	7
formula of oxide	Na_2O	MgO	Al_2O_3	SiO_2	P_4O_6 P_4O_{10}	SO_2 SO_3	Cl_2O_7
oxidation state of element in oxide	+1	+2	+3	+4	+3 +5	+4 +6	+7

increase in highest oxidation state

The amount of oxygen atoms per mole of the element increases steadily across Period 3.

For each element in the Period, there is an increase of 0.5 mole of O per mole of element.

$Na_1O_{0.5}$ Mg_1O_1 $Al_1O_{1.5}$ Si_1O_2 $P_1O_{2.5}$ S_1O_3 $Cl_1O_{3.5}$

Periodicity means a repeating trend. This is one of the important ideas of chemistry – a trend across one period is repeated across other periods.

This periodicity is also seen across Periods 2 and 4:

Period 2	Li_2O	BeO	B_2O_3	CO_2
Period 3	Na_2O	MgO	Al_2O_3	SiO_2
Period 4	K_2O	CaO	Ga_2O_3	GeO_2

Preparation of oxides from the elements

AQA ▶ M5   CCEA ▶ M4

Oxides of the Period 3 elements Na to Cl can be prepared by heating each element in oxygen. These are redox reactions:

- the Period 3 element is oxidised
- oxygen is reduced.

Metal oxides

Equations for the reactions of oxygen with the metals sodium, magnesium and aluminium are shown below.

At room temperature and pressure:
Na_2O, MgO and Al_2O_3 are white solids.

$$4Na(s) + O_2(g) \xrightarrow{\text{yellow flame}} 2Na_2O(s)$$

$$2Mg(s) + O_2(g) \xrightarrow{\text{white flame}} 2MgO(s)$$

$$4Al(s) + 3O_2(g) \xrightarrow{\text{white flame}} 2Al_2O_3(s)$$

- Na_2O and MgO are **ionic compounds**.
- Al_2O_3 has bonding that is **intermediate** between ionic and covalent.

Non-metal oxides

Phosphorus and sulfur exist as P_4 and S_8 molecules.

Sulfur, S_8, is usually simplified in equations as S.

Equations for the reactions of phosphorus and sulfur with oxygen are shown below.

$$P_4(s) + 5O_2(g) \xrightarrow{\text{white flame}} P_4O_{10}(s)$$

$$S(s) + O_2(g) \xrightarrow{\text{blue flame}} SO_2(g)$$

At room temperature and pressure:
- P_4O_{10} is a white solid
- SO_2 is a colourless gas
- SO_3 is a colourless liquid.

SO_2 reacts further with oxygen in the presence of a catalyst (V_2O_5):

$$2SO_2(g) + O_2(g) \longrightarrow 2SO_3(l)$$

- P_4O_{10}, SO_2 and SO_3 are **covalent compounds**.

Trend in the boiling points of the Period 3 oxides

AQA ▶ M5   WJEC ▶ M5
CCEA ▶ M4

The table below compares the boiling points of some Period 3 oxides with their structure and bonding.

Key points from AS

- **Bonding, structure and properties**
  Revise AS pages 67–71
- **Trends in boiling points of Period 3 elements**
  Revise AS pages 74–75

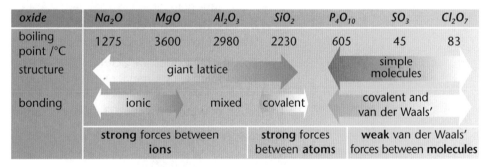

oxide	Na_2O	MgO	Al_2O_3	SiO_2	P_4O_{10}	SO_3	Cl_2O_7
boiling point /°C	1275	3600	2980	2230	605	45	83
structure	← giant lattice →				simple molecules →		
bonding	← ionic →	mixed	covalent		covalent and van der Waals' →		
	strong forces between ions			strong forces between atoms	weak van der Waals' forces between molecules		

Giant structures and boiling point

During your study of AS Chemistry, you learnt that the boiling points of the elements and compounds are dependent upon bonding and structure.

The same principles can be applied many times in chemistry.

The oxides with **giant structures** ($Na_2O \rightarrow SiO_2$):

- have **high boiling points**
- require a large amount of energy to break the **strong forces** between their particles.

The particles making up a giant lattice can be different.

- Na_2O and MgO have ionic bonding and the **strong** forces are electrostatic attractions acting between positive and negative **ions**.
- Al_2O_3 has bonding intermediate between ionic and covalent. **Strong** forces act between particles that are **intermediate** between ions and atoms.
- SiO_2 has covalent bonding and the **strong** forces are 'shared pairs of electrons' acting between the **atoms**.

P_4O_{10}, SO_2, SO_3 and Cl_2O_7 all exist as covalently bonded molecules. The forces between the molecules though are van der Waals' forces.

Simple molecular structures and boiling point

The oxides with simple molecular structures ($P_4O_{10} \rightarrow Cl_2O_7$):

- have low boiling points
- require a small amount of energy to break the weak van der Waals' forces acting between the molecules.

The action of water on the Period 3 oxides

Reactions of sodium and magnesium oxides

Metal oxides form alkalis in water.

Although MgO reacts with water, the magnesium hydroxide formed is only slightly soluble in water forming a weak alkaline solution only.

$$Na_2O(s) + 2H_2O(l) \longrightarrow 2NaOH(aq) \qquad pH = 14$$

$$MgO(s) + 2H_2O(l) \longrightarrow Mg(OH)_2(aq) \qquad pH = 11$$

Each hydroxide dissociates in water, releasing OH^- ions into solution:

$$NaOH(aq) \longrightarrow Na^+(aq) + OH^-(aq)$$

Sodium and magnesium metals react with water forming the metal hydroxide and hydrogen gas. The reaction with sodium is rapid but magnesium reacts very slowly.

Oxides of aluminium and silicon

Al_2O_3 and SiO_2 have very strong lattices which cannot be broken down by water. Consequently these compounds are insoluble in water.

Reactions of non-metal oxides

Non-metal oxides form acids in water. Equations for the reactions of $P_4O_{10}(s)$, $SO_2(g)$ and $SO_3(l)$ with water are shown below.

$$P_4O_{10}(s) + 6H_2O(l) \longrightarrow 4H_3PO_4(aq) \qquad \textit{phosphoric acid}$$

$$SO_2(g) + H_2O(l) \longrightarrow H_2SO_3(aq) \qquad \textit{sulfurous acid}$$

$$SO_3(l) + H_2O(l) \longrightarrow H_2SO_4(aq) \qquad \textit{sulfuric acid}$$

$$Cl_2O_7(s) + H_2O(l) \longrightarrow 2HClO_4(aq) \qquad \textit{chloric(VII) acid}$$

Each acid dissociates in the water, releasing H^+ ions into solution.

E.g. $\quad H_2SO_4(aq) \longrightarrow H^+(aq) + HSO_4^-(aq)$

Key points from AS

- **The Group 1 elements**
  Revise AS pages 76–77
- **The Group 2 elements**
  Revise AS pages 77–78

> An important general rule is:
>
> - **metal oxides** are **basic**
>   When soluble, metal oxides form alkaline solutions in water.
> - **non-metal oxides** are **acidic**
>   When soluble, non-metal oxides form acidic solutions in water.
>
> **KEY POINT**

The action of water on Period 3 oxides is summarised below.

oxide	Na_2O	MgO	Al_2O_3	SiO_2	P_4O_{10}	SO_3	Cl_2O_7
action of water	alkali		insoluble		acid		

The reactions of oxides with acids and bases

Basic oxides, Na_2O and MgO

Basic oxides are neutralised by acids to form a salt and water.

e.g. $\quad Na_2O(s) + 2HCl(aq) \longrightarrow 2NaCl(aq) + H_2O(l)$

$\qquad MgO(s) + H_2SO_4(aq) \longrightarrow MgSO_4(aq) + H_2O(l)$

Acidic oxides, P_4O_{10}, SO_2, SO_3 and Cl_2O_7

Acidic oxides are **neutralised** by bases to form a salt and water.

e.g.
$$P_4O_{10}(s) + 12NaOH(aq) \longrightarrow 4Na_3PO_4(aq) + 6H_2O(l)$$
$$SO_2(g) + 2KOH(aq) \longrightarrow K_2SO_3(aq) + H_2O(l)$$
$$SO_3(s) + 2KOH(aq) \longrightarrow K_2SO_4(aq) + H_2O(l)$$
$$Cl_2O_7(s) + 2NaOH(aq) \longrightarrow 2NaClO_4(aq) + H_2O(l)$$

Aluminium oxide, Al_2O_3

Al_2O_3 is **neutralised** by both acids and bases and is **amphoteric**.

> **KEY POINT**
>
> An **amphoteric** oxide is one that is neutralised by both acids and bases.

With hot dilute HCl(aq),
$$Al_2O_3(s) + 6HCl(aq) \longrightarrow 2AlCl_3(aq) + 3H_2O(l)$$
With hot concentrated NaOH(aq),
$$Al_2O_3(s) + 2NaOH(aq) + 3H_2O(l) \longrightarrow 2NaAl(OH)_4(aq)$$

Silicon(IV) oxide, SiO_2

SiO_2 is **neutralised** by hot concentrated bases:
$$2KOH(aq) + SiO_2(s) \longrightarrow K_2SiO_3(aq) + H_2O(l)$$

Progress check

1 (a) Across the Periodic Table, what pattern is shown in the formulae of the Period 3 oxides?
   (b) Why do elements in the **same** group form compounds with **similar** formulae?

2 The reactions of elements with oxygen are redox reactions. Use oxidation numbers to show that the reaction of aluminium with oxygen is a redox reaction.

1 (a) For each element in the period, there is an increase of 0.5 mole of O per mole of the element.
  (b) Although the outer shell is different, there is the same number of electrons in the outer shell.
2 $4Al(s) + 3O_2(g) \longrightarrow 2Al_2O_3(s)$
  Al changes oxidation number from 0 to +3 (oxidation)
  O changes oxidation state from 0 to −2 (reduction)

The formulae of the Period 3 chlorides

CCEA   M4

The relationship of the formulae of some Period 3 chlorides with electron structure and oxidation state is shown below.

Key points from AS

- **The modern Periodic Table**
  Revise AS pages 72–75
- **Redox reactions**
  Revise AS pages 42–44

element	Na	Mg	Al	Si	P
electrons in outer shell	1	2	3	4	5
formula of chloride	NaCl	$MgCl_2$	Al_2Cl_6	$SiCl_4$	PCl_3 PCl_5
oxidation state of element in chloride	+1	+2	+3	+4	+3 +5

increase in highest oxidation state ➡

The oxidation state of the element in its chloride is equal to the number of chlorine atoms bonded to the element.

The amount of chlorine atoms per mole of the element increases steadily across Period 3.

For each element in the Period, there is an increase of 1 mole of Cl per mole of element.

$$NaCl \quad MgCl_2 \quad Al_2Cl_6 \quad SiCl_4 \quad PCl_5$$

The same trend is seen across each Period of the Periodic Table.

The reason is the same – the number of electrons in the outer shell increases steadily across each period.

As with the Period 3 oxides, this periodicity in formulae is also seen as a repeating trend across Periods 2 and 4. The table below shows the formulae of the chlorides from Period 2 to Period 4 of the Periodic Table.

Period 2	$LiCl$	$BeCl_2$	BCl_3	CCl_4
Period 3	$NaCl$	$MgCl_2$	$AlCl_3$	$SiCl_4$
Period 4	KCl	$CaCl_2$	$GaCl_3$	$GeCl_4$

Trend in the boiling points of the Period 3 chlorides

Al_2Cl_6, $SiCl_4$ and PCl_5 exist as covalently bonded molecules. The forces between the molecules though are van der Waals' forces.

The table below compares the boiling points of some Period 3 chlorides with structure and bonding.

chloride	NaCl	MgCl₂	Al₂Cl₆	SiCl₄	PCl₅
boiling point /°C	1465	1412	178	58	160
structure	giant lattice		simple molecules		
bonding	ionic		covalent and van der Waals'		
forces	strong forces between ions		weak van der Waals' forces between molecules		

Key points from AS

- **Bonding, structure and properties**
  Revise AS pages 67–71
- **Trends in boiling points of Period 3 elements**
  Revise AS pages 74–75

Giant structures and boiling point

The chlorides with **giant** structures ($NaCl \longrightarrow MgCl_2$)

- have **high boiling points**
- require a large amount of energy to break the **strong forces** between their particles
- $NaCl$ and $MgCl_2$ have ionic bonding and the **strong** forces are electrostatic attractions acting between positive and negative **ions**.

The chlorides with **simple molecular** structures ($Al_2Cl_6 \longrightarrow PCl_5$)

- have low boiling points
- require a small amount of energy to break the weak **van der Waals' forces** acting between the **molecules**.

Phosphorus pentachloride: ionic or covalent?

Phosphorus pentachloride, PCl_5, exists as a covalent molecule in the gaseous state. However phosphorus pentachloride exists in the solid state in the **ionic** form, $[PCl_6]^- [PCl_4]^+$.

Thus, solid PCl_3 and PCl_5 have different structures with PCl_5 having a much higher melting point and boiling point than PCl_3.

Comparison between the oxides and chlorides of Period 3

The structure and bonding of the Period 3 oxides and chlorides are compared below.

For **oxides**, bonding and structure change at **different** points.

- Bonding changes from ionic to covalent between MgO and SiO_2 with Al_2O_3 having intermediate bonding.
- Structure changes from giant lattice to simple molecular between SiO_2 and P_4O_{10}.

For **chlorides**, both bonding and structure change at the **same** point.

Between $MgCl_2$ and Al_2Cl_6:

- bonding changes from ionic to covalent **and**
- structure changes from giant to simple molecular.

The action of water on the chlorides of Period 3

CCEA ▶ M4

Dissolving ionic chlorides

The ionic chlorides **dissolve** in water forming a **neutral** or very weak acidic solution.

$$NaCl(s) \quad + aq \longrightarrow Na^+(aq) \quad + Cl^-(aq) \qquad pH = 7$$
$$MgCl_2(s) \quad + aq \longrightarrow Mg^{2+}(aq) + 2Cl^-(aq) \qquad pH = 6$$

This periodicity of properties is repeated across each period.

Reactions of covalent chlorides

The covalent chlorides are **hydrolysed** by water in **a vigorous reaction**. Strong acid solutions are formed containing hydrochloric acid.

Equations for the reactions of $Al_2Cl_6(s)$, $SiCl_4(l)$ and $PCl_5(s)$ with water are shown below.

$$Al_2Cl_6(s) \quad + 6H_2O(l) \longrightarrow 2Al(OH)_3(s) \quad + 6HCl(aq)$$
$$SiCl_4(l) \quad + 4H_2O(l) \longrightarrow Si(OH)_4(s) \quad + 4HCl(aq)$$
$$PCl_5(s) \quad + 4H_2O(l) \longrightarrow H_3PO_4(aq) \quad + 5HCl(aq)$$

> **KEY POINT**
>
> An important general rule is:
> - **ionic chlorides** form **neutral** solutions in water
> - **covalent chlorides** form **acidic** solutions in water.

The action of water on the Period 3 oxides is summarised below.

chloride	NaCl	MgCl₂	AlCl₃	SiCl₄	PCl₅
action of water	neutral	very weak acid		strong acid	

Progress check

1 (a) What is the trend in pH shown by the chlorides of Period 3?
  (b) Water is added to sodium chloride and phosphorus pentachloride to form aqueous solutions with different pH values. Explain, with equations, why these solutions have different pH values.

PCl₅ reacts with water forming H₃PO₄ and HCl both generating H⁺ ions in solution. ∴ the solution is acidic.
NaCl(aq) simply dissolves in water and does not generate excess H⁺ or OH⁻ ions in solution. ∴ NaCl(aq) is neutral.
PCl₅(s) + 4H₂O(l) ⟶ H₃PO₄(aq) + 5HCl(aq)
(b) NaCl(s) + aq ⟶ Na⁺(aq) + Cl⁻(aq)
1 (a) neutral to acidic

3.2 Chemistry of the p-block elements

After studying this section you should be able to:

- *understand general properties of the p-block elements*
- *understand the electron deficiency of Group 3 compounds*
- *describe the relative stabilities of the oxidation states in Group 4*
- *explain the trend in oxidising power of the Group 7 elements*
- *explain the trend in reducing power of the Group 7 halides*

LEARNING SUMMARY

General properties

Electron configurations of the p-block elements

group	3	4	5	6	7	0
outer shell electrons	s^2p^1	s^2p^2	s^2p^3	s^2p^4	s^2p^5	s^2p^6
Period 2: 2nd shell	B	C	N	O	F	Ne
Period 3: 3rd shell	Al	Si	P	S	Cl	Ar

The inert pair effect

On descending Groups 3, 4 and 5, the two electrons in the outer s-orbital (the s^2 pair) are less involved in bonding – the **inert pair effect**.

- At the **top** of the group, the inert pair effect is minor. **All outer shell electrons** are involved in **covalent** bonding.

- At the **bottom** of the group, the inert pair effect is significant. **Only p-electrons** are involved in **ionic** bonding.

Expansion of the octet

The maximum number of electron pairs that can surround a central atom is greater in Period 3 (Na–Ar) than in Period 2 (Li–Ne).

- In Period 2, N forms halides with the general formula NX_3 only: NF_3, NCl_3, NBr_3

- In Period 3, P forms halides with the general formulae PX_3 and PX_5: PF_3 and PF_5, PCl_3 and PCl_5, PBr_3 and PBr_5

PF_5, PCl_5 and PBr_5 have 'expanded their octets' with 10 electrons around the central P atom.

Some compounds and ions in the p-block are **amphoteric**.

> An **amphoteric** substance is one that reacts as either an acid or base.
>
> **KEY POINT**

Al_2O_3 is an **amphoteric** oxide.

Amphoteric behaviour of Al^{3+}.

- *Acidic nature*: With hot dilute HCl(aq), a salt forms:

    $$Al_2O_3(s) + 6HCl(aq) \longrightarrow 2AlCl_3(aq) + 2H_2O(l)$$

- *Basic nature*: With hot concentrated NaOH(aq), a salt forms:

    $$Al_2O_3(s) + 2NaOH(aq) + 3H_2O(l) \longrightarrow 2NaAl(OH)_4(aq)$$

PbO is an **amphoteric** oxide.

Amphoteric behaviour of Pb^{2+}.

- *Acidic nature*: PbO reacts with bases to form salts:

$$PbO(s) + 2OH^-(aq) \longrightarrow PbO_2^{2-}(aq) + H_2O(l)$$

- *Basic nature*: PbO reacts with acids to form salts:

$$PbO(s) + 2H^+(aq) \longrightarrow Pb^{2+}(aq) + H_2O(l)$$

Group 3

WJEC   M5

Many Group 3 compounds (e.g. BF_3, BCl_3 and $AlCl_3$) are **electron deficient** – one of the **p-orbitals** in B and Al is **unused**.

- BF_3, BCl_3 and $AlCl_3$ all react to form **donor-acceptor compounds** by accepting an electron pair.

- The donor-acceptor compounds below are **not** electron-deficient.

The Al_2Cl_6 dimer

At room temperature, aluminium chloride exists as a dimer, with a dative covalent bond bridging from one molecule to the other.

Notice that **all** of the **p-orbitals** in B and Al are **used** and that Al now has a stable octet.

Formation of BF_3NH_3

The electron deficiency of BF_3, BCl_3 and $AlCl_3$ allows the formation of donor-acceptor compounds such as BF_3NH_3.

The affinity of $AlCl_3$ for chlorine species (as in the formation of Al_2Cl_6) finds a use in industrially important catalysts:

These ionic liquids are being developed as 'clean technology' solvents and catalysts for processes such as the polymerisation of alkenes.

- $AlCl_3$ as a halogen carrier in the chlorination of benzene

- low melting temperature ionic liquids, containing the chloroaluminate(III) ion, $AlCl_4^-$.

Boron nitride, BN

Boron nitride, BN, forms different structures.

Cubic 3D structure

- There is a tetrahedral arrangement around each atom in the structure (as in diamond).

BN is finding increasing use as lubricants, wear-resistant coatings and nanotubes for wire sleeving, catalyst support and semiconduction.

A hexagonal structure

- Each layer is bonded weakly to the next (as in graphite) using the two outer shell electrons 'left over' from each N atom.

Boron nitride has hardness, chemical inertness, high melting temperature and semiconductor properties.

Group 4

C	+4 stable
Si	
Ge	
Sn	
Pb	+2 stable

As Group 4 is descended, the obvious trend is from non-metal to metal.

Group 4 compounds have two main oxidation states +2 and +4.

- At the top of the group (C), the +4 oxidation state is more stable.
- At the bottom of the group, the +2 oxidation state is more stable.

Carbon monoxide is the only common example of the +2 oxidation state in a carbon compound. CO is a strong reducing agent and is readily oxidised to CO_2; the more stable +4 oxide of carbon.

- In the extraction of iron from iron(III) oxide in the blast furnace, CO is the reducing agent:

$$Fe_2O_3 + 3CO \longrightarrow 2Fe + 3CO_2$$

$$+2 \xrightarrow{\hspace{2cm}} +4 \qquad\qquad \text{oxidation}$$

Note that the reducing agent (CO) gets oxidised.

At the bottom of the group, Pb(IV) compounds act as oxidising agents and can readily be reduced to the more stable +2 oxidation state of lead.

- PbO_2 oxidises concentrated hydrochloric acid:

$$PbO_2 + 4HCl \longrightarrow PbCl_2 + Cl_2 + 2H_2O$$

$$+4 \xrightarrow{\hspace{2cm}} +2 \qquad\qquad \text{reduction}$$

Note that the oxidising agent (PbO_2) gets reduced

Properties of oxides: CO_2 and PbO

Oxide	$CO_2(g)$	$PbO(g)$
bonding	covalent	ionic/intermediate
structure	simple molecular	giant ionic

Acid–base properties

- CO_2 is an **acidic** gas, that forms a weak acidic solution with water:

$$CO_2(g) + aq \longrightarrow CO_2(aq)$$
$$CO_2(aq) + H_2O(l) \rightleftharpoons H^+(aq) + HCO_3^-(aq)$$

- PbO is an **amphoteric** oxide.

  Basic nature: PbO reacts with acids to form salts:

$$PbO(s) + 2H^+(aq) \longrightarrow Pb^{2+}(aq) + H_2O(l)$$

  Acidic nature: PbO reacts with bases to form salts:

$$PbO(s) + 2OH^-(aq) \longrightarrow PbO_2^{2-}(aq) + H_2O(l)$$

Properties of chlorides: CCl_4, $SiCl_4$, $PbCl_2$

Chloride	$CCl_4(l)$	$SiCl_4(l)$	$PbCl_2(s)$
bonding	covalent	covalent	mainly ionic
structure	simple molecular	simple molecular	giant ionic

Reaction with water

- CCl_4 does **not** react with water; two layers are formed.
- $SiCl_4$ is **hydrolysed** in a violent reaction with water, forming a strong acidic solution.

$$SiCl_4(l) + 4H_2O(l) \longrightarrow Si(OH)_4(s) + 4HCl(g)$$

- $PbCl_2$ is **slightly soluble** in cold water; more soluble in hot water.

Reactions of Pb^{2+}(aq) with aqueous NaOH, Cl⁻ and I⁻

Pb^{2+}(aq) reacts with NaOH(aq) in two stages.

A precipitation reaction takes place:

$$Pb^{2+}(aq) + 2OH^-(aq) \longrightarrow Pb(OH)_2(s) \qquad \text{white precipitate}$$

With an **excess of NaOH(aq)**, a **colourless** solution forms:

$$Pb(OH)_2(s) + 2OH^-(aq) \longrightarrow Pb(OH)_4^{2-}(aq)$$

Reactions of Pb^{2+}(aq) with aqueous Cl⁻

A precipitation reaction takes place:

$$Pb^{2+}(aq) + 2Cl^-(aq) \longrightarrow PbCl_2(s) \qquad \text{white precipitate}$$

With an **excess of Cl⁻(aq)**, a **colourless** solution forms:

$$PbCl_2(s) + 2Cl^-(aq) \longrightarrow PbCl_4^{2-}(aq)$$

Reactions of Pb^{2+}(aq) with aqueous I⁻

A precipitation reaction takes place:

$$Pb^{2+}(aq) + 2I^-(aq) \longrightarrow PbI_2(s) \qquad \text{yellow precipitate}$$

Group 7

WJEC ▷ M5

Key points from AS

- **Group 7 and their compounds**
  Revise AS pages 80–85

Disproportionation of chlorine in dilute aqueous alkalis

In dilute alkaline solutions, chlorine undergoes disproportionation.

$$Cl_2(aq) + 2NaOH(aq) \longrightarrow NaCl(aq) + NaClO(aq) + H_2O(l)$$

$0 \xrightarrow{\quad -1 \quad} -1$ *chlorine reduced*

$0 \xrightarrow{\quad +1 \quad} +1$ *chlorine oxidised*

Oxidising power of halogens

The oxidising power of the halogens **decreases** down the group. This can be demonstrated by **displacement reactions** of aqueous halides using Cl_2, Br_2 and I_2.

The $E^{\ominus}$ values below show that **halogens** gain electrons more readily and become **stronger oxidising agents** as the group is **ascended**.

F_2
Cl_2
Br_2
I_2

Increased strength as oxidising agent

	redox system					$E^{\ominus}$ / V	
strongest oxidising agent	$F_2(g)$	+	$2e^-$	⇌	$2F^-(aq)$	+2.87	*strongest reducing agent*
	$Cl_2(g)$	+	$2e^-$	⇌	$2Cl^-(aq)$	+1.36	
	$Br_2(g)$	+	$2e^-$	⇌	$2Br^-(aq)$	+1.09	
	$I_2(g)$	+	$2e^-$	⇌	$2I^-(aq)$	+0.54	

Reducing power of halides

Halide ions react with concentrated sulfuric acid producing a range of products depending on the halide used.

HCl

HBr

HI

Increased strength as reducing agent

- HCl does not reduce H_2SO_4
- HBr does not reduce H_2SO_4 to SO_2 (S reduced from +6 to +4)
- HI does not reduce H_2SO_4 to H_2S (S reduced from +6 to –2)

This difference is caused by the **increasing reducing power** of the **hydrogen halides** as the group is **descended**.

The $E^{\ominus}$ values below show that **halides** lose electrons more readily and become **stronger reducing agents** as the group is **descended**.

3.3 The transition elements

After studying this section you should be able to:

- *explain what is meant by the terms d-block element and transition element*
- *deduce the electronic configurations of atoms and ions of the d-block elements Sc → Zn*
- *know the typical properties of a transition element*

LEARNING SUMMARY

Key points from AS

- **The Periodic Table**
  Revise AS page 72–85

During AS Chemistry, you studied the metals in the s-block of the Periodic Table. For A2 Chemistry, this understanding is extended with a detailed study of the elements scandium to zinc in the d-block of the Periodic Table. Many of the principles introduced during AS Chemistry will be revisited, especially redox chemistry, and structure and bonding.

The d-block elements

AQA	M5	SALTERS	M4
EDEXCEL	M5	WJEC	M5
OCR	M5	CCEA	M5

The d-block is found in the centre of the Periodic Table. For A2 Chemistry, you will be studying mainly the d-block elements in Period 4 of the Periodic Table: Sc, Ti, V, Cr, Mn, Fe, Co, Ni, Cu and Zn.

Electronic configurations of d-block elements

The diagram below shows the sub-shell being filled across Period 4 of the Periodic Table.

4s		3d									4p					
K	Ca	Sc	Ti	V	Cr	Mn	Fe	Co	Ni	Cu	Zn	Ga	Ge	As	Se	Br	Kr

Key points from AS

- **Sub-shells and orbitals**
  Revise AS pages 21–23
- **Filling the sub-shells**
  Revise AS pages 23–24
- **Sub-shells and the Periodic Table**
  Revise AS page 24

> The 3d sub-shell is at a higher energy and fills **after** the 4s sub-shell.

> See also the stability from a half-full p sub-shell.

- The elements Sc ⟶ Zn have their highest energy electrons in the 4s and 3d sub-shells.
- Across the d-block, electrons are filling the 3d sub-shell. The diagram below shows the outermost electron shell for Sc ⟶ Zn.

Notice how the orbitals are filled:

- the orbitals in the 3d sub-shell are first occupied singly to prevent any repulsion caused by pairing.

Notice chromium and copper:

- chromium has one electron in each orbital of the 4s and 3d sub-shells ⟶ extra stability
- copper has a full 3d sub-shell ⟶ extra stability.

		4s	3d				
Sc	[Ar] $3d^1 4s^2$	↑↓	↑				
Ti	[Ar] $3d^2 4s^2$	↑↓	↑	↑			
V	[Ar] $3d^3 4s^2$	↑↓	↑	↑	↑		
Cr	[Ar] $3d^5 4s^1$	↑	↑	↑	↑	↑	↑
Mn	[Ar] $3d^5 4s^2$	↑↓	↑	↑	↑	↑	↑
Fe	[Ar] $3d^6 4s^2$	↑↓	↑↓	↑	↑	↑	↑
Co	[Ar] $3d^7 4s^2$	↑↓	↑↓	↑↓	↑	↑	↑
Ni	[Ar] $3d^8 4s^2$	↑↓	↑↓	↑↓	↑↓	↑	↑
Cu	[Ar] $3d^{10} 4s^1$	↑	↑↓	↑↓	↑↓	↑↓	↑↓
Zn	[Ar] $3d^{10} 4s^2$	↑↓	↑↓	↑↓	↑↓	↑↓	↑↓

Transition elements

> Successive ionisation energies provide evidence for electronic configurations of the d-block elements Sc to Zn.
> This is most evident by the presence of peaks matching the $3d^5$ half-filled shell.

The elements in the d-block, Ti→Cu, are called transition elements.

KEY POINT

- A transition element has **at least one ion** with a **partially-filled d sub-shell**.

Although scandium and zinc are d-block elements, they are **not** *transition elements*. Neither element forms an ion with a partially filled d sub-shell.

Scandium forms one ion only, Sc^{3+} with the 3d sub-shell **empty**.

$$Sc\ [Ar]3d^1 4s^2 \xrightarrow{\textit{loss of 3 electrons}} Sc^{3+}\ only:\quad [Ar]$$

Zinc forms one ion only, Zn^{2+} with the 3d sub-shell **full**.

$$Zn\ [Ar]3d^{10} 4s^2 \xrightarrow{\textit{loss of 2 electrons}} Zn^{2+}\ only:\quad [Ar]3d^{10}$$

d–block elements

Sc	Ti	V	Cr	Mn	Fe	Co	Ni	Cu	Zn

transition elements

Key points from AS

• **The s-block elements**
  Revise AS pages 76–79

Properties of transition elements

1 high density

2 high m. and b. pt.

3 moderate to low reactivity

4 two or more oxidation states

5 coloured ions

6 complex ions with ligands

7 catalysts

Typical properties of transition elements

The transition elements are all metals – they are good conductors of heat and electricity. In addition, some general properties distinguish the transition elements from the s-block metals.

Density

• The transition elements are more **dense** than other metals.
  • They have smaller atoms than the metals in Groups 1 and 2. The small atoms are able to pack closely together $\longrightarrow$ high density.

Melting point and boiling point

• The transition elements have **higher melting and boiling points** than other metals.
  • Within the metallic lattice, ions are **smaller** than those of the s-block metals – the metallic bonding between the metal ions and the delocalised electrons is strong.

Reactivity

• The transition elements have **moderate to low reactivity**.
  • Unlike the s-block metals, they do **not** react with cold water. Many transition metals react with dilute acids although some, such as gold, silver and platinum, are extremely unreactive.

Oxidation states

• Most transition elements have compounds with **two or more oxidation states**.

Colour of compounds

• The transition elements have **coloured compounds and ions**.
  • Most transition metals have at least one oxidation state that is coloured.

Complex ions

• The ions of transition elements form **complex ions** with ligands.

Catalysis

• Many transition elements can act as **catalysts**.

Formation of ions

AQA	M5	SALTERS	M4
EDEXCEL	M5	WJEC	M5
OCR	M5	CCEA	M5

The energy levels of the 4s and 3d sub-shells are very close together.

> • Transition elements are able to form **more than one ion**, each with a different oxidation state, by losing the **4s** electrons and different numbers of **3d** electrons.
> • When forming ions, the 4s electrons are **lost first**, before the 3d electrons.

KEY POINT

The Fe^{3+} ion, [Ar]3d^5 is more stable than the Fe^{2+} ion, [Ar]3d^{5}4s^1.

Fe^{3+} has a half-full 3d sub-shell ⟶ stability.

The 4s and 3d energy levels are very close together and both are involved in bonding.

When forming ions, the 4s electrons are **lost before** the 3d electrons.

Note that this is different from the order of **filling** – 4s before 3d.

Once the 3d sub-shell starts to fill, the 4s electrons are repelled to a higher energy level and are lost first.

Forming Fe^{2+} and Fe^{3+} ions from iron

Iron has the electronic configuration [Ar]3d^{6}4s^2

Iron forms two common ions, Fe^{2+} and Fe^{3+}.

An Fe atom loses **two 4s electrons** ⟶ Fe^{2+} ion.

An Fe atom loses **two 4s electrons** and **one 3d electron** ⟶ Fe^{3+} ion.

The variety of oxidation states

The table below summarises the stable oxidation states of the elements scandium to zinc. Those in bold type represent the commonest oxidation numbers of the elements in their compounds.

Sc	Ti	V	Cr	Mn	Fe	Co	Ni	Cu	Zn
	+1	+1	+1	+1	+1	+1	+1	+1	
	+2	+2	+2	+2	+2	+2	+2	+2	+2
+3	+3	+3	+3	+3	+3	+3	+3	+3	
	+4	+4	+4	+4	+4	+4	+4		
		+5	+5	+5	+5	+5			
			+6	+6	+6				
				+7					

- The variety of oxidation states results from the close similarity in energy of the 4s and the 3d electrons.

- The number of available oxidation states for the element **increases** from Sc → Mn.
  - All of the available 3d and 4s electrons may be used for bond formation.

- The number of available oxidation states for the element **decreases** from Mn → Zn.
  - There is a decreasing number of unpaired d-electrons available for bond formation.

- Higher oxidation states involve covalency because of the high charge densities involved.
  - In practice, for oxidation states of +4 and above, the bonding electrons are involved in covalent bond formation.

Refer to the electronic configurations of the d-block elements, shown on page 84.

Importance of transition elements (WJEC only)

The transition elements have great economic importance, e.g. iron and other transition elements in the various types of steel.

In living systems, many transition elements are essential as ions in small quantities as 'trace elements', e.g. Cu^{2+} is an essential part of many enzymes, such as *cytochrome c oxidase*.

Progress check

1 Write down the electronic configuration of the following ions:
  (a) Ni^{2+} (b) Cr^{3+} (c) Cu$^+$ (d) V^{3+}.

2 What is the oxidation state of the metal in each of the following?
  (a) MnO$_2$ (b) CrO$_3$ (c) MnO$_4^-$ (d) VO$_2^+$

2 (a) +4 (b) +6 (c) +7 (d) +5.

1 (a) [Ar]3d^8 (b) [Ar]3d^3 (c) [Ar]3d^{10} (d) [Ar]3d^2.

3.4 Transition element complexes

After studying this section you should be able to:

- *explain what is meant by the terms 'complex ion' and 'ligand'*
- *predict the formula and possible shape of a complex ion*
- *know that ligands can be unidentate, bidentate and multidentate*
- *understand that some complexes have stereoisomers*
- *know that transition metal ions can be identified by their colour*
- *know that electronic transitions are responsible for colour*
- *explain how colorimetry can be used to determine the concentration and formula of a complex ion*

LEARNING SUMMARY

Ligands and complex ions

AQA	M5	SALTERS	M4
EDEXCEL	M5	WJEC	M5
OCR	M5	CCEA	M5

Transition metal ions are small and densely charged. They strongly attract electron-rich species called **ligands** forming **complex ions**.

> **KEY POINT**
>
> A ligand is a molecule or ion that bonds to a metal ion by:
> - forming a coordinate (dative covalent) bond
> - donating a lone pair of electrons into a vacant orbital.
>
> Common ligands include: H_2O: , :Cl^-, :NH_3, :CN^-

A ligand has a lone pair of electrons.

> **KEY POINT**
>
> A **complex ion** is a central metal ion surrounded by ligands.
> The **coordination number** is the total **number** of **coordinate bonds** from ligands to the central transition metal ion of a complex ion.

Key points from AS

- **Electron pair repulsion theory**
  Revise AS pages 60–61

For AS, you learnt that electron pair repulsion is responsible for the shape of a molecule or ion.

Shapes of complex ions

The size of a ligand helps to decide the shape of the complex ion.

Six coordinate complexes

Six water molecules are able to fit around a Cu^{2+} ion to form:

- the complex ion $[Cu(H_2O)_6]^{2+}$
- with a coordination number of **6**.

The six electron pairs surrounding the central Cu^{2+} ion in $[Cu(H_2O)_6]^{2+}$ repel one another as far apart as possible to form a complex ion with an **octahedral** shape.

The hexaaquacopper(II) complex ion, $[Cu(H_2O)_6]^{2+}$

$[Cu(H_2O)_6]^{2+}$
octahedral
6 coordinate

$$\left[\begin{array}{c} H_2O \\ H_2O \overset{90°}{\underset{Cu}{\Big|}} OH_2 \\ H_2O \quad OH_2 \\ H_2O \end{array} \right]^{2+}$$

Four coordinate complexes

Chloride ions are larger than water molecules and it is only possible for **four** chloride ions to fit around the central copper(II) ion to form:

- the complex ion $[CuCl_4]^{2-}$
- with a coordination number of **4**.

The **four** electron pairs surrounding the central Cu^{2+} ion in $[CuCl_4]^{2-}$ repel one another as far apart as possible to form a complex ion with a **tetrahedral** shape.

The tetrachlorocuprate(II) complex ion $[CuCl_4]^{2-}$

Notice the overall charge on the complex ion $[CuCl_4]^{2-}$ is 2–.
Cu^{2+} and 4 Cl^- → 2– ions.

$[CuCl_4]^{2-}$
tetrahedral
4 coordinate

General rules for deciding the shape of a complex ion

Although there are exceptions, the following general rules are useful.

> **KEY POINT**
>
> Complex ions with small ligands such as H_2O and NH_3 are usually **6-coordinate** and **octahedral**.
>
> Complex ions with large Cl^- ligands are usually **4-coordinate** and **tetrahedral**.

The table below compares complex ions formed from cobalt(II) and chromium(III) ions.

ligand	complex ions from Co^{2+}	complex ions from Cr^{3+}	shape
H_2O	$[Co(H_2O)_6]^{2+}$	$[Cr(H_2O)_6]^{3+}$	octahedral
NH_3	$[Co(NH_3)_6]^{2+}$	$[Cr(NH_3)_6]^{3+}$	octahedral
Cl^-	$[CoCl_4]^{2-}$	$[CrCl_4]^-$	tetrahedral

The $[Ag(NH_3)_2]^+$ complex ion is present in Tollens' reagent (ammonical silver nitrate) used as a test for the aldehyde functional group (see pages 116–117).

- Some complex ions contain more than one type of ligand. For example, copper(II) forms a complex ion with a mixture of water and ammonia ligands, $[Cu(NH_3)_4(H_2O)_2]^{2+}$.

- Ag^+ and Cu^+ forms linear complexes that are 2-coordinate: e.g. $[Ag(H_2O)_2]^+$, $[Ag(NH_3)_2]^+$, $[AgCl_2]^-$ and $[CuCl_2]^-$.

Ligands have teeth

AQA   M5   SALTERS   M4
EDEXCEL M5   CCEA   M5
OCR   M5

Ligands such as H_2O, NH_3 and Cl^- are called **monodentate** ligands. They form only one coordinate bond to the central metal ion.

A molecule or ion with more than one oxygen or nitrogen atom may form more than one coordinate bond to the central metal ion.

Ligands that can form **two** coordinate bonds to the central metal ion are called **bidentate** ligands. Examples of bidentate ligands are ethane-1,2-diamine, $NH_2CH_2CH_2NH_2$ and the ethanedioate ion, $(COO^-)_2$.

Monodentate means **one** tooth.

Bidentate ligands have **two** teeth.

Multidentate ligands have **many** teeth.

Each 'tooth' is a coordinate bond.

Multidentate ligands can form many coordinate bonds to the central metal ion. For example, the hexadentate ligand, $edta^{4-}$, is able to form **six** coordinate bonds to the central metal ion. The diagram of $edta^{4-}$ shows four oxygen atoms and two nitrogen atoms able to form coordinate bonds.

$edta^{4-}$

Stereoisomerism in complexes

AQA   M5   EDEXCEL   M5
OCR   M5   CCEA   M5

Stereoisomers have the same structural isomers but different arrangements in space. Transition metal complexes show two types of stereoisomerism:

- *cis-trans* isomerism
- optical isomerism.

Cis-trans isomerism

Cis-trans isomerism occurs in square planar complexes with two ligands of one kind and two of another kind, e.g. $Ni(NH_3)_2Cl_2$.

cis-isomer
groups on same side

trans-isomer
groups on opposite side

Platin

The structures of *cis*-platin and *trans*-platin are shown below. Both structures have a square planar shape with a 90° bond angle.

cis-platin

trans-platin

Cis-platin is used as a chemotherapy drug in the treatment of some cancers. *Cis*-platin forms coordinate bonds to a basic site in the DNA of cancer cells. This process prevents the cancerous DNA from replicating, effectively killing the cancerous cells. Careful treatment is required to avoid harmful side-effects of the drug.

Optical isomerism (OCR only)

Optical isomers are non-superimposable mirror images of one another. Some octahedral complexes with multidentate ligands form optical isomers, e.g. $[Ni(NH_2CH_2CH_2NH_2)_3]^{2+}$.

The two optical isomers rotate plane-polarised light in opposite directions.

Colour and complex ions

AQA	M5	SALTERS	M4
EDEXCEL	M5	WJEC	M5
OCR	M5	CCEA	M5

Complex ions have different colours

Many transition metal ions have different colours. These colours indicate the possible identity of a transition metal ion. The table on page 90 shows the colours of some **aqua** complex ions of d-block elements. Notice that different oxidation states of a d-block element can have different colours.

Sc	Ti	V	Cr	Mn	Fe	Co	Ni	Cu	Zn
								+1 colourless	
				+2 pale pink	+2 pale green	+2 pink	+2 green	+2 blue	+2 colourless
+3 colourless	+3 violet	+3 blue	+3 ruby		+3 red-brown				
		+5 yellow							
			+6 yellow or orange						
				+7 purple					

Why are transition element ions coloured?

AQA	M5	SALTERS	M5
EDEXCEL	M5	WJEC	CH5

Splitting the 3d energy level

All five d-orbitals in the outer d sub-shell of an **isolated** transition element ion have the same energy. However, when ligands bond to the central ion, the d-orbitals move to two different energy levels. The gap between the energy levels depends upon:

- the ligand
- the coordination number
- the transition metal ion.

This diagram shows how water ligands split the energy levels of the five 3d orbitals in a copper(II) ion.

Absorption of light energy

An electron can be promoted from the lower 3d energy level by absorbing energy **exactly** equal to the energy gap ΔE. This energy is provided by radiation from the visible and ultraviolet regions of the spectrum.

Radiation with a frequency f has an energy hf, where h = Planck's constant, 6.63×10^{-34} J s.

So, to promote an electron through as energy gap ΔE, a quantity of light energy is needed given by:

$$\Delta E = hf$$

The diagram below shows what happens when a complex ion absorbs light energy.

Energy and frequency

The difference in energy between the d-orbitals, ΔE, and the frequency of the absorbed radiation, f, are linked by the following relationship:

$\Delta E = hf$

h = Planck's constant, 6.63×10^{-34} J s.

90

The blue colour of $[Cu(H_2O)_6]^{2+}$ results from:

- **absorption** of light energy in the red, yellow and green regions of the spectrum. This absorbed radiation provides the energy for an electron to be excited to a higher energy level
- **reflection** of blue light only, giving the copper(II) hexaaqua ion its characteristic blue colour. The blue region of the spectrum is **not** absorbed.

Copper has another ion, Cu^+, with the electronic configuration: $[Ar]3d^{10}$.

The Cu^+ ion is colourless because:

- the 3d sub-shell is full, $[Ar]3d^{10}$, preventing electron transfer.

> **KEY POINT**
> The colour of a transition metal complex ion results from the **transfer** of an **electron** between the orbitals of an **unfilled** d sub-shell.

> Only those ions that have a partially filled d sub-shell are coloured. Cu^{2+} is $[Ar]3d^94s^2$

> Ag^+ complexes are also colourless because the 3d sub-shell is full.

Absorbance and reflectance spectra (Salters only)

The absorbance and reflectance spectra of a pigment are shown below. Note that the spectra show peaks the opposite way around.

> **Key points from AS**
>
> - **Atomic spectra of hydrogen**
>   *Revise AS pages 28–29*

> Different techniques can be used to piece together analytical information about substances.
>
> For example, analysis of paintings may include:
> - gas chromatography, GC (see pages 163–164)
> - atomic emission and absorption spectroscopy (see AS pages 28–29)
> - visible spectroscopy (reflection and absorption).

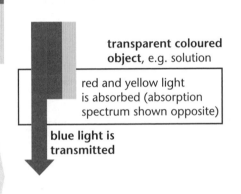

transparent coloured object, e.g. solution

red and yellow light is absorbed (absorption spectrum shown opposite)

blue light is transmitted

blue light is reflected (reflectance spectrum shown opposite)

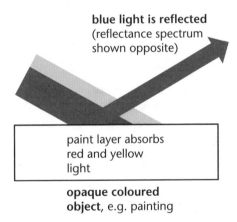

paint layer absorbs red and yellow light

opaque coloured object, e.g. painting

Using colorimetry

AQA   M5   SALTERS   M4
CCEA   M5

A colorimeter measures the amount of light absorbed by a coloured solution. The concentration and formula of a complex ion can be determined from the intensity of light absorbed by the colorimeter.

Finding an unknown concentration of a coloured solution (AQA and Salters only)

- A suitable filter and wavelength is chosen for the readings.
- Solutions of a coloured complex ion of known concentration are prepared.

- The absorbances of the solutions of known concentration are measured.
- A calibration curve is plotted.

Colorimetry can also be used as a method for monitoring reaction rates (see pages 18–27).

- The solution of the complex ion with an unknown concentration is then placed in the colorimeter and the absorbance measured.
- The unknown concentration can be determined from the calibration curve.

Finding the formula of a coloured complex (CCEA only)

Colorimetry can be used to determine the formula of a coloured complexion.

The formula of a complex ion by colorimetry

The CCEA specification lists $[Cu(NH_3)_4(H_2O)_2]^{2+}$ and $[Fe(SCN)(H_2O)_5]^{2+}$ as specific examples.

- A suitable filter and wavelength is chosen for the readings.
- Aqueous solutions of Cu^{2+}(aq) and NH_3(aq) are prepared.
- Mixtures are now prepared with different relative proportions of the Cu^{2+}(aq) and NH_3(aq).

The maximum absorption of light occurs when the Cu^{2+}/NH_3 ratio is closest to the actual formula of the complex ion.

- The absorbance of each solution is measured in a colorimeter.
- A graph is plotted to find the maximum absorbance – this shows the amounts of the Cu^{2+} and NH_3 present on the complex ion.

From the graph, the maximum absorbance is when $Cu^{2+} : NH_3 = 1 : 4$

In Cu^{2+}(aq), the complex ion is $[Cu(H_2O)_6]^{2+}$

∴ 4 NH_3 molecules have replaced 4 H_2O ligands in $[Cu(H_2O)_6]^{2+}$ and the formula of the complex ion is $[Cu(NH_3)_4(H_2O)_2]^{2+}$

The same method could be used to find the formula of any other complex ion.

Progress check

1 Predict the formula of the following complex ions:
(a) iron(III) with water ligands
(b) vanadium(III) with chloride ligands
(c) nickel(II) with ammonia ligands.

2 Explain the origin of colour in a complex ion that is yellow.

2 The 3d orbitals are split between two energy levels. A 3d electron from the lower 3d energy level absorbs visible light in the blue and red regions of the spectrum. The absorbed energy allows the d-electron to be promoted to a vacancy in the orbitals of the higher 3d energy level. With the red and blue regions of the spectrum absorbed, only yellow light is reflected, giving the complex ion its colour.

1 (a) $[Fe(H_2O)_6]^{3+}$ (b) $[VCl_6]^{3-}$ (c) $[Ni(NH_3)_6]^{2+}$.

3.5 Ligand substitution of complex ions

After studying this section you should be able to:

- *describe what is meant by ligand substitution*
- *understand that ligand exchange may produce changes in colour and coordination number*
- *understand stability of complex ions in terms of stability constants*
- *understand edta titrations of complex ions*

LEARNING SUMMARY

Exchange between ligands

AQA	M5	SALTERS	M4
EDEXCEL	M5	WJEC	M5
OCR	M5	CCEA	M5

Ligand substitution usually produces a change in colour.

A **ligand substitution** reaction takes place when a ligand in a complex ion exchanges for another ligand. A change in ligand usually changes the energy gap between the 3d energy levels. With a different ΔE value, light with a different frequency is absorbed, producing a colour change.

Exchange between H_2O and NH_3 ligands

The **similar sizes** of water and ammonia molecules ensure that ligand exchange takes place with **no change in coordination number**.

For example, addition of an excess of concentrated aqueous ammonia to aqueous nickel(II) ions results in ligand substitution of ammonia ligands for water ligands. Both complex ions have an octahedral shape with a coordination number of six.

Remember that the **size** of the ligand is a major factor in deciding the coordination number (see page 87):

- H_2O and NH_3 have similar sizes – same coordination number
- H_2O and Cl^- have different sizes – different coordination numbers.

$$[Ni(H_2O)_6]^{2+} \quad + \quad 6\ddot{N}H_3 \longrightarrow [Ni(NH_3)_6]^{2+} \quad + \quad 6H_2\ddot{O}$$

Exchange between H_2O and Cl^- ligands

You should also be able to construct a balanced equation for any ligand exchange reaction.

The **different sizes** of water molecules and chloride ions ensure that ligand exchange takes place **with a change in coordination number**.

For example, addition of an excess of concentrated hydrochloric acid (as a source of Cl^- ions) to aqueous cobalt(II) ions results in ligand substitution of chloride ligands for water ligands. The complex ions have different shapes with different coordination numbers.

octahedral   change in coordinate number   tetrahedral
6 coordinate   4 coordinate

$$\left[\begin{array}{c} OH_2 \\ H_2O_{,,,}\!\!\underset{|}{\overset{|}{Co}}\!\!^{,,,}OH_2 \\ H_2O \quad OH_2 \\ OH_2 \end{array}\right]^{2+} + \quad 4\ddot{Cl}^- \longrightarrow \left[\begin{array}{c} Cl \\ Co \\ Cl \quad Cl \\ Cl \end{array}\right]^{2-} + \quad 6H_2\ddot{O}$$

pink solution   blue solution

$$[Co(H_2O)_6]^{2+} \quad + \quad 4\ddot{Cl}^- \longrightarrow [CoCl_4]^{2-} \quad + \quad 6H_2\ddot{O}$$

Ligand substitutions of copper(II) and cobalt(II)

Ligand substitutions of copper(II) and cobalt(II) complexes are shown below.

Concentrated hydrochloric acid is used as a source of Cl⁻ ligands.

Concentrated aqueous ammonia is used as a source of NH_3 ligands.

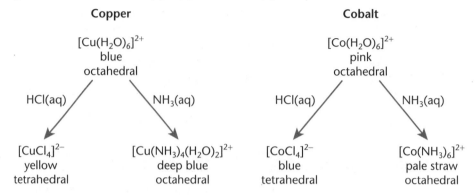

Copper

$[Cu(H_2O)_6]^{2+}$
blue
octahedral

HCl(aq) / NH₃(aq)

$[CuCl_4]^{2-}$
yellow
tetrahedral

$[Cu(NH_3)_4(H_2O)_2]^{2+}$
deep blue
octahedral

Cobalt

$[Co(H_2O)_6]^{2+}$
pink
octahedral

HCl(aq) / NH₃(aq)

$[CoCl_4]^{2-}$
blue
tetrahedral

$[Co(NH_3)_6]^{2+}$
pale straw
octahedral

Incomplete substitution

Substitution may be incomplete.

- Aqueous ammonia only exchanges **four** from the six water ligands in $[Cu(H_2O)_6]^{2+}$.

$$[Cu(H_2O)_6]^{2+} + 4NH_3 \longrightarrow [Cu(NH_3)_4(H_2O)_2]^{2+} + 4H_2O$$
blue solution   deep blue solution

- Aqueous thiocyanate ions, SCN⁻, only exchanges **one** from the six water ligands in $[Fe(H_2O)_6]^{3+}$.

$$[Fe(H_2O)_6]^{3+} + SCN^-(aq) \longrightarrow [Fe(H_2O)_5(SCN)]^{2+} + H_2O$$
pale brown solution   deep red solution

This reaction is used as a test for the Fe³⁺ ion – the deep red-brown colour of $[Fe(H_2O)_5(SCN)]^{2+}$ is intense and extremely small traces of Fe³⁺ ions can be detected using this ligand substitution reaction.

Haemoglobin

AQA ▸ M5   CCEA ▸ M5
OCR ▸ M5

Haemoglobin is a complex ion of Fe²⁺. A haem group consists of an Fe²⁺ ion, held in a ring, known as a porphyrin. The Fe²⁺ ion, which is the site of oxygen binding, bonds with four nitrogen atoms in the centre of the ring in a square planar geometry. The protein globin bonds below and O_2 is able to bond weakly above.

The porphyrin ring in haemoglobin

O_2 can be easily lost when required and is replaced by a weakly bonded water ligand. When haemoglobin reaches the lungs again, fresh O_2 is able to bond to Fe²⁺, displacing the water.

Carbon monoxide, CO, is a serious poison for the blood as the polar molecule binds much more strongly to the Fe²⁺ ion than O_2 and cannot be displaced. This prevents oxygen from being carried by the blood.

Stability of complex ions

The stability of a complex ion depends upon the ligands. For example, a complex ion of copper(II) is more stable with ligands of ammonia than with water ligands.

Bidentate or multidentate ligands (such as edta) lead to a particularly stable complex. This is due to an increase in entropy:

e.g. $[Cu(H_2O)_6]^{2+} + edta^{4-} \xrightarrow[\text{ENTROPY}]{\text{INCREASE IN}} [Cu(edta)]^{2-} + 6H_2O$

$\underbrace{\hspace{3cm}}_{2 \text{ mol}}$ $\underbrace{\hspace{3cm}}_{7 \text{ mol}}$

> The concentration of water is virtually constant. Constant terms are not included in expressions for equilibrium constants.

The stability of a complex ion is measured as a **stability constant**, K_{stab}:

$$[Cu(H_2O)_6]^{2+} + 4NH_3(aq) \rightleftharpoons [Cu(NH_3)_4(H_2O)_2]^{2+} + 4H_2O(l)$$

$$K_{stab} = \frac{[Cu(NH_3)_4(H_2O)_2]^{2+}}{[Cu(H_2O)_6]^{2+}[NH_3(aq)]^4} = 1 \times 10^{12} \text{ dm}^{12} \text{ mol}^{-4} \text{ at } 25°C$$

> The data is expressed on a logarithmic scale because of the very large range of values.

Stability constants usually measure the stability of a complex compared with the metal aqua-ion. The greater the value of K_{stab}, the more stable the complex ion.

complex ion	log K_{stab}	
$[Fe(H_2O)_5(SCN)]^{2+}$	3.9	
$[CuCl_4]^{2-}$	5.6	increased
$[Ni(NH_3)_6]^{2+}$	8.6	stability
$[Ni(edta)]^{2-}$	19.3	

Edta titrations

> The structure of edta is discussed on page 88.

Edta can be used for complexometric titrations in which the formation of a coloured complex is used to indicate the end-point of a titration.

Disodium edta, $Na_2H_2(edta)$, is typically used to prepare solutions for titration. In a weak alkaline aqueous solution, this dissociates forming $edta^{4-}(aq)$ ions.

Most 2+ metal cations form a complex with $edta^{4-}$:

$$M^{2+}(aq) + edta^{4-}(aq) \longrightarrow M(edta)^{2-}(aq)$$

Note that the M^{2+} and $edta^{4-}$ reacts in a **1 : 1** molar ratio.

Edta is used as a 'sequestering agent' in detergents to soften hard water. Edta acts by complexing to Ca^{2+} ions that cause water hardness.

Edta is used in medicine to prevent clotting of blood. Edta acts by complexing to Ca^{2+} ions, required for the clotting action.

Determination of Ca^{2+}(aq) or Mg^{2+}(aq) ions

> The titration is carried out in the presence of a weakly alkaline buffer.

> Calculation from titration results follows common principles. See pages 43–44 (acid-base) and pages 96–98 (redox) for examples and hints.

A complexometric indicator, such as Eriochrome Black T, is used.

- The indicator binds to the metal cations in solution to form a red-coloured complex.
- Edta is added from the burette.
- Edta binds to metal cations much more strongly than the indicator and displaces the indicator from the metal cations as it is added.
- The colour change at the end point is from **red to blue**.

Progress check

1 Write equations for the following ligand substitutions:
(a) $[Ni(H_2O)_6]^{2+}$ with six ammonia ligands
(b) $[Fe(H_2O)_6]^{3+}$ with four chloride ligands
(c) $[Cr(H_2O)_6]^{3+}$ with six cyanide ligands, CN^-.

1 (a) $[Ni(H_2O)_6]^{2+} + 6NH_3 \longrightarrow [Ni(NH_3)_6]^{2+} + 6H_2O$
(b) $[Fe(H_2O)_6]^{3+} + 4Cl^- \longrightarrow [FeCl_4]^- + 6H_2O$
(c) $[Cr(H_2O)_6]^{3+} + 6CN^- \longrightarrow [Cr(CN)_6]^{3-} + 6H_2O$.

3.6 Redox reactions of transition metal ions

After studying this section you should be able to:

- describe redox behaviour in transition elements
- construct redox equations, using relevant half-equations
- perform calculations involving simple redox titrations

Redox reactions

Transition elements have variable oxidation states with characteristic colours (see page 90). Many **redox** reactions take place in which transition metals ions change their oxidation state by **gaining** or **losing** electrons.

The iron(II) – manganate(VII) reaction

> **Key points from AS**
>
> - **Redox reactions**
>   *Revise AS pages 42–44*

Iron(II) ions are oxidised by acidified manganate(VII) ions.

- Acidified manganate(VII) ions are reduced to manganate(II) ions.

reduction: $\quad MnO_4^-(aq) + 8H^+(aq) + 5e^- \longrightarrow Mn^{2+}(aq) + 4H_2O(l)$
$\qquad\qquad\qquad +7 \qquad\qquad\qquad\qquad\qquad\qquad\quad +2$
$\qquad\qquad\qquad$ purple $\longrightarrow$ very pale pink

> The reaction is easy to see.
>
> The deep purple MnO_4^- ions are reduced to the very pale pink Mn^{2+} ions, which are virtually colourless in solution.

- Iron(II) ions are oxidised to iron(III) ions.

oxidation: $\quad Fe^{2+}(aq) \longrightarrow Fe^{3+}(aq) + e^-$
$\qquad\qquad\qquad +2 \qquad\qquad\quad +3$

To give the overall equation:

- the electrons are balanced

$$MnO_4^-(aq) + 8H^+(aq) + 5e^- \longrightarrow Mn^{2+}(aq) + 4H_2O(l)$$
$$5Fe^{2+}(aq) \longrightarrow 5Fe^{3+}(aq) + 5e^-$$

- the half-equations are added

$$5Fe^{2+}(aq) + MnO_4^-(aq) + 8H^+(aq) \longrightarrow 5Fe^{3+}(aq) + Mn^{2+}(aq) + 4H_2O(l)$$

Redox titrations

Redox titrations can be used in analysis.

Essential requirements are:

- an oxidising agent
- a reducing agent
- an easily-seen colour change (with or without an indicator).

> It is important to use an acid that does **not** react with either the oxidising or reducing agent – dilute sulphuric acid is usually used.
>
> For example, hydrochloric acid cannot be used because HC is oxidised to Cl_2 by MnO_4^-.

Redox titrations using the acidified manganate(VII)

- $KMnO_4$ is reacted with a reducing agent such as Fe^{2+} under acidic conditions (see above).
- Purple $KMnO_4$ is added from the burette to a measured amount of the acidified reducing agent.
- At the end-point, the colour changes from colourless to pale pink, showing that all the reducing agent has exactly reacted. The pale-pink colour indicates the first trace of an excess of purple manganate(VII) ions.
- This titration is **self-indicating** – no indicator is required, the colour change from the reduction of MnO_4^- ions being sufficient to indicate that the reaction is complete.

> The most common redox titration encountered at A Level is that between manganate(VII) and acidified iron(II) ions.

Key points from AS

- **Calculations in acid–base titrations**
  Revise AS page 40

Calculations for redox titrations follow the same principles as those used for acid–base titrations, studied during AS Chemistry.

The concentration and volume of $KMnO_4$ are known so the amount of MnO_4^- ions can be found.

Using the equation determine the number of moles of the second reagent.

If there is sampling of the original solution, you will need to scale.

The estimation of iron in iron tablets

Five iron tablets with a combined mass of 0.900 g were dissolved in acid and made up to 100 cm³ of solution. In a titration, 10.0 cm³ of this solution reacted exactly with 10.4 cm³ of 0.0100 mol dm⁻³ potassium manganate(VII). What is the percentage by mass of iron in the tablets?

As with all titrations, we must consider **five** pieces of information:

- the balanced equation

  $$5Fe^{2+}(aq) + MnO_4^-(aq) + 8H^+(aq) \rightarrow 5Fe^{3+}(aq) + Mn^{2+}(aq) + 4H_2O(l)$$

- the concentration c_1 and reacting volume V_1 of $KMnO_4(aq)$
- the concentration c_2 and reacting volume V_2 of $Fe^{2+}(aq)$.

From the titration results, the amount of $KMnO_4$ can be calculated:

$$\text{amount of } KMnO_4 = c \times \frac{V}{1000} = 0.0100 \times \frac{10.4}{1000} = 1.04 \times 10^{-4} \text{ mol}$$

From the equation, the amount of Fe^{2+} can be determined:

$$5Fe^{2+}(aq) + MnO_4^-(aq) + 8H^+(aq) \rightarrow 5Fe^{3+}(aq) + Mn^{2+}(aq) + 4H_2O(l)$$

5 mol　　　**1 mol** *(balancing numbers)*

$\therefore$ 5 x 1.04×10^{-4} mol Fe^{2+} reacts with 1.04×10^{-4} mol MnO_4^-

$\therefore$ amount of Fe^{2+} that reacted = 5.20×10^{-4} mol

Find the amount of Fe^{2+} in the solution prepared from the tablets:

10.0 cm³ of $Fe^{2+}(aq)$ contains 5.20×10^{-4} mol Fe^{2+} (aq)

The 100 cm³ solution of iron tablets contains　$10 \times (5.20 \times 10^{-4})$
$$= 5.20 \times 10^{-3} \text{ mol } Fe^{2+}$$

Find the percentage of Fe^{2+} in the tablets (A_r: Fe, 55.8)

5.20×10^{-3} mol Fe^{2+} has a mass of $5.20 \times 10^{-3} \times 55.8 = 0.290$ g

$$\therefore \text{ % of } Fe^{2+} \text{ in tablets} = \frac{\text{mass of } Fe^{2+}}{\text{mass of tablets}} \times 100 = \frac{0.290}{0.900} \times 100 = 32.2\%$$

For A2, you are expected to tackle unstructured titration calculations. The principles are the same, irrespective of the type of titration.

Further redox titrations

Providing there is a visible colour change, many other redox reactions can be used for redox titrations.

For example, acidified dichromate(VI) ions is an oxidising agent which can also oxidise Fe^{2+} ions to Fe^{3+}.

reduction:　　$Cr_2O_7^{2-}(aq) + 14H^+(aq) + 6e^- \longrightarrow 2Cr^{3+}(aq) + 7H_2O(l)$

oxidation:　　　　　　　　　$Fe^{2+}(aq) \longrightarrow Fe^{3+}(aq) + e^-$

overall:　　$6Fe^{2+}(aq) + Cr_2O_7^{2-}(aq) + 14H^+(aq) \rightarrow 6Fe^{3+}(aq) + 2Cr^{3+}(aq) + 7H_2O(l)$

Iodine-thiosulfate titrations

EDEXCEL	M5	WJEC	M5
OCR	M5	CCEA	M5

Iodine-thiosulfate titrations can be used to determine iodine concentrations, either directly or by liberating iodine using a more powerful oxidising agent.

Iodine oxidises thiosulfate ions:

$$I_2(aq) + 2S_2O_3^{2-}(aq) \longrightarrow 2I^-(aq) + S_4O_6^{2-}(aq)$$

Starch is a sensitive test for the presence of iodine. If added too early in this titration, the deep-blue colour perseveres and the end-point cannot be detected with accuracy.

- Thiosulfate is added from the burette to the iodine solution until the deep-brown colour of iodine becomes a light-straw colour.
- Starch is now added, forming a deep-blue colour.
- Thiosulfate is added dropwise until the deep-blue colour becomes colourless. This is the end-point and shows that all the iodine has just been reacted.

The estimation of copper in a brass

1.65 g of a sample of brass was reacted with concentrated nitric acid. The solution was neutralised and diluted to 250 cm³ with water.

25.0 cm³ of this solution was pipetted into a flask. An excess of aqueous potassium iodide was then added to liberate iodine:

equation 1 $2Cu^{2+}(aq) + 4I^-(aq) \longrightarrow 2CuI(s) + I_2(s)$

Titration of this solution required 21.20 cm³ of 0.100 mol dm⁻³ sodium thiosulfate.

equation 2 $2S_2O_3^{2-}(aq) + I_2(aq) \longrightarrow 2I^-(aq) + S_4O_6^{2-}(aq)$

Calculate the percentage, by mass, of copper in the brass sample.

From the titration results, the amount (in moles) of $Na_2S_2O_3$ can be calculated:

> *This is an unstructured titration calculation. See also pages 43–44 for general hints on solving this type of problem.*

$$\text{amount of } Na_2S_2O_3 = c \times \frac{V}{1000} = 0.100 \times \frac{21.20}{1000} = 0.00212 \text{ mol}$$

> *The concentration and volume of $Na_2S_2O_3$ are known.*

From the equations, the amount (in moles) of Cu^{2+} can be determined:

From *equation 2*, 2 mol $S_2O_3^{2-}$ reacts with 1 mol I_2

From *equation 1*, 1 mol I_2 reacts with 2 mol Cu^{2+}

> *Using the equations, determine the number of moles of Cu^{2+}.*

∴ 2 mol $S_2O_3^{2-}$ ≡ 1 mol I_2 ≡ 2 mol Cu^{2+}

∴ 0.00212 mol $S_2O_3^{2-}$ ≡ 0.00212/2 mol I_2 ≡ 0.00212 mol Cu^{2+}

amount of Cu^{2+} = 0.00212 mol

The amount of Cu^{2+} of the 250 cm³ solution prepared from the brass can be deduced:

25.0 cm³ of $Cu^{2+}(aq)$ in the titration contains 0.00212 mol Cu^{2+}.

> *Don't forget to take into account any need to scale up.*

250 cm³ of the $Cu^{2+}(aq)$ solution from the brass contains 10 x 0.00212 = 0.0212 mol Cu^{2+}.

Finally, the percentage, by mass, of copper in brass can be calculated:

0.0212 mol Cu produced 0.0212 mol Cu^{2+}

> *The final step is now easy provided that you have remembered:*
>
> $$n = \frac{\text{mass}}{\text{molar mass}}$$

mass of copper in brass = 63.5 x 0.0212 = 1.35 g

∴ percentage of copper in brass = $\frac{1.35}{1.65}$ x 100 = 81.8 %.

Further examples of redox reactions

AQA   M5   WJEC   M5
EDEXCEL   M5   CCEA   M5

Vanadium

Vanadium(V) can be reduced to vanadium(II) using zinc in acid solution as the reducing agent. The formation of different oxidation states of vanadium can be followed by colour changes.

oxidation state	+2	+3	+4	+5
species	V^{2+} (purple)	V^{3+} (green)	VO^{2+} (blue)	VO_2^+ (yellow)

Zn/HCl

Chromium

The oxidation states of chromium can be interchanged using:

- hydrogen peroxide in alkaline solution as the oxidising agent
- zinc in acid solution as the reducing agent.

> *For moving up oxidation states H_2O_2/OH^- is a good general oxidising agent.*
>
> *For moving down oxidation states Zn/HCl is a good general reducing agent.*

oxidation state	+2	+3	+6
species	Cr^{2+} (blue)	Cr^{3+} (green)	CrO_4^{2-} (yellow) / $Cr_2O_7^{2-}$ (orange)

This conversion can be explained by applying le Chatelier's principle.

Addition of acid increases [H⁺(aq) – the equilibrium moves to the right, counteracting this change.

Added alkali reacts with H⁺(aq) ions present in the equilibrium system. [H⁺(aq) decreases – the equilibrium moves to the left, counteracting this change.

The dichromate(VI) – chromate(VI) conversion

The table on the previous page shows that the dichromate(VI) ion $Cr_2O_7^{2-}$ and the chromate(VI) ion CrO_4^{2-} have the **same** oxidation state. These ions can be interconverted at different pH values.

$$2H^+(aq) + 2CrO_4^{2-}(aq) \quad \rightleftharpoons \quad Cr_2O_7^{2-}(aq) + H_2O(l)$$

acid →

yellow ← alkali   orange

Cobalt

Cobalt(II) can be oxidised to Co(III) using:

- hydrogen peroxide in alkaline solution or
- air in the presence of ammonia as an oxidising agent.

oxidation state	+2		+3
species	$[Co(NH_3)_6]^{2+}$ (light straw)	H_2O_2/OH^- *or* NH_3/air →	$[Co(NH_3)_6]^{3+}$ (brown)

Disproportionation in transition metal chemistry (Edexcel only)

Copper metal has an oxidation state of 0. Copper compounds exist in the oxidation states +1 and +2. We can predict redox reactions that may take place involving these three species by treating redox systems as if they are half-cells.

$$Cu^{2+}(aq) + e^- \rightleftharpoons Cu^+(aq) \qquad E^\ominus = +0.16 \text{ V}$$
$$Cu^+(aq) + e^- \rightleftharpoons Cu(s) \qquad E^\ominus = +0.52 \text{ V}$$

- $E_{cell} = (+0.52) - (+0.16) = +0.36$ V.

The Cu^{2+}/Cu^+ system has the more negative $E^\ominus$ value and its half-reaction will proceed to the left, donating electrons:

$$Cu^{2+}(aq) + e^- \quad \longleftarrow \quad Cu^+(aq) \qquad E^\ominus = +0.16 \text{ V}$$
$$Cu^+(aq) + e^- \quad \longrightarrow \quad Cu(s) \qquad E^\ominus = +0.52 \text{ V}$$

Notice that a reaction takes place between reactants from different sides of each half-equation.

We would therefore predict that **Cu⁺** would react with **Cu⁺** and that this **disproportionation** will take place:

$$2Cu^+ \longrightarrow Cu^{2+} + Cu$$

This disproportionation reaction can be predicted from electrode potentials.

+1 ———→ 0	*reduction*	$Cu^+ + e^- \longrightarrow Cu$
+1 ——→ +2	*oxidation*	$Cu^+ \longrightarrow Cu^{2+} + e^-$

Progress check

1 Write a full equation from the following pairs of half-equations. For each pair, identify the changes in oxidation number, what has been oxidised and what has been reduced.
   (a) $Zn \longrightarrow Zn^{2+} + 2e^-$
       $VO_2^+ + 4H^+ + 3e^- \longrightarrow V^{2+} + 2H_2O$
   (b) $Cr^{3+} + 8OH^- \longrightarrow CrO_4^{2-} + 4H_2O + 3e^-$
       $H_2O_2 + 2e^- \longrightarrow 2OH^-$

2 In a redox titration, 25.0 cm³ of an acidified solution containing $Fe^{2+}(aq)$ ions reacted exactly with 21.8 cm³ of 0.0200 mol dm⁻³ potassium manganate(VII). Calculate the concentration of $Fe^{2+}(aq)$ ions.

2 0.0872 mol dm⁻³

Cr: +3 → +6; O: –1 → –2; Cr³⁺ oxidised; H₂O₂ reduced.
(b) 2Cr³⁺ + 3H₂O₂ + 10OH⁻ ⟶ 2CrO₄²⁻ + 8H₂O
V: +5 → +2; Zn: 0 → +2; VO₂⁺ reduced; Zn oxidised.
1 (a) 2VO₂⁺ + 3Zn + 8H⁺ ⟶ 2V²⁺ + 3Zn²⁺ + 4H₂O

3.7 Catalysis

After studying this section you should be able to:

- *understand how a transition element acts as a catalyst*
- *explain how a catalyst acts in heterogeneous catalysis*
- *explain how a catalyst acts in homogeneous catalysis*

LEARNING SUMMARY

Key points from AS

- **How do catalysts work?**
  Revise AS page 108
- **Heterogeneous and homogeneous catalysis**
  Revise AS pages 108–109

The two different classes of catalyst, homogeneous and heterogeneous, were discussed in detail during AS Chemistry. Both types are used industrially but heterogeneous catalysis is much more common. The AS coverage is summarised below and expanded to include extra examples of transition element catalysis.

Transition elements as catalysts

AQA	MS	SALTERS	M4
EDEXCEL	MS	WJEC	M5
OCR	MS	CCEA	M5

An important use of transition metals and their compounds is as catalysts for many industrial processes. Nickel and platinum are extensively used in the petroleum and polymer industries.

> Transition metal ions are able to act as catalysts by changing their oxidation states. This is made possible by using the partially full d-orbitals for gaining or losing electrons.

KEY POINT

Heterogeneous catalysis

AQA	MS	SALTERS	M4
EDEXCEL	MS	WJEC	M5
		CCEA	M5

Key points from AS

- **Heterogeneous and homogeneous catalysis**
  Revise AS pages 108–109

Transition metals use d and s-electrons to form weak bonds with reactant molecules at the catalyst surface.

A **heterogeneous** catalyst has a **different** phase from the reactants.

- Many examples of heterogeneous catalysts involve reactions between **gases**, catalysed by a **solid** catalyst which is often a transition metal or one of its compounds.

The process involves:

- **diffusion** of gas molecules onto the surface of the iron catalyst
- **adsorption** of the gases to the surface of the catalyst
- **weakening of bonds**, allowing a chemical reaction to take place
- **diffusion** of the product molecules from the surface of the catalyst, allowing more gas molecules to diffuse onto its surface.

Transition metal ions as heterogeneous catalysts

The catalytic converter

- Rh/Pt/Pd catalysts are used in catalytic converters for the removal of polluting gases, such as CO and NO, produced in a car engine.
- The **solid** Rh/Pt/Pd catalyst is held on a ceramic honeycomb support, giving a large surface area for the catalyst which can be spread extremely thinly on the support. The high surface area of the catalyst increases the chances of a reaction and less of the expensive catalysts are needed, keeping down costs.

Iron

Iron-containing catalysts are used in many industrial processes, the most important being to form ammonia from nitrogen and hydrogen in the Haber process.

$$N_2(g) + 3H_2(g) \rightleftharpoons 2NH_3(g)$$

Chromium(III) oxide

Chromium(III) oxide, Cr_2O_3, is used to catalyse the manufacture of methanol from carbon monoxide and hydrogen.

$$CO(g) + 2H_2(g) \rightleftharpoons CH_3OH(g)$$

Vanadium

A vanadium(V) oxide, V_2O_5, catalyst is used in the contact process for sulfur trioxide production from which sulfuric acid is manufactured.

This catalysis proceeds via an **intermediate state**.

- The vanadium(V) oxide catalyst first oxidises sulfur dioxide to sulfur trioxide. The vanadium is **reduced** from the +5 to +4 oxidation state, forming vanadium(IV) oxide $V_2O_4(s)$ as the **intermediate state**.

$$SO_2(g) + V_2O_5(s) \longrightarrow SO_3(g) + V_2O_4(s) \qquad \textit{vanadium reduced}$$

+4 $\longrightarrow$ +6

+5 $\longrightarrow$ +4
+5 $\longrightarrow$ +4

> Notice that the oxidation number of each atom has been shown. Two V atoms have been reduced from +5 to +4.

- The intermediate V_2O_4 is then oxidised back to the +5 oxidation state by oxygen, forming vanadium(V) oxide.

$$\tfrac{1}{2}O_2(g) + V_2O_4(s) \longrightarrow V_2O_5(s) \qquad \textit{vanadium oxidised}$$

0 $\longrightarrow$ −2

+4 $\longrightarrow$ +5
+4 $\longrightarrow$ +5

This is a chain reaction because the vanadium(V) oxide is then able to oxidise further sulfur dioxide.

Note:

- Although V_2O_5 has been involved in the mechanism, the overall reaction does not include V_2O_5. V_2O_5 is unchanged at the end of the reaction.
- The equation for the overall reaction taking place is:
  $$SO_2(g) + \tfrac{1}{2}O_2(g) \rightleftharpoons SO_3(g) \qquad \textit{The contact process}$$
- The vanadium is able to catalyse the reaction by interchanging its +5 and +4 oxidation states.

Poisoning of catalysts (AQA only)

A key requirement of a heterogeneous catalyst is to bind reactant molecules to the surface of the catalyst by adsorption.

The strength of this adsorption is critical.

- Lead bonds very strongly to the catalyst. The adsorption is so strong that molecules are unable to leave the surface and the catalyst is poisoned and rendered useless. Before catalytic converters could be introduced, unleaded petrol was developed. Otherwise, the lead in the fuel would poison the catalyst.

> Catalysts can become coated by impurities and can become 'poisoned' – efficiency is reduced as active sites are blocked.

Nickel and platinum are commonly used as heterogeneous catalysts.

- The bonding of reactant molecules is sufficient to allow a reaction to take place but weak enough to allow molecules to escape following reaction.

Homogeneous catalysis

AQA ▸ M5   SALTERS ▸ M4

A homogeneous catalyst has the **same** phase as the reactants.

- During homogeneous catalysis, the catalyst initially reacts with the reactants forming an **intermediate state** with **lower activation energy**.

Key points from AS

- **How catalysts work**
  Revise AS page 108
- **Homogeneous catalysis**
  Revise AS page 109

- The catalyst is then regenerated as the reaction completes, allowing the catalyst to react with further reactants.
- Overall the catalyst is **not** used up, but it is actively involved in the process by a chain reaction.

Transition metal ions as homogeneous catalysts

The reaction between I^- and $S_2O_8^{2-}$, catalysed by Fe^{2+}(aq) ions

The reaction between I^- and $S_2O_8^{2-}$ is very slow:

- it can be catalysed by Fe^{2+} ions
- the Fe^{2+} ions are recycled in a chain reaction.

> Transition metal ions often change their oxidation states during their catalytic action.
> Here: $Fe^{2+} \longrightarrow Fe^{3+}$

chain reaction: $\quad S_2O_8^{2-}(aq) + 2Fe^{2+}(aq) \longrightarrow 2SO_4^{2-}(aq) + 2Fe^{3+}(aq)$

$\qquad\qquad\qquad\quad 2Fe^{3+}(aq) + 2I^-(aq) \longrightarrow I_2(aq) + 2Fe^{2+}(aq)$

overall: $\qquad\qquad\quad S_2O_8^{2-}(aq) + 2I^-(aq) \longrightarrow I_2(aq) + 2SO_4^{2-}(aq)$

The overall reaction between I^- and $S_2O_8^{2-}$ involves two negative ions. These negative ions will repel one another, making it difficult for a reaction to take place. Notice that, in each stage of the mechanism, the catalyst provides positive ions which attract, and react with, each negative ion in turn.

Autocatalysis by Mn^{2+}(aq) ions

> Notice that, as in the first example, this reaction is between two negative ions.
>
> The mechanism of this reaction proceeds in a similar manner – the catalyst provides positive ions which react with each negative ion.

In warm acidic conditions, manganate(VII) ions, MnO_4^-, oxidise ethanedioate ions, $C_2O_4^{2-}$, to carbon dioxide.

$$2MnO_4^-(aq) + 5C_2O_4^{2-}(aq) + 8H^+(aq) \to 2Mn^{2+}(aq) + 10CO_2(g) + H_2O(l)$$

The purple manganate(VII) colour disappears very slowly at first, indicating a slow reaction. As soon as Mn^{2+}(aq) ions start to form, the colour disappears immediately because the Mn^{2+}(aq) ions catalyse the reaction. This is called **autocatalysis**.

The development of new catalysts

EDEXCEL   M5

The development of new catalysts is a priority area for chemical research today.

- Ethanoic acid, CH_3COOH, used to be prepared by oxidation of butane. The preparation had a poor percentage yield and was wasteful in terms of energy and atom economy.

> New catalysts provide bigger profits for companies, better use of available raw materials and less pollution to the environment.

- Research into a new synthesis of ethanoic acid, using new catalysts, has resulted in the development of a new synthesis, using methanol and carbon monoxide.

$$CH_3OH(l) + CO(g) \longrightarrow CH_3COOH$$

- An iridium-based catalyst is now used that produces near to 100% atom economy.

New catalysts lead to more efficient processes in which products can be made quicker, with less energy, better yields and improved atom economies.

Progress check

1 (a) State what is meant by homogeneous and heterogeneous catalysis.
(b) State an example of a homogeneous and heterogeneous catalyst.

2 How does a transition metal act as a catalyst?

2 Transition metal changes oxidation states by gaining or losing electrons from partially filled d-orbitals.
Heterogeneous: iron catalysing the reaction between N_2 and H_2 for ammonia production (Haber process).
(b) Homogeneous: Fe^{2+} catalysing the reaction between I^- and $S_2O_8^{2-}$.
Heterogeneous: catalyst and reactants have different phases.
1 (a) Homogeneous: catalyst and reactants have the same phase.

3.8 Reactions of metal aqua-ions

After studying this section you should be able to:

- describe the precipitation reactions of metal aqua-ions with bases
- describe the acidity of transition metal aqua-ions
- describe the acid–base behaviour of metal hydroxides

LEARNING SUMMARY

Simple precipitation reactions of metal aqua-ions

AQA	M5	SALTERS	M4
EDEXCEL	M5	WJEC	M5
OCR	M5	CCEA	M5

*Notice that NaOH(aq) and NH₃(aq) **both** act as bases.*

A precipitation reaction takes place between **aqueous alkali** and an aqueous solution of a **metal(II)** or **metal(III) cation**.

This results in the formation of a **precipitate** of the **metal hydroxide**, often with a characteristic colour.

Suitable aqueous alkalis include aqueous sodium hydroxide, NaOH(aq), and aqueous ammonia, NH₃(aq).

Aqueous ammonia provides OH⁻(aq) ions.
$NH_3(aq) + H_2O(l) \rightleftharpoons NH_4^+(aq) + OH^-(aq)$

These precipitation reactions can be represented simply as follows.

$$Cu^{2+}(aq) + 2OH^-(aq) \longrightarrow Cu(OH)_2(s)$$
$$Cr^{3+}(aq) + 3OH^-(aq) \longrightarrow Cr(OH)_3(s)$$

The hydroxides of all transition metals are insoluble in water.

The characteristic colour of the precipitate can help to identify the metal ion. The colours of some hydroxide precipitates are shown below.

hydroxide	$Fe(OH)_2(s)$	$Fe(OH)_3(s)$	$Co(OH)_2(s)$	$Cu(OH)_2(s)$	$Cr(OH)_3(s)$
colour	green	brown	blue–green	blue	green

See also:

'Reactions of metal aqua-ions with aqueous bases' page 105.

The precipitate has no charge.

AQA and Edexcel prefer to show hydroxide precipitates based on six ligands, e.g. Cu(OH)₂(H₂O)₄(s) – but most Boards will credit the simplified formulae such as Cu(OH)₂(s).

Species in solution are charged.

Reaction of complex metal aqua-ions with aqueous alkali

Equations can be written using complex aqua-ions for the reactions above, each producing a **precipitate** of the **hydrated hydroxide**.

$$[Cu(H_2O)_6]^{2+}(aq) + 2OH^-(aq) \longrightarrow Cu(OH)_2(H_2O)_4(s) + 2H_2O(l)$$
blue precipitate

$$[Cr(H_2O)_6]^{3+}(aq) + 3OH^-(aq) \longrightarrow Cr(OH)_3(H_2O)_3(s) + 3H_2O(l)$$
green precipitate

Excess aqueous sodium hydroxide

Metal(III) hydroxides **dissolve** in an **excess** of dilute aqueous sodium hydroxide forming charged **anions**.

$$Al(OH)_3(H_2O)_3(s) + OH^-(aq) \rightleftharpoons [Al(OH)_4]^-(aq) + 3H_2O(l)$$
aluminate ions

$$Cr(OH)_3(H_2O)_3(s) + 3OH^-(aq) \rightleftharpoons [Cr(OH)_6]^{3-}(aq) + 3H_2O(l)$$
chromate(III) ions

Excess aqueous ammonia

Edexcel and Salters prefer to use [Cu(NH₃)₄]²⁺ for the complex formed between Cu²⁺ and NH₃.

Excess ammonia usually results in **ligand exchange** forming a soluble ammine complex:

$$Cr(H_2O)_3(OH)_3(s) + 6NH_3(aq) \longrightarrow [Cr(NH_3)_6]^{3+}(aq) + 3H_2O(l) + 3OH^-(aq)$$
purple solution

If aqueous ammonia is slowly added to an aqueous solution of a **metal(II)** or **metal(III) cation**:

- a precipitate of the metal hydroxide first forms: **acid–base reaction**
- the precipitate then dissolves in excess ammonia: **ligand substitution**.

103

Precipitation as acid–base equilibria

AQA ▶ M5   CCEA ▶ M5
EDEXCEL ▶ M5

Fission of O–H bond

Metal(II) aqua-ions are weaker acids than metal(III) aqua-ions.

Examples of metal aqua-ions with 3+ cations include $[Al(H_2O)_6]^{3+}$, $[V(H_2O)_6]^{3+}$, $[Cr(H_2O)_6]^{3+}$ and $[Fe(H_2O)_6]^{3+}$.

Acidity of metal aqua-ions

Metal(II) and metal(III) aqua-ions behave as weak acids. This is achieved by:

- fission of the O–H bond in one of the water ligands of the complex ion
- donation of a proton to a water molecule.

Metal(II) cations

- With a metal(II) aqua-ion, the equilibrium lies well to the left-hand side: only a very weak acid is formed.

$$[Cu(H_2O)_6]^{2+}(aq) + H_2O(l) \rightleftharpoons [Cu(H_2O)_5(OH)]^+(aq) + H_3O^+(l)$$
very weakly acidic

Metal(III) cations

- Metal(III) aqua-ions are slightly more acidic than metal(II) aqua-ions: the equilibrium position has moved slightly to the right.

$$[Fe(H_2O)_6]^{3+}(aq) + H_2O(l) \rightleftharpoons [Fe(H_2O)_5(OH)]^{2+}(aq) + H_3O^+(aq)$$
weakly acidic

> **KEY POINT**
> The aqua-ions of metal(III) cations have a greater charge/size ratio and greater acidity than aqua-ions of metal(II) cations.

Precipitation

The precipitation reaction of a transition metal with hydroxide ions can be expressed as a series of acid–base equilibria.

The equilibrium set up in water by the hexaaqua ion of iron(III) is:

$$[Fe(H_2O)_6]^{3+}(aq) + H_2O(l) \rightleftharpoons [Fe(H_2O)_5(OH)]^{2+}(aq) + H_3O^+(aq)$$

OH^- reacts with H_3O^+:
$OH^- + H_3O^+ \longrightarrow 2H_2O$

With the weak alkali Na_2CO_3(aq), metal(II) aqua-ions precipitate metal **carbonates**.

The more acidic metal(III) aqua-ions precipitate metal **hydroxides**.

Metal(III) carbonates do not exist.

On addition of aqueous hydroxide ions:

- H_3O^+ ions are removed from the equilibrium, which shifts to the right.

The $[Fe(H_2O)_5(OH)]^{2+}$ ion now sets up a second equilibrium:

$$[Fe(H_2O)_5(OH)]^{2+}(aq) + H_2O(l) \rightleftharpoons [Fe(H_2O)_4(OH)_2]^+(aq) + H_3O^+(aq)$$

- Again, the hydroxide ion removes H_3O^+ ions from the aqueous equilibrium, which shifts to the right.
- This process continues. Eventually **all charge** will be **removed** from the iron(III) complex. Then the uncharged **hydrated metal hydroxide** precipitates.

$$[Fe(H_2O)_4(OH)_2]^+(aq) + H_2O(l) \rightleftharpoons [Fe(H_2O)_3(OH)_3](s) + H_3O^+(aq)$$

Acid–base properties of metal hydroxides

AQA ▶ M5   WJEC ▶ M5
EDEXCEL ▶ M5   CCEA ▶ M5

Many insoluble metal hydroxides are **amphoteric** – they can act as both an acid and a base.

Metal hydroxides as acids

See also:
'Reaction of complex metal aqua-ions with aqueous alkali' page 103.

Some insoluble metal hydroxides can act as acids, donating protons to strong alkalis and forming soluble anions.

- Metal(III) hydroxides react with dilute aqueous sodium hydroxide.

$$Al(OH)_3(H_2O)_3(s) + OH^-(aq) \rightleftharpoons [Al(OH)_4(H_2O)_2]^-(aq) + H_2O(l)$$
aluminate ions

$$Cr(OH)_3(H_2O)_3(s) + 3OH^-(aq) \rightleftharpoons [Cr(OH)_6]^{3-}(aq) + 3H_2O(l)$$
chromate(III) ions

In general, metal(III) hydroxides form anions with the general formula $[M(OH)_6]^{3-}$.

- Metal(II) hydroxides are weaker acids and do not usually react with aqueous sodium hydroxide.

Metal hydroxides as bases (AQA and Edexcel only)

All metal hydroxides can act as bases, removing protons from strong acids.

This reaction reverses the direction of the acid-base equilibria that produce hydrated hydroxide precipitates (see page 104).

$$Cu(OH)_2(H_2O)_4(s) + 2H^+(aq) \rightleftharpoons [Cu(H_2O)_6]^{2+}(aq)$$
blue precipitate

$$Cr(OH)_3(H_2O)_3(s) + 3H^+(aq) \rightleftharpoons [Cr(H_2O)_6]^{3+}(aq)$$
green precipitate

Reactions of metal aqua-ions with aqueous bases

AQA	M5	SALTERS	M4
EDEXCEL	M5	WJEC	M5
OCR	M5	CCEA	M5

Make sure that you check carefully with your specification here. The Boards themselves do not always agree. The reactions are complex and different simplifications have been made by different Boards.

In exams, a great emphasis is placed on these reactions. You will need to learn the colours of all solutions and precipitates in your course.

Reactions with OH$^-$(aq) and NH$_3$(aq)

You are expected to know reactions of metal aqua ions with aqueous OH$^-$(aq) ions (probably as NaOH(aq)) and with aqueous ammonia, NH$_3$(aq).

The tables below summarise what you are expected to know for each Board so make sure that you do not learn more than you have to!

	AQ	ED	OC	SA	WJ	CC
Fe^{2+}	✓	✓	✓	✓	✓	✓
Co^{2+}	✓		✓			✓
Cu^{2+}	✓	✓	✓	✓	✓	✓
Mn^{2+}	✓					✓
Ni^{2+}	✓					✓
Zn^{2+}	✓					
Cr^{3+}	✓	✓			✓	✓
Fe^{3+}	✓	✓	✓	✓	✓	✓
Al^{3+}	✓					

	OH$^-$	OH$^-$ excess	NH$_3$	NH$_3$ excess
AQA	✓	✓	✓	✓
EDEXCEL	✓	✓	✓	✓
OCR	✓		✓	✓
SALTERS	✓		✓	✓
WJEC	✓		✓	✓
CCEA	✓	✓	✓	✓

aqua ion	OH$^-$(aq) or NH$_3$(aq) as a base		NH$_3$(aq) as a ligand
	NaOH(aq) or dilute NH$_3$(aq) (small amount)	excess NaOH(aq)	excess/conc. NH$_3$(aq)
$[Fe(H_2O)_6]^{2+}$ green	$Fe(OH)_2(s)$ / $Fe(OH)_2(H_2O)_4(s)$ green	no change	no change
$[Co(H_2O)_6]^{2+}$ pink	$Co(OH)_2(s)$ / $Co(OH)_2(H_2O)_4(s)$ blue–green	no change	$[Co(NH_3)_6]^{2+}$ pale straw
$[Cu(H_2O)_6]^{2+}$ blue	$Cu(OH)_2(s)$ / $Cu(OH)_2(H_2O)_4(s)$ pale blue	no change	$[Cu(NH_3)_4(H_2O)_2]^{2+}$ deep blue
$[Mn(H_2O)_6]^{2+}$ pale pink	$Mn(OH)_2(s)$ / $Mn(OH)_2(H_2O)_4(s)$ pale brown	no change	no change
$[Ni(H_2O)_6]^{2+}$ colourless	$Ni(OH)_2(s)$ / $Ni(OH)_2(H_2O)_4(s)$ pale green	no change	$[Ni(NH_3)_6]^{2+}$ blue
$[Zn(H_2O)_6]^{2+}$ colourless	$Zn(OH)_2(s)$ / $Zn(OH)_2(H_2O)_4(s)$ white	$[Zn(OH)_4]^{2-}(aq)$ colourless	$[Zn(NH_3)_4]^{2+}$ colourless
$[Cr(H_2O)_6]^{3+}$ ruby	$Cr(OH)_3(s)$ / $Cr(OH)_3(H_2O)_3(s)$ green	$[Cr(OH)_6]^{3-}(aq)$ green	$[Cr(NH_3)_6]^{3+}(aq)$ purple
$[Fe(H_2O)_6]^{3+}$ pale violet	$Fe(OH)_3(s)$ / $Fe(OH)_3(H_2O)_3(s)$ brown	no change	no change
$[Al(H_2O)_6]^{3+}$ colourless	$Al(OH)_3(s)$ / $Al(OH)_3(H_2O)_3(s)$ white	$[Al(OH)_4(H_2O)_2]^-(aq)$ colourless	no change

- Of the 2+ ions, only $Zn(OH)_2(s)$ reacts with excess $OH^-(aq)$.
- $Fe(OH)_2(s)$ is oxidised in air forming a brown precipitate of $Fe(OH)_3(s)$.
- $[Co(NH_3)_6]^{2+}$ darkens in air as it is oxidised to $[Co(NH_3)_6]^{3+}$ (see page 99).
- $Mn(OH_2)(s)$ forms a dark-brown precipitate of manganese(III) oxide, $Mn_2O_3(s)$.

Reactions of metal aqua-ions with aqueous carbonate ions (AQA only)

Metal(II) ions

Metal(II) ions form a precipitate of the metal carbonate. The chemistry is complex and the equations here are acceptable simplifications.

$$Fe^{2+}(aq) + CO_3{}^{2-}(aq) \longrightarrow FeCO_3(s)$$
green
$$Co^{2+}(aq) + CO_3{}^{2-}(aq) \longrightarrow CoCO_3(s)$$
pink
$$Cu^{2+}(aq) + CO_3{}^{2-}(aq) \longrightarrow CuCO_3(s)$$
green

Metal(III) ions

Metal(III) aqua-ions behave as weak acids (see page 104).

A hydroxide precipitate is formed together with CO_2 gas.

$$[Cr(H_2O)_6]^{3+} + 1\tfrac{1}{2}CO_3{}^{2-}(aq) \longrightarrow Cr(OH)_3(H_2O)_3(s) + 1\tfrac{1}{2}CO_2(g) + 1\tfrac{1}{2}H_2O(l)$$
green
$$[Fe(H_2O)_6]^{3+} + 1\tfrac{1}{2}CO_3{}^{2-}(aq) \longrightarrow Fe(OH)_3(H_2O)_3(s) + 1\tfrac{1}{2}CO_2(g) + 1\tfrac{1}{2}H_2O(l)$$
brown
$$[Al(H_2O)_6]^{3+} + 1\tfrac{1}{2}CO_3{}^{2-}(aq) \longrightarrow Al(OH)_3(H_2O)_3(s) + 1\tfrac{1}{2}CO_2(g) + 1\tfrac{1}{2}H_2O(l)$$
white

- The acidity of the metal(III) ion means that this reaction is essentially the same as that between an acid such as hydrochloric acid and a carbonate.
- Consequently, metal(III) carbonates do not exist.

Progress check

1 Write equations for the following reactions of metal aqua-ions with aqueous alkali. What is the colour of each precipitate?

(a) $Co^{2+}(aq)$ (b) $Fe^{2+}(aq)$ (c) $[Ni(H_2O)_6]^{2+}$ (d) $[Fe(H_2O)_6]^{3+}$.

2 Write equations to show what happens when excess $NH_3(aq)$ is added to the following hydrated metal hydroxides.

(a) $Co(OH)_2(H_2O)_4$ (b) $Cu(OH)_2(H_2O)_4$ (c) $Cr(OH)_3(H_2O)_3$.

2 (a) $Co(OH)_2(H_2O)_4(s) + 6NH_3(aq) \longrightarrow [Co(NH_3)_6]^{2+}(aq) + 4H_2O(l) + 2OH^-(aq)$ (pale straw)
(b) $Cu(OH)_2(H_2O)_4(s) + 4NH_3(aq) \longrightarrow [Cu(NH_3)_4(H_2O)_2]^{2+}(aq) + 2H_2O(l) + 2OH^-(aq)$ (deep-blue)
(c) $Cr(OH)_3(H_2O)_3(s) + 6NH_3(aq) \longrightarrow [Cr(NH_3)_6]^{3+}(aq) + 3H_2O(l) + 3OH^-(aq)$ (purple)

1 (a) $Co^{2+}(aq) + 2OH^-(aq) \longrightarrow Co(OH)_2(s)$ (blue-green)
(b) $Fe^{2+}(aq) + 2OH^-(aq) \longrightarrow Fe(OH)_2(s)$ (green)
(c) $[Ni(H_2O)_6]^{2+}(aq) + 2OH^-(aq) \longrightarrow Ni(OH)_2(H_2O)_4(s) + 2H_2O(l)$ (pale green)
(d) $[Fe(H_2O)_6]^{3+}(aq) + 3OH^-(aq) \longrightarrow Fe(OH)_3(H_2O)_3(s) + 3H_2O(l)$ (brown)

Sample question and model answer

This question looks at different transition elements.

(a) Write the electron configuration of a vanadium atom and a cobalt(III) ion.

V: $1s^2 2s^2 2p^6 3s^2 3p^6 3d^3 4s^2$ ✓
Co^{3+}: $1s^2 2s^2 2p^6 3s^2 3p^6 3d^6$ ✓

[2]

Remember:
4s fill before 3d
4s empty before 3d

(b) When concentrated hydrochloric acid is added to an aqueous solution containing copper(II) ions, the colour changes. Write the formulae of the two copper complexes involved, their colours, their shapes and the co-ordination numbers of the copper. Write an equation for the reaction and explain why the addition of dilute hydrochloric acid does not produce the same colour change.

Aqueous copper(II) contains the complex $[Cu(H_2O)_6]^{2+}$ ✓ which is pale blue. ✓ It has an octahedral shape ✓ and a coordination number of 6. ✓
After addition of concentrated hydrochloric acid, the complex ion $[CuCl_4]^{2-}$ ✓ is formed, which is yellow. ✓ It has a tetrahedral shape ✓ and a coordination number of 4. ✓

Equation: $[Cu(H_2O)_6]^{2+} + 4Cl^- \longrightarrow CuCl_4^{2-} + 6H_2O$ ✓✓

The concentration of chloride ligands in **dilute** hydrochloric acid is much smaller than the concentration of water ligands. ✓

[11]

This is standard bookwork but it also reinforces important principles:
H_2O forms octahedral complexes with a coordination number of 6.
Cl^- forms tetrahedral complexes with a coordination number of 4.

(c) A 0.626 g sample of hydrated iron(II) sulfate was dissolved in water and the solution made up to 250 cm³. A 25.0 cm³ sample of this solution was acidified with dilute sulfuric acid and titrated with potassium dichromate(VI). 25.85 cm³ of 0.00145 mol dm⁻³ potassium dichromate(VI) were required for exact reaction.

The half-equation for the reduction of acidified dichromate ions is shown below.
$$Cr_2O_7^{2-}(aq) + 14H^+(aq) + 6e^- \longrightarrow 2Cr^{3+}(aq) + 7H_2O(l)$$

(i) Write the half-equation for the oxidation of Fe^{2+} and construct the equation for the overall reaction with acidified dichromate (VI) ions.

$Fe^{2+}(aq) \longrightarrow Fe^{3+}(aq) + e^-$ ✓
$6Fe^{2+}(aq) + Cr_2O_7^{2-}(aq) + 14H^+(aq) \longrightarrow 6Fe^{3+}(aq) + 2Cr^{3+}(aq) + 7H_2O(l)$ ✓

Learn how to combine redox half-equations. Although this titration is different from the permanganate titrations that you have carried out, the same principles are used.

Even if your equation is wrong, you can still score in the next part provided that your method is built upon sound chemical principles.

Show your working!

(ii) Using the information above, calculate the molar mass of the hydrated iron(II) sulfate and determine the number of moles of water of crystallisation present in one mole of hydrated iron(II) sulfate.

amount of $Cr_2O_7^{2-} = c \times \dfrac{V}{1000} = 0.00145 \times \dfrac{25.85}{1000} = 3.75 \times 10^{-5}$ mol ✓

From the equation, the amount of $Fe^{2+} = 6 \times$ amount of $Cr_2O_7^{2-}$. ✓

∴ amount of Fe^{2+} that reacted $= 6 \times 3.75 \times 10^{-5}$ mol $= 2.25 \times 10^{-4}$ mol ✓

In 250 cm³ solution, amount of $Fe^{2+} = 10 \times 2.25 \times 10^{-4} = 2.25 \times 10^{-3}$ mol ✓

∴ $\dfrac{0.626}{2.25 \times 10^{-3}} = 278$ g of hydrated iron(II) sulfate contains 1 mol Fe^{2+} ✓

M of hydrated iron(II) sulfate $= 278$ g mol⁻¹ ✓

M of $FeSO_4 = 55.8 + 32.1 + 16.0 \times 4 = 151.9$ g mol⁻¹ ✓

Number of waters of crystallisation $= \dfrac{278.0 - 151.9}{18.0} = \dfrac{120.1}{18.0} = 7$ ✓

Don't forget the scaling stage. The original solution was 250 cm³ but you have only taken 25 cm³ for the titration.

Show your working!

(iii) Explain how the volume of potassium dichromate(VII) solution needed in the titration would be different if the solution of iron(II) sulfate had been left for some time before being titrated.

Less dichromate(VI) solution would have been needed ✓ because some of the Fe^{2+} would have been oxidised by air to Fe^{3+} ✓

[12]

[Total: 25]

Practice examination questions

1 (a) Complete the following table for the Period 3 oxides.

	Mg	Al	Si	P	S
Oxidation number	+2	+3	+4	+5	+6
Formula of oxide					

[2]

(b) Explain the trend in oxidation number. [1]

(c) Write equations, if any, to show the effect of water on these oxides. [4]

(d) What is the relationship between the structure and bonding of the Period 3 oxides and the pH of any resulting solution? [3]

[Total: 10]

2 (a) Write the electron configuration of a nickel atom and a Ni^{2+} ion. [2]

(b) Nickel is both a d-block element and a transition element. State what is meant by each of the terms. [2]

(c) In aqueous solution, nickel sulfate, forms a six-coordinate complex ion which gives a green colour to the solution.

(i) What feature of the water molecule allows it to form a complex ion with Ni^{2+}?

(ii) Write the formula of the nickel complex ion formed in aqueous solution.

(iii) What types of bond are present in this nickel complex ion?

(iv) Suggest the shape of, and bond angles in, this complex ion. [6]

(d) Consider the following reactions.

(i) Write the formula of the green precipitate, **A**, and write an ionic equation for its formation above.

(ii) Predict the formula of **B**.

(iii) Write an equation for the formation of $[Ni(NH_3)_6]^{2+}$ from the aqueous nickel complex ion and suggest the type of reaction taking place. [5]

[Total: 15]

Practice examination questions *(continued)*

3 (a) Deduce the oxidation state of the transition metal in each of the following species.

   (i) Cr in CrO_4^{2-}

   (ii) Cu in $[CuCl_2]^-$

   (iii) V in $[VO(H_2O)_5]^{2+}$ [3]

(b) Chromium(III) can be oxidised in alkaline conditions by hydrogen peroxide, H_2O_2. Use the half-equations below to construct the overall equation for this reaction.

$$Cr^{3+} + 8OH^- \longrightarrow CrO_4^{2-} + 4H_2O + 3e^-$$

$$H_2O_2 + 2e^- \longrightarrow 2OH^-$$ [1]

(c) Give two examples of the use of transition elements as catalysts in industrial processes. [2]

[Total: 6]

4 The concentration of an aqueous solution of hydrogen peroxide can be determined by titration. Aqueous potassium manganate(VII), $KMnO_4$, is titrated against a solution of hydrogen peroxide in the presence of acid.

The half-equations are shown below.

$$H_2O_2(aq) \longrightarrow 2H^+(aq) + O_2(g) + 2e^-$$

$$MnO_4^-(aq) + 8H^+(aq) + 5e^- \longrightarrow Mn^{2+}(aq) + 4H_2O(l)$$

(a) (i) Deduce the oxidation state of the manganese in the MnO_4^- ion.

   (ii) Construct the equation for the reaction between H_2O_2, MnO_4^- ions and H^+ ions. [2]

(b) State the role of hydrogen peroxide in this reaction. [1]

(c) After acidification, 25.0 cm³ of a dilute aqueous solution of hydrogen peroxide reacted exactly with 23.80 cm³ of 0.0150 mol dm⁻³ $KMnO_4$. Calculate the concentration, in mol dm⁻³, of hydrogen peroxide in the solution. [3]

[Total: 6]

5 Cobalt and nickel both form complex ions with the ligand ethane-1,2-diamine, $NH_2CH_2CH_2NH_2$.

(a) (i) Explain how ligands bond to a metal ion in a complex ion.

   (ii) What name is given to this type of ligand? [3]

(b) Cobalt forms the complex compound, $[Co(NH_2CH_2CH_2NH_2)_3]Cl_3$.

   (i) What is the oxidation state of cobalt in this compound?

   (ii) What is the electron configuration of cobalt in this compound? [2]

(c) In solution, nickel forms the complex ion $[Ni(NH_2CH_2CH_2NH_2)_3]^{2+}$.

   (i) Deduce the co-ordination number of nickel in this complex ion.

   (ii) State the shape around nickel in this complex ion.

   (iii) Outline how you could prepare a solution containing the complex ion $[Ni(NH_2CH_2CH_2NH_2)_3]^{2+}$ from an aqueous solution of nickel(II) chloride. Include an equation in your answer. [4]

[Total: 9]

Chapter 4

Chemistry of organic functional groups

The following topics are covered in this chapter:

- Isomerism and functional groups
- Aldehydes and ketones
- Carboxylic acids
- Esters
- Acylation

- Arenes
- Reactions of arenes
- Phenols and alcohols
- Amines

4.1 Isomerism and functional groups

After studying this section you should be able to:

- understand what is meant by structural isomerism and stereoisomerism
- explain the term chiral centre and identify any chiral centres in a molecule of given structural formula
- understand that many natural compounds are present as one optical isomer only
- understand that many pharmaceuticals are chiral drugs
- recognise common functional groups

LEARNING SUMMARY

Key points from AS

- **Basic concepts**
  Revise AS pages 119–124

During AS Chemistry, you learnt about the basic concepts used in organic chemistry. You should revise these thoroughly before you start the A2 part of this course.

Isomerism

AQA	M4	SALTERS	M4, M5
EDEXCEL	M4	WJEC	M4
OCR	M4	CCEA	M4

Structural and *E/Z* isomerism were introduced during AS Chemistry. These are reviewed below and *E/Z* isomerism is discussed in the wider context of **stereoisomerism**.

Key points from AS

- **Structural isomerism**
  Revise AS pages 121–122
- **E/Z isomerism**
  Revise AS pages 129–130

Structural isomerism

Structural isomers are molecules with the same molecular formula but with different structural arrangements of atoms (structural formulae).

Two structural isomers of $C_2H_4O_2$ are shown below:

Stereoisomerism

Stereoisomers are molecules with the same structural formula but their atoms have different positions in space.

There are two types of stereoisomerism, each arising from a different structural feature:

- *E/Z* isomerism about a C=C double bond
- **optical** isomerism about a **chiral** carbon centre.

E/Z isomerism

E/Z isomerism occurs in molecules with:

- a C=C double bond and
- two **different** groups attached to **each** carbon in the C=C bond.

The double bond prevents rotation.

E.g. *E/Z* isomers of 1,2-dichloroethene, ClCH=CHCl.

In simple cases in which 2 of the groups are the same, E/Z isomerism is often referred to as cis-trans isomerism.

Each E/Z isomer has the same structural formula.

cis-isomer
(groups on one side)
Z isomer

trans-isomer
(groups on opposite sides)
E isomer

Optical isomers

> **KEY POINT**
>
> Optical isomerism occurs in the molecules of a compound with a **chiral** (or *asymmetric*) carbon atom. A chiral carbon atom has **four** different groups attached to it.

E.g. the optical isomers of an amino acid, $RCHNH_2COOH$ (see pages 148–151).

Optical isomers are usually drawn as 3D diagrams. It is then easy to picture the mirror images.

chiral (or asymmetric) carbon atom
– 4 different groups attached

mirror plane

Optical isomers are also called enantiomers.

Optical isomers:

- are non-superimposable mirror images of one another
- rotate plane-polarised light in opposite directions
- are chemically identical.

Chirality and drug synthesis

Society discovered the consequences of harmful side-effects from the 'wrong' optical isomer with the use of thalidomide. One optical isomer combated the effects of morning sickness in pregnant women. The other optical isomer was the cause of deformed limbs of unborn babies.

Partly through this lesson, drugs are now often used as the optically pure form, comprising just the required optical isomer.

A synthetic amino acid, made in the laboratory, is optically inactive and does not rotate plane-polarised light:
- it contains equal amounts of each optical isomer – a **racemic** mixture or **racemate**.

A natural amino acid, made by living systems, is optically active:
- it contains only one of the optical isomers.

The difference between the optical isomers present in natural and synthetic organic molecules has important consequences for drug design. The synthesis of pharmaceuticals often requires the production of chiral drugs containing a single optical isomer. Although one of the optical isomers may have beneficial effects, the other may be harmful and may lead to undesirable side effects. See also page 173.

Progress check

1 Show the alkenes that are structural isomers of C_4H_8.
2 Show the *E/Z* isomers of C_4H_8.
3 Show the optical isomers of C_4H_9OH.

1 $CH_3CH_2CH=CH_2$; $CH_3CH=CHCH_3$; $(CH_3)_2C=CH_2$

111

Chemistry of organic functional groups

Common functional groups

	AQA	M4	SALTERS	M4, M5
EDEXCEL	M4	WJEC	M4
OCR	M4	CCEA	M4

The functional groups in the table below contain most of the functional groups you will meet in the A Level Chemistry course, including those met in AS Chemistry. It cannot be stressed enough just how important it is that you can instantly recognise a functional group. Without this, your progress in Organic Chemistry will be very limited.

It is essential that you can instantly identify a functional group within a molecule so that you can apply the relevant chemistry.

You must learn all of these!

Key points from AS

• **Functional groups**
  Revise AS pages 120–121

name	functional group	examples structural formula		prefix or suffix (for naming)
alkane	C–H	$CH_3CH_2CH_3$ *propane*	$CH_3CH_2CH_3$	-ane
alkene	$\diagdown C=C \diagup$	CH_3CHCH_2 *propene*	H_3C ... $C=C$ ... H, H	-ene
halogenoalkane	—Br	CH_3CH_2Br *bromoethane*	$CH_3CH_2—Br$	bromo-
alcohol	—OH	CH_3CH_2OH *ethanol*	$CH_3CH_2—OH$	-ol
aldehyde	$-C{\diagup}^O_{\diagdown H}$	CH_3CHO *ethanal*	$H_3C-C{\diagup}^O_{\diagdown H}$	-al
ketone	$-C{\diagup}^O_{\diagdown}$	CH_3COCH_3 *propanone*	$H_3C-C{\diagup}^O_{\diagdown CH_3}$	-one
carboxylic acid	$-C{\diagup}^O_{\diagdown OH}$	CH_3COOH *ethanoic acid*	$H_3C-C{\diagup}^O_{\diagdown OH}$	-oic acid
ester	$-C{\diagup}^O_{\diagdown O-}$	CH_3COOCH_3 *methyl ethanoate*	$H_3C-C{\diagup}^O_{\diagdown O-CH_3}$	-oate
acyl chloride	$-C{\diagup}^O_{\diagdown Cl}$	CH_3COCl *ethanoyl chloride*	$H_3C-C{\diagup}^O_{\diagdown Cl}$	–oyl chloride
amine	—NH₂	$CH_3CH_2NH_2$ *ethylamine*	$CH_3CH_2—NH_2$	-amine
amide	$-C{\diagup}^O_{\diagdown NH_2}$	CH_3CONH_2 *ethanamide*	$H_3C-C{\diagup}^O_{\diagdown NH_2}$	-amide
nitrile	$-C\equiv N$	CH_3CN *ethanenitrile*	$H_3C—CN$	-nitrile

The nitrile carbon atom is included in the name.

CH_3CN contains the longest carbon chain with **two** carbon atoms and its name is based upon ethane – hence ethanenitrile.

4.2 Aldehydes and ketones

After studying this section you should be able to:

- *understand the polarity and physical properties of carbonyl compounds*
- *describe the oxidation of alcohols*
- *describe the reduction of carbonyl compounds to form alcohols*
- *describe nucleophilic addition to aldehydes and ketones*
- *describe a test to detect the presence of the carbonyl group*
- *describe tests to detect the presence of an aldehyde group*

LEARNING SUMMARY

Carbonyl compounds General formula: $C_nH_{2n}O$

AQA	M4	SALTERS	M4
EDEXCEL	M4	WJEC	M4
OCR	M4	CCEA	M4

During AS Chemistry, you learnt about how alcohols can be oxidised to carbonyl compounds: aldehydes and ketones. For A2 Chemistry, you will learn about the reactions of aldehydes and ketones.

Key points from AS

- **Oxidation of alcohols**
  Revise AS pages 135–136

Types and naming of carbonyl compounds

The carbonyl group, C=O, is the functional group in aldehydes and ketones.

aldehyde, RCHO

ketone, RCOR'

ethanal
CH_3CHO

butanal
$CH_3CH_2CH_2CHO$

propanone
CH_3COCH_3

pentan-2-one
$CH_3COCH_2CH_2CH_3$

Polarity of carbonyl compounds

The properties of aldehydes and ketones are dominated by the polar carbonyl group, C=O.

Carbon and oxygen have different electronegativities, resulting in a polar C=O bond: carbonyl compounds have polar molecules.

$$\overset{\delta+}{C}=\overset{\delta-}{O}$$ oxygen is more electronegative than carbon producing a dipole

Physical properties of carbonyl compounds

The polarity in propanone is such that it mixes with polar solvents such as water and also dissolves many organic compounds.

The low boiling point also makes it easy to remove by evaporation, a property exploited by its use in paints and varnishes.

The polarity of the carbonyl group is less than that of the hydroxyl group in alcohols. Thus, aldehydes and ketones have weaker dipole–dipole interactions and lower boiling points than alcohols of comparable molecular mass.

$$\overset{\delta+}{C}=\overset{\delta-}{O} \xrightarrow{\text{stronger dipole}} -\overset{}{C}-\overset{\delta-}{O}\overset{}{\underset{\delta+}{H}}$$

carbonyl group in
aldehyde or ketone

hydroxyl group in
alcohols

The Sheffield College

Hillsborough LRC
Telephone: 0114 260 2254

Chemistry of organic functional groups

Oxidation of alcohols

EDEXCEL	M4	SALTERS	M4
OCR	M4	WJEC	M4
		CCEA	M4

You studied the oxidation of different types of alcohols during AS Chemistry. The link between alcohols, carbonyl compounds and carboxylic acids is shown below.

Key points from AS

- **Oxidation of alcohols**
  Revise AS pages 135–136

Oxidation of primary alcohols

The orange dichromate ions, $Cr_2O_7^{2-}$, are reduced to green Cr^{3+} ions.

A primary alcohol can be oxidised to an aldehyde and then to a carboxylic acid.

This is carried out using an oxidising agent such as a mixture of concentrated sulfuric acid, H_2SO_4 (source of H^+) and potassium dichromate, $K_2Cr_2O_7$ (source of $Cr_2O_7^{2-}$).

- By heating and distilling the product immediately, oxidation can be stopped at the aldehyde stage.

$$CH_3CH_2OH + [O] \longrightarrow CH_3CHO + H_2O$$

For balanced equations, the oxidising agent can be shown simply as [O].

- By refluxing with an excess of the oxidising agent, further oxidation takes place to form the carboxylic acid.

$$CH_3CH_2OH + 2[O] \longrightarrow CH_3COOH + H_2O$$

Oxidation of secondary alcohols

By heating with $H^+/Cr_2O_7^{2-}$, a secondary alcohol can be oxidised to a ketone. No further oxidation normally takes place.

The equation for the oxidation of propan-2-ol is shown below.

$$CH_3(CHOH)CH_3 + [O] \longrightarrow CH_3COCH_3 + H_2O$$

Reduction of carbonyl compounds

AQA	M4	WJEC	M4
EDEXCEL	M4	CCEA	M4
OCR	M4		

Aldehydes and ketones can be reduced to alcohols using a reducing agent containing the hydride ion, H^-.

Suitable reducing agents are:
- sodium tetrahydridoborate(III) (*sodium borohydride*), $NaBH_4$, in water (heat)
- lithium tetrahydridoaluminate(III) (*lithium aluminium hydride*), $LiAlH_4$, in ether.

Aldehydes are reduced to primary alcohols:

For balanced equations, the reducing agent can be shown simply as [H].

aldehyde   primary alcohol

$NaBH_4$ and $LiAlH_4$ both reduce the C=O double bond in aldehydes and ketones.

They do **not** reduce the C=C bond in alkenes.

Ketones are reduced to secondary alcohols:

ketone   secondary alcohol

Nucleophilic addition to carbonyl compounds

The electron-deficient carbon atom of the polar $C^{\delta+}=O^{\delta-}$ bond attracts **nucleophiles**. This allows an **addition** reaction to take place across the C=O double bond of aldehydes and ketones. This is called **nucleophilic addition**.

$$\overset{\delta+}{\underset{}{C}}=\overset{\delta-}{O} \quad \text{electron-rich nucleophile attracted to } \overset{\delta+}{C}$$

Reduction as nucleophilic addition (AQA and OCR only)

> The reaction of carbonyl compounds with hydrogen cyanide is also an example of nucleophilic addition.

The reduction of aldehydes and ketones to alcohols using $NaBH_4$ or $LiAlH_4$ is an example of **nucleophilic addition**. The reducing agent can be considered to release hydride ions, H^-.

$$NaBH_4 \longrightarrow H^- + NaBH_3^+$$

The hydride ion acts as a nucleophile in the first stage of the reaction.

Mechanism

$$H_3C-\overset{\delta+}{C}\overset{\overset{\delta-}{O}}{\underset{H}{<}} \quad :H^- \longrightarrow H_3C-\underset{\underset{H}{|}}{\overset{\overset{\cdot\cdot}{O}^-}{C}}-H \xrightarrow[\text{with } H_2O]{\text{protonation}} H_3C-\underset{\underset{H}{|}}{\overset{\overset{O^{\diagup H}}{|}}{C}}-H \; + \; OH^-$$

:H⁻ nucleophile donates electron pair

primary alcohol

Nucleophilic addition of hydrogen cyanide, HCN (not OCR)

> HCN is added across the C=O double bond.

In the presence of cyanide ions, CN^-, hydrogen cyanide, HCN, is added across the C=O bond in aldehydes and ketones.

aldehyde	+	HCN $\longrightarrow$ hydroxynitrile
CH_3CHO	+	HCN $\longrightarrow$ $CH_3CH(OH)CN$

$$H_3C-C\overset{\overset{O}{\diagup}}{\underset{H}{\diagdown}} \xrightarrow{\text{KCN(aq) / HCN}} H_3C-\underset{\underset{H}{|}}{\overset{\overset{OH}{|}}{C}}-C\equiv N$$

> This hydroxynitrile has optical isomers.

Hydrogen cyanide is a very poisonous gas and it is usually generated in solution as H^+ and CN^- ions using:
- sodium cyanide, NaCN as a source of CN^-
- dilute sulfuric acid as a source of H^+.

Mechanism

> The presence of cyanide ions is essential to provide the nucleophile for the first step of this mechanism.

$$H_3C-\overset{\delta+}{C}\overset{\overset{\delta-}{O}}{\underset{H}{<}} \quad :C\equiv N \longrightarrow H_3C-\underset{\underset{H}{|}}{\overset{\overset{\overset{\cdot\cdot}{O}^-}{|}}{C}}-C\equiv N \xrightarrow{H^+ \text{ transfer}} H_3C-\underset{\underset{H}{|}}{\overset{\overset{O^{\diagup H}}{|}}{C}}-C\equiv N$$

:CN⁻ nucleophile donates electron pair

'hydroxynitrile'

Increasing the carbon chain length (not OCR)

The nucleophilic addition of hydrogen cyanide is useful for increasing the length of a carbon chain. The nitrile product can then easily be reacted further in organic synthesis.
- Nitriles are easily *hydrolysed* by water in hot dilute acid to form a carboxylic acid.
- Nitriles are easily *reduced* by sodium in ethanol to form an amine.

The diagrams below show how 2-hydroxypropanenitrile, synthesised above, can be converted into a carboxylic acid and an amine.

2-hydroxypropanoic acid
(lactic acid)

Nitriles from halogenolkanes (WJEC only)

A nitrile can also be prepared by heating under reflux a halogenoalkane with an ionic cyanide, such as NaCN, in ethanol.

$$CH_3CH_2Br + CN^- \longrightarrow CH_3CH_2C{\equiv}N + Br^-$$

Testing for the carbonyl group

| EDEXCEL | M4 | WJEC | M4 |
| OCR | M4 | CCEA | M4 |

Carbonyl compounds produce an orange–yellow crystalline solid with Brady's reagent.

The carbonyl group can be detected using Brady's reagent – a solution of 2,4-dinitrophenylhydrazine (2,4-DNPH) in dilute acid.

- With 2,4-DNPH, both aldehydes and ketones produce bright **orange–yellow crystals** which identify the carbonyl group, C=O.

orange crystalline precipitate

The carbonyl group can also be detected using IR spectroscopy, see page 165 (see also AS pages 143–144).

This is a **condensation reaction** – water is lost.

- If first recrystallised, the crystals have very sharp melting points which can be compared with known melting points from databases. Thus, the actual carbonyl compound can be identified.

Testing for the aldehyde group

AQA	M4	WJEC	M4
EDEXCEL	M4	CCEA	M4
OCR	M4		

An aldehyde can be distinguished from a ketone by using a combination of these two tests.

Both aldehyde and ketone produce a yellow–orange precipitate with 2,4-DNPH.

Only the aldehydes react in the three tests below.

Ketones cannot normally be oxidised and they **do not** react with Tollens' reagent, Fehling's solution or acidified dichromate(VI).

The oxidation of aldehydes provides the basis of chemical tests used to identify this functional group.

> **KEY POINT**
>
> In each test:
> - the aldehyde **reduces** the reagents used in the test, producing a visible colour change
> - the aldehyde is **oxidised** to a carboxylic acid.
> $$RCHO + [O] \longrightarrow RCOOH$$

Heat aldehyde with Tollens' reagent

Tollens' reagent is a solution of silver nitrate in aqueous ammonia. The silver ions are reduced by an aldehyde producing a **silver mirror**.

Tollens' reagent contains the $[Ag(NH_3)_2]$ complex ion (see page 88).

> **KEY POINT**
>
> Tollens' reagent $\longrightarrow$ **silver mirror**
>
> $Ag^+(aq) + e^- \longrightarrow Ag(s)$

Heat aldehyde with Fehling's (or Benedict's) solution

Fehling's and Benedict's solutions contain Cu^{2+} ions dissolved in aqueous alkali. The Cu^{2+} ions are reduced to copper(I) ions, Cu^+, producing a **brick-red precipitate** of Cu_2O.

Key points from AS

- **Oxidation of primary alcohols**
  Revise AS pages 135–136

> **KEY POINT**
>
> Benedict's / Fehling's solution $\longrightarrow$ **brick-red precipitate** of Cu_2O
>
> $2Cu^{2+}(aq) + 2e^- + 2OH^-(aq) \longrightarrow Cu_2O(s) + H_2O(l)$

Heat aldehyde with $H^+/Cr_2O_7^{2-}$

Acidified dichromate(VI) can also be used to oxidise alcohols.

Concentrated sulfuric acid, H_2SO_4, is used as a source of H^+ ions and potassium dichromate(VI), $K_2Cr_2O_7$, as a source of $Cr_2O_7^{2-}$ ions. The **orange** $Cr_2O_7^{2-}$ ions are reduced to **green** chromium(III) ions, Cr^{3+}.

Test for the presence of the methyl carbonyl group

EDEXCEL M4 WJEC M4

The presence of a methyl carbonyl group can be detected by heating a compound with iodine, I_2 in aqueous sodium hydroxide, $OH^-(aq)$.

$$H_3C - \overset{\overset{\displaystyle O}{\|}}{C} -$$

methyl carbonyl

Methyl carbonyl compounds produce pale-yellow crystals with I_2/OH^-.

- Methyl carbonyls produce **pale-yellow crystals** of triiodomethane (*iodoform*), CHI_3, with an antiseptic smell.
- $CH_3CHO + 3I_2 + 4OH^- \longrightarrow CHI_3 + HCOO^- + 3H_2O + 3I^-$

Progress check

1 (a) Draw the structure of:
    (i) 3-methylpentan-2-one
    (ii) 3-ethyl-2-methylpentanal.

2 **Three** isomers of C_4H_8O are carbonyl compounds.
  (a) (i) Show the formula for each isomer.
    (ii) Classify each isomer as an *aldehyde* or a *ketone*.
    (iii) Name each isomer.
  (b) Write the structural formulae of the **three** alcohols that could be formed by reduction of these isomers.

(b) $CH_3CH_2CH_2CH_2OH$; $CH_3CH_2CHOHCH_3$; $(CH_3)_2CHCH_2OH$

2 (a) (i)

(iii)
methylpropanal
aldehyde

butanone
ketone

(ii)
butanal
aldehyde

2 (a) (i)

1 (a) (i)

(ii)

4.3 Carboxylic acids

LEARNING SUMMARY

After studying this section you should be able to:

- *understand the polarity and physical properties of carboxylic acids*
- *describe acid reactions of carboxylic acids to form salts*
- *describe the esterification of carboxylic acids with alcohols*

Carboxylic acids   General formula: $C_nH_{2n+1}COOH$ RCOOH

AQA	M4	SALTERS	M4
EDEXCEL	M4	WJEC	M4
OCR	M4	CCEA	M4

The combination of carbonyl and hydroxyl groups in the carboxyl group modifies the chemistry of both groups.

Carboxylic acids have their own set of reactions and react differently from carbonyl compounds and alcohols.

The carboxyl group

The functional group in carboxylic acids is the **carboxyl** group, COOH. Although this combines both the **carbonyl** group and a **hydroxyl** group its properties are very different from either.

carboxyl group

Naming of carboxylic acids

Numbering starts from the carbon atom of the carboxyl group.

4-methylpentanoic acid
$(CH_3)_2CH_2CH_2CH_2COOH$

Natural carboxylic acids

Carboxylic acids are found commonly in nature. Their acidity is comparatively weak and their presence in food often gives a sour taste. Some examples of natural carboxylic acids are shown below.

structure	name	natural source
HCOOH	methanoic acid (*formic acid*)	ants, stinging nettles
CH₃COOH	ethanoic acid (*acetic acid*)	vinegar
COOH | COOH	ethanedioic acid (*oxalic acid*)	rhubarb
OH | H₃C—CH—COOH	2-hydroxypropanoic acid (*lactic acid*)	sour milk
CH₂COOH | HO—C—COOH | CH₂COOH	2-hydroxypropane-1,2,3-tricarboxylic acid (*citric acid*)	oranges, lemons

Polarity

The carboxyl group is a combination of two polar groups: the hydroxyl –OH, **and** carbonyl C=O groups. This makes a carboxylic acid molecule more polar than a molecule of an alcohol or a carbonyl compound.

carbonyl group in aldehyde or ketone | hydroxyl group in alcohols | carboxyl group in carboxylic acids

The properties of carboxylic acids are dominated by the carboxyl group, COOH.

Physical properties of carboxylic acids

The COOH group dominates the physical properties of short-chain carboxylic acids. Hydrogen bonding takes place between carboxylic acid molecules, resulting in:

- higher melting and boiling points than alkanes of comparable M_r
- solubility in water.

The solubility of alcohols in water decreases with increasing carbon chain length as the non-polar contribution to the molecule becomes more important.

Carboxylic acids as 'acids'

Carboxylic acids are only weak acids because they only partially dissociate in water.

$$CH_3COOH \rightleftharpoons CH_3COO^- + H^+$$

- Only 1 molecule in about 100 actually dissociates.
- Only a small proportion of the potential H^+ ions is released.

Carboxylic acids are the 'organic acids'.

For more details of the dissociation of weak acids, see pages 35–36.

Carboxylates: salts of carboxylic acids

Carboxylic acid salts, 'carboxylates', are formed by neutralisation of a carboxylic acid by an alkali. In the example below, ethanoic acid produces ethanoate ions.

$$
\underset{\substack{\text{carboxylic acids exist} \\ \text{in acidic conditions}}}{H-\overset{\displaystyle H}{\underset{\displaystyle H}{C}}-C\overset{\displaystyle O}{\underset{\underset{\delta- \quad \delta+}{O-H}}{}}} \;+\; OH^- \longrightarrow \underset{\substack{\text{carboxylates exist} \\ \text{in alkaline conditions}}}{H-\overset{\displaystyle H}{\underset{\displaystyle H}{C}}-C\overset{\displaystyle O}{\underset{O^-}{}}} \;+\; H_2O
$$

On evaporation of water, a carboxylate salt crystallises out as an ionic compound. With aqueous sodium hydroxide as the alkali, sodium ethanoate, $CH_3COO^-Na^+$, is produced as the ionic salt.

Acid reactions of carboxylic acids

Key points from AS

- **Typical reactions of an acid**
  Revise AS page 46

Carboxylic acids take part in typical acid reactions. Note in the examples below that each salt formed is a carboxylate.

- They are **neutralised by alkalis**, forming a salt and water only.
  $$CH_3COOH \;+\; NaOH \longrightarrow CH_3COONa + H_2O$$

- They **react with carbonates**, forming a salt, carbon dioxide and water.
  $$2CH_3COOH + CaCO_3 \longrightarrow (CH_3COO)_2Ca + CO_2 + H_2O$$

- They **react with** reactive **metals**, forming a salt and hydrogen.
  $$2CH_3COOH + Mg \longrightarrow (CH_3COO)_2Mg + H_2$$

Carboxylic acids react by the usual 'acid reactions' producing carboxylate salts.

> **KEY POINT**
> Carboxylic acids are the only common organic group able to release carbon dioxide gas from carbonates. This provides a useful test to show the presence of a carboxyl group.

Properties of carboxylates

Carboxylates such as sodium ethanoate, $CH_3COO^-Na^+$, are ionic compounds. They have typical properties of an ionic compound.

- They are solids at room temperature with high melting and boiling points.
- They have a giant ionic lattice structure.
- They dissolve in water, totally dissociating into ions.

Reduction of carboxylic acids

Just as primary alcohols can be oxidised to carboxylic acids, the reverse process can take place using a strong reducing agent such as lithium tetrahydridoalumuninate(III) (*lithium aluminium hydride*), $LiAlH_4$ in dry ether. (See also: Reduction of carbonyl compounds, page 114.)

$$RCOOH + 4[H] \longrightarrow RCH_2OH + H_2O$$

Esterification

Esters are formed by reaction of a carboxylic acid with an alcohol.

Esterification is the formation of an ester by reaction of a **carboxylic acid** with an **alcohol** in the presence of an **acid catalyst** (e.g. concentrated sulfuric acid).

$$\text{carboxylic acid} + \text{alcohol} \longrightarrow \text{ester} + \text{water}$$

The esterification of ethanoic acid by methanol is shown below:

$$CH_3COOH + CH_3OH \longrightarrow CH_3COOCH_3 + H_2O$$

Conditions

- An acid catalyst (a few drops of conc. H_2SO_4) and reflux.
- The yield is usually poor due to incomplete reaction.

Purifying solids (Salters only)

The solvent is critical.

Without a difference in solubility at high and low temperatures, hardly any crystals will appear on cooling.

Many organic compounds are solids and they will need to be purified. The easiest method of doing this is by **recrystallisation**.

The organic solid must be:

- very **soluble** in the solvent at **higher temperatures** – the solvent is saturated by the substance at higher temperatures

- **much less soluble**, or nearly so, in the solvent at **lower temperatures** – on cooling, the substance crystallises out, leaving impurities in solution.

Progress check

1 Write down the structural formula of:
(a) propanoic acid
(b) the propanoate ion.

2 Explain why a carboxylic acid has a higher boiling point than the corresponding alcohol.

2 Carboxylic acid has both polar carbonyl and hydroxyl groups. Alcohols have hydroxyl group only. Therefore, a carboxylic acid has greater intermolecular forces.

1 (a) CH_3CH_2COOH
(b) $CH_3CH_2COO^-$

4.4 Esters

After studying this section you should be able to:

- *understand the physical properties of esters*
- *describe the acid and base hydrolysis of esters*
- *understand that fats and oils are saturated and unsaturated esters*
- *describe the hydrolysis of fats and oils in soap making*

LEARNING SUMMARY

Esters

General formula: $C_nH_{2n+1}COOC_mH_{2m+1}$ RCOOR'

AQA	M4	SALTERS	M4
EDEXCEL	M4	WJEC	M4
OCR	M4	CCEA	M4

The functional group in esters is the COOR' group, with an alkyl group in place of the acidic proton of a carboxylic acid.

Naming of esters

The name of an ester is based on the carboxylic acid from which the ester is derived. The ester below, methyl butanoate, is derived from butanoic acid C_3H_7COOH with a methyl group in place of the acidic proton.

butanoate from butanoic acid $CH_3CH_2CH_2COOH$
$CH_3CH_2CH_2-C$ (with $=O$ and $O-CH_3$)
methyl from methanol CH_3OH

methyl butanoate

In the name of **methyl butanoate**:

- the alkyl group comes first as the ...*yl*: **methyl**
- the carboxylic acid part comes second as the ...*oate*: **butanoate**

Natural esters

Esters are found commonly in nature as fats and oils. They often have pleasant smells and contribute to the flavouring of many foods as shown below.

> Esters are common organic compounds present in fats and oils. They are also used as solvents, plasticisers, in food flavourings and as perfumes.

structure	name	source
$HCOOCH_3$	methyl methanoate	raspberries
$C_3H_7COOC_4H_9$	butyl butanoate	pineapple

Physical properties of esters

Unlike carboxylic acids, esters are neutral. They are less polar than carboxylic acids. The absence of an –OH group means that esters cannot form hydrogen bonds and are generally insoluble in water.

Hydrolysis of esters

AQA	M4	SALTERS	M4
EDEXCEL	M4	WJEC	M4
OCR	M4	CCEA	M4

The hydrolysis of an ester is the reverse reaction to esterification (see page 120):

hydrolysis
ester + water ⇌ carboxylic acid + alcohol
esterification

> Note that this reaction is reversible. The direction of reaction can be controlled by the reagents and reaction conditions used.

> **Hydrolysis is the breaking down of a compound using water as the reagent.**
>
> KEY POINT

Hydrolysis takes place by refluxing the ester with dilute aqueous acid or alkali.

- Acid hydrolysis ⟶ alcohol + carboxylic acid.
- Alkaline hydrolysis ⟶ alcohol + carboxylate.

Esterification **produces** water.

Hydrolysis **reacts** with water.

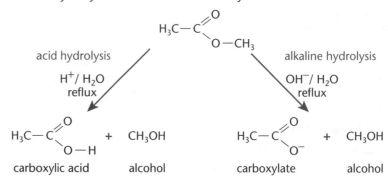

acid hydrolysis H^+/H_2O reflux

alkaline hydrolysis OH^-/H_2O reflux

carboxylic acid   alcohol   carboxylate   alcohol

Fats and oils

AQA	M4	SALTERS	M5
EDEXCEL	M4	CCEA	M4
OCR	M4		

Most fats and oils are mixed esters from different fatty acids. So 'R' in these structures may refer to three different chains.

Natural fats and oils are *triglyceryl esters* of fatty acids (long chain carboxylic acids) and propane-1,2,3-triol (*glycerol*).

```
RCOO—CH₂          R—COOH          HO—CH₂
     |                                  |
RCOO—CH           R—COOH          HO—CH
     |                                  |
RCOO—CH₂          R—COOH          HO—CH₂
```

fat or oil   fatty acids   glycerol
triglyceryl ester

Saturated and unsaturated fats

Saturated fats tend to be solids at room temperature and are mainly from animal products. Unsaturated fats tend to be oils and are mainly from vegetable products.

Saturated and unsaturated fatty acids can be obtained from fats and oils by hydrolysis (see page 123). An unsaturated fatty acid would have at least one double C=C bond in one of the alkyl carbon chains.

Examples of saturated and unsaturated fatty acids

octadecanoic acid, 18,0

octadec-9-enoic acid, 18,1(9);

octadeca-9,12-dienoic acid, 18,2(9,12)

- Note that the unsaturated fatty acids above are *trans* acids. The *cis* isomers are less compact and are far healthier.
- Many triglyceryl esters contain different alkyl carbon chains derived from different fatty acids.

Scientists have discovered that *trans* fatty acids pose health problems, increasing cholesterol with an increased risk of coronary heart disease, strokes and obesity.

In margarine production, vegetable oils are hardened by partial **catalytic hydrogenation**.

- Partial hydrogenation leaves some double bonds intact. The oil is reacted just enough to solidify the oily texture. This prevents the formation of **polysaturates**, with no C=C double bonds, which are linked to unhealthy diets.
- Margarines are often sold as partially hydrogenated **polyunsaturates** to promote the health value of unsaturated fats.

Iodine value (CCEA only)

The iodine value of a fat or oil can be determined from the following procedure:

- Add Wij's reagent and keep in the dark for 30 minutes.
- Add excess KI.
- Titrate with sodium thiosulfate. (See pages 97–98).
- Add starch indicator and titrate until the blue–black colour disappears.

Iodine value is used to measure the degree of unsaturation in a fat or oil.

> **Iodine value** is the mass of iodine in grams that reacts with 100 grams of a fat or oil.
>
> **KEY POINT**

- A solution of iodine is yellow/brown in colour.
- Iodine adds across any C=C bonds in a fat or oil, decolourising the solution.
- The greater the iodine value, the more C=C bonds present and the greater the unsaturation.

Hydrolysis of fats and oils

The hydrolysis of fats and oils is an important reaction used in soap production in which the fat or oil is boiled with aqueous alkali. In alkaline hydrolysis with aqueous NaOH, each mole of the fat or oil produces:

- **three** moles of the fatty acid salt, $3RCOO^-Na^+$ and
- **one** mole of glycerol (a triol), $HOCH_2CHOHCH_2OH$.

$$
\begin{array}{l}
RCOO-CH_2 \\
RCOO-CH \\
RCOO-CH_2
\end{array}
+ \; 3\,NaOH \;
\xrightarrow{\text{NaOH(aq)}}
\;
\begin{array}{l}
3\,RCOO^-Na^+ \\
\text{salt of} \\
\text{carboxylic acid}
\end{array}
+
\begin{array}{l}
HO-CH_2 \\
HO-CH \\
HO-CH_2
\end{array}
$$

Saponification number (CCEA only)

Saponification number is the number of mg of KOH needed to saponify 1g of fat.

- If a fat has long fatty acid chains, a relatively large proportion of the total mass of the fat comes from the carbon chains.

- The greater the saponification number, the smaller the relative molecular mass of the fat and the shorter the fatty acid chain length.

Biodiesel

Transesterification is also being investigated for the development of low-fat spreads as an alternative to hydrogenation of vegetable oils to produce margarine.

Esters of fatty acids are being developed for use as fuels such as biodiesel. Use of biodiesel as a fuel increases the contribution to energy requirements from renewable fuels. Biodiesel is a mixture of esters of long chain carboxylic acids.

Vegetable oils can be converted into biodiesel by **transesterification** using methanol in the presence of an alkaline catalyst, e.g.

$$
\begin{array}{l}
RCOO-CH_2 \\
RCOO-CH \\
RCOO-CH_2
\end{array}
+ \; 3\,CH_3OH \;
\xrightarrow[\text{catalyst}]{\text{NaOH}}
\;
\begin{array}{l}
3\,RCOO-CH_3 \\
\text{methyl ester}
\end{array}
+
\begin{array}{l}
HO-CH_2 \\
HO-CH \\
HO-CH_2
\end{array}
$$

The methyl ester is the easiest to prepare but methanol has the disadvantage that it is toxic. Research is being done to develop the ethyl ester made from ethanol. Ethanol is easy to produce from fermentation of sugars.

Progress check

1. How is methyl propanoate made from a named carboxylic acid and alcohol?
2. (a) Explain what is meant by the term *hydrolysis*.
   (b) Name the products of the acid and alkaline hydrolysis of ethyl butanoate.

1 Reflux propanoic acid with methanol in the presence of a few drops of concentrated sulfuric acid as catalyst.
2 (a) Breaking down a molecule using water.
   (b) Acid hydrolysis: ethanol and butanoic acid.
   Alkaline hydrolysis: ethanol and butanoate ions.

4.5 Acylation

LEARNING SUMMARY

After studying this section you should be able to:

- describe the formation of acyl chlorides from carboxylic acids
- describe nucleophilic addition-elimination reactions of acyl chlorides
- know the advantages of ethanoic anhydride for industrial acylations

Acyl chlorides

General formula: $C_nH_{2n+1}COCl$ $RCOCl$

The functional group in acyl chlorides is the COCl group:

Acyl chlorides are named from the parent carboxylic acid.

The examples below show that the suffix '*-oic acid*' is changed to '*-oyl chloride*' in the corresponding acyl chloride.

| ethanoic acid | ethanoyl chloride | propanoic acid | propanoyl chloride |

Properties

Acyl chlorides are the most reactive organic compounds that are commonly used. Unlike most other organic functional groups, acyl chlorides do **not** occur naturally because of their high reactivity with water.

> Acyl chlorides are the only common organic compounds that react violently with water.

The relatively large δ+ charge attracts the lone pair of a nucleophile

The electron-withdrawing effects of both the **chlorine** atom and carbonyl **oxygen** atom produces a relatively large δ+ charge on the carbonyl carbon atom. Nucleophiles are strongly attracted to the electron-deficient carbon atom, increasing the reactivity.

Acyl chlorides in organic synthesis

The high reactivity of acyl chlorides compared with carboxylic acids makes them particularly useful in the organic synthesis of related compounds.

Advantages of acyl chlorides over carboxylic acids:

- A good yield of product – reactions go to completion.
- Reactions often occur quickly and at lower temperatures.

Using acyl chlorides in synthesis (not AQA)

The high reactivity of an acyl chloride means that it is usually prepared from the parent carboxylic acid '*in situ*', i.e. when it is needed.

Acyl chlorides are prepared by reacting a carboxylic acid with:
- phosphorus pentachloride

> With acyl chlorides, anhydrous conditions are **essential** – acyl chlorides react with water.

$$RCOOH + PCl_5 \longrightarrow RCOCl + POCl_3 + HCl$$

- or sulfur dichloride oxide, $SOCl_2$

$$RCOOH + SOCl_2 \longrightarrow RCOCl + SO_2 + HCl$$

- The required nucleophile is then added to the acyl chloride.

Reactions of acyl chlorides with nucleophiles

AQA	M4	SALTERS	M4
EDEXCEL	M4	WJEC	M4
		CCEA	M4

Nucleophiles of the type H–Y: react readily with acyl chlorides.

This is an **addition-elimination** reaction involving:

- addition of HY across the C=O double bond followed by
- elimination of HCl.

Addition-elimination reactions of acyl chlorides

Acyl chlorides can be reacted with different nucleophiles to produce a range of related functional groups. In each addition-elimination reaction, hydrogen chloride is eliminated as the second product.

The reaction scheme below shows the reactions of an acyl chloride RCOCl with the nucleophiles water, H_2O, methanol, CH_3OH, ammonia, NH_3 and methylamine, CH_3NH_2.

The high reactivity of an acyl chloride means that these reactions take place at room temperature.

(WJEC and Salters only)
Acyl chlorides also react with phenols to form esters.

carboxylic acid ... **ester**

$$R-C(=O)O-H \quad + \quad HCl \qquad\qquad R-C(=O)O-CH_3 \quad + \quad HCl$$

$$H_2O \qquad CH_3OH$$

$$R-C(=O)Cl$$

concentrated NH_3 ... CH_3NH_2

$$R-C(=O)NH_2 \quad + \quad HCl \qquad\qquad R-C(=O)NHCH_3 \quad + \quad HCl$$

primary amide ... **secondary amide**

Ammonia and methylamine are bases – they react with the HCl eliminated:

$$NH_3 + HCl \longrightarrow NH_4^+Cl^-$$
$$CH_3NH_2 + HCl \longrightarrow CH_3NH_3^+Cl^-$$

Mechanism (AQA only)

The mechanism below shows the **nucleophilic addition-elimination** reaction of ethanoyl chloride with methanol to form an ester. Each nucleophile in the reaction scheme above will react in a similar manner.

addition of CH₃OH ... **elimination of HCl**

nucleophile

$$H_3C-C \quad \longrightarrow \quad H_3C-\overset{:O^-}{\underset{Cl}{C}}-O \quad \xrightarrow{-Cl^-} \quad H_3C-C \quad \xrightarrow{-H^+} \quad H_3C-C(=O)O-CH_3$$

lone pair attracted to $C^{\delta+}$

125

Chemistry of organic functional groups

Acid anhydrides

AQA M4 WJEC CH4
OCR M4

Acyl chlorides are ideal for small-scale preparations in the laboratory. However, they are too expensive and too reactive for large-scale preparations, for which they are replaced by acid anhydrides.

The equation below shows the reaction between ethanoic anhydride and methanol:

Notice the molecular structure of ethanoic anhydride – two ethanoic acid molecules have been condensed together with loss of H_2O. Hence the 'anhydride' from ethanoic acid.

acid anhydride

carboxylic acid as second product

- The reaction is slower and easier to control on a large scale.
- This is the same essential reaction as with an acyl chloride but RCOOH forms instead of HCl as the second product.

Synthesis of aspirin

Aspirin can be synthesised by acylation of 2-hydroxybenzenecarboxylic acid (*salicylic acid*) using ethanoic anhydride.

aspirin

ethanoic acid as second product

Progress check

1 Write down the structural formula of the organic product formed from the reaction of propanoyl chloride with:
(a) water
(b) ammonia.

2 What could you react together to make N-ethylbutanamide, $CH_3CH_2CH_2CONHCH_2CH_3$?

3 Write an equation for the preparation of aspirin using an acyl chloride.

3

2 $CH_3CH_2CH_2COCl$ and $CH_3CH_2NH_2$

(b) $CH_3CH_2CONH_2$

1 (a) CH_3CH_2COOH

126

4.6 Arenes

After studying this section you should be able to:

- *apply rules for naming simple aromatic compounds*
- *understand the delocalised model of benzene*
- *explain the resistance to addition of benzene compared with alkenes*

LEARNING SUMMARY

Aromatic organic compounds

AQA	M4	SALTERS	M5
EDEXCEL	M5	WJEC	M4
OCR	M4	CCEA	M5

Organic compounds with pleasant smells were originally classified as aromatic compounds. Many of these contain a benzene ring in their structure and nowadays an aromatic compound is one structurally derived from benzene, C_6H_6.

The diagrams below show different representations of a benzene molecule. It is usual practice to omit the carbon and hydrogen labels.

Arenes burn with a smoky flame. This reflects the relatively low hydrogen to carbon ratio compared to alkanes and alkenes.

Arenes

An **arene** is an aromatic hydrocarbon containing a benzene ring. Benzene is the simplest arene and substituted arenes have alkyl groups attached to the benzene ring. Examples of arenes are shown below.

benzene   methylbenzene   ethylbenzene

Functional groups

Arenes can have a functional group next to an **aryl** group (a group containing a benzene ring):

  —X   or C_6H_5X

Aryl group   *Functional group*

An aryl group contains a benzene ring.

- An aryl group is often represented simply as Ar—.
- The simplest aryl group is the **phenyl** group, C_6H_5, derived from benzene, C_6H_6.

Naming of aromatic organic compounds

The benzene ring of an aromatic compound is numbered from the carbon atom attached to a functional group or alkyl side-chain.
The names can be derived in two ways:

- Some compounds (e.g. hydrocarbons, chloroarenes and nitroarenes) are regarded as substituted benzene rings.

chlorobenzene   1,3-dimethylbenzene   2,4-dinitromethylbenzene

> You should be able to suggest names for simple arenes.

- Other compounds (e.g. phenols and amines) are considered as phenyl compounds of a functional group.

phenol   phenylamine   2,4,6-trichlorophenol
not hydroxybenzene   **not** aminobenzene

The stability of benzene

AQA	M4	SALTERS	M5
EDEXCEL	M5	WJEC	M4
OCR	M4	CCEA	M5

Two structures are used to represent benzene:

- the **Kekulé** structure, developed between 1865 and 1872
- the modern **delocalised**, structure developed in the 1930s.

The Kekulé structure of benzene

> The Kekulé model of a benzene molecule has alternate double and single bonds making up the ring.

The original Kekulé structure showed benzene as a hexagonal molecule with alternate double and single bonds. Each carbon atom is attached to one hydrogen atom. This model was later modified to one with two isomers, rapidly interconverting into one another.

The Kekulé structure of benzene

> The chemical name for the Kekulé structure of benzene is **cyclohexa-1,3,5-triene**, after the positions of the double bonds in the ring.

The delocalised structure of benzene

The delocalised structure of benzene shows a benzene molecule as a hybrid state between Kekulé's two isomers with no separate single and double bonds.

In this hybrid state:

> The delocalised model of a benzene molecule has identical carbon–carbon bonds making up the ring.

- each carbon atom contributes one electron from its p-orbital to form π-bonds
- the π-bonds are spread out or **delocalised** over the whole ring.

The double bond in an alkene is a **localised** π-bond between two carbon atoms. In the delocalised structure of benzene, each bond is identical, with electron density spread out to encompass and stabilise the whole ring. The diagram below shows one of the π-bonds formed by delocalisation of electrons in a benzene molecule.

Key point from AS

- **Alkenes**
  Revise AS page 129

> This model helps to explain the low reactivity of benzene compared with alkenes (see also page 131–132).

overlap of p-orbitals forms
delocalised π-bonds above
and below the benzene ring

p-orbitals

planar molecule
bond-angle: 120°

Although the Kekulé structure is used for some purposes, the delocalised structure is a better representation of benzene. You will find both representations in books.

The delocalised structure of a benzene molecule is shown as a hexagon to represent the carbon skeleton and a circle to represent the six delocalised electrons.

 delocalised electrons
– all carbon-carbon
bonds identical

The shape of a benzene molecule

Key points from AS

• **Electron-pair repulsion theory**
Revise AS pages 60–61

Using electron-pair repulsion theory:

• there are **three** centres of electron density surrounding each carbon atom
• the shape around each carbon atom is trigonal planar with bond angles of 120°.

This results in a benzene molecule that is **planar**.

3 electron centres surround each carbon atom

Experimental evidence for delocalisation

AQA	M4	SALTERS	M5
EDEXCEL	M5	WJEC	M4
OCR	M4	CCEA	M5

Bond length data

The Kekulé structure of benzene as cyclohexa-1,3,5-triene suggests two bond lengths for the separate single and double bonds:

• C—C bond length = 0.154 nm
• C=C bond length = 0.134 nm

Experiment shows only one C—C bond length of 0.139 nm, between the bond lengths for single and double carbon-carbon bonds.

0.154 nm   0.134 nm
0.134 nm   0.154 nm
0.154 nm   0.134 nm

all C–C bonds are the same length: 0.139 nm

> This shows that each carbon-carbon bond in the benzene ring is intermediate between a single and a double bond.
>
> **KEY POINT**

Thermochemical evidence

Hydrogenation of cyclohexene

Each molecule of cyclohexene has **one** C=C double bond. The enthalpy change for the reaction of cyclohexene with hydrogen is shown below:

+ H$_2$ ⟶

$\Delta H^\ominus = -120$ kJ mol^{-1}

Hydrogenation of benzene

The Kekulé structure of benzene as cyclohexa-1,3,5-triene has **three** double C=C bonds. It would be expected that the enthalpy change for the hydrogenation of this structure would be three times the enthalpy change for the **one** C=C bond in cyclohexene.

The stability of benzene can also be demonstrated using thermochemical data for the reactions of bromine with cyclohexene and benzene.

predicted enthalpy change:
$\Delta H^\ominus = 3 \times -120 = -360$ kJ mol^{-1}

- When benzene is reacted with hydrogen, the enthalpy change obtained is far less exothermic, $\Delta H^\ominus = -208$ kJ mol^{-1}.

> **KEY POINT**
>
> - The difference between the thermochemical data for cyclohexa-1,3,5-triene and benzene suggests that benzene has **more stable bonding** than the Kekulé structure.
> - The delocalisation or resonance energy of benzene of -152 kJ mol^{-1} is the difference between the two enthalpy changes above. This is extra energy that must be provided to break the delocalised benzene ring.

Progress check

1 Name the **three** aromatic isomers of $C_6H_4Br_2$.

2 State two pieces of experimental evidence that support the delocalised structure of benzene.

3 Explain why alkenes, such as cyclohexene, are so much more reactive with electrophiles than arenes such as benzene.

3 Alkenes have localised π-bonds with a larger electron density than the delocalised π-bonds in benzene. The greater electron density is able to attract electrophiles more strongly. Also, the stability of the benzene ring must be disrupted if benzene is to react.

2 The enthalpy change of hydrogenation of benzene is less exothermic than three times the enthalpy change of hydrogenation of cyclohexene.
All the carbon-carbon bonds in the benzene ring are the same length.

1 1,2-dibromobenzene; 1,3-dibromobenzene; 1,4-dibromobenzene.

4.7 Reactions of arenes

After studying this section you should be able to:

- describe electrophilic substitution of arenes: nitration, halogenation, alkylation, acylation and sulfonation
- describe the mechanism of electrophilic substitution in arenes
- understand the importance of reactions of arenes in the synthesis of commercially important materials

LEARNING SUMMARY

Electrophilic substitution reactions of arenes

AQA	M4	SALTERS	M5
EDEXCEL	M5	WJEC	M4
OCR	M4	CCEA	M5

Many electrophiles react with alkenes by **addition**. However, electrophiles react with arenes by **substitution**, replacing a hydrogen atom on the ring. The difference in behaviour results from the high stability of the delocalised π-bonds in benzene compared with the localised π-bonds in alkenes (see pages 128–129).

> - Benzene reacts with only very reactive electrophiles.
> - The typical reaction of an arene is **electrophilic substitution**.
>
> KEY POINT

In this section, reactions of benzene are discussed to illustrate electrophilic substitution reactions of arenes.

Nitration of arenes

AQA	M4	SALTERS	M5
EDEXCEL	M5	WJEC	M4
OCR	M4	CCEA	M5

The nitration of arenes produces aromatic nitro compounds, which are important for the synthesis of many important products including explosives and dyes (see page 140).

Nitration of benzene

Benzene is nitrated by concentrated nitric acid at 55°C in the presence of concentrated sulfuric acid, which acts as a catalyst.

Although some heat is required (55°C), too much may give further nitration of the benzene ring forming 1,3-dinitrobenzene.

$$\text{benzene} + HNO_3 \xrightarrow[55°C]{H_2SO_4} \text{nitrobenzene} + H_2O$$

Mechanism

The nitronium ion is also called a nitryl cation.

- The role of the concentrated sulfuric acid is to generate the **nitronium ion**, NO_2^+, as the active electrophile:

$$HNO_3 + H_2SO_4 \longrightarrow H_2NO_3^+ + HSO_4^-$$
$$H_2NO_3^+ \longrightarrow NO_2^+ + H_2O$$

- The powerful NO_2^+ electrophile then reacts with benzene.

*This is **electrophilic substitution.***

attack of NO_2^+ electrophile　　　　proton loss

$$+ H^+$$

- The H^+ formed regenerates a molecule of H_2SO_4.

$$H^+ + HSO_4^- \longrightarrow H_2SO_4$$

*The H_2SO_4 therefore acts as a **catalyst.***

- The H_2SO_4 molecule reacts with more nitric acid to form more nitronium ions.

Comparing halogenation of arenes and alkenes

EDEXCEL	M5	SALTERS	M5
OCR	M4	WJEC	M4
		CCEA	M5

Key points from AS

- **Alkenes**
  Revise AS page 129
- **Addition reactions of alkenes**
  Revise AS pages 130–132

Bromination of alkenes

Alkenes and cycloalkenes react with bromine by **electrophilic addition**. The reaction takes place in the dark at room temperature. The bromination of cyclohexene is shown below:

- Using the same conditions with benzene, there is **no reaction**.
- The stability of the delocalised system resists addition that would disrupt this stability (see pages 128–129).

Bromination of arenes

Arenes react with bromine by **electrophilic substitution**. The reaction takes place only in the presence of a **halogen carrier**, which acts as a catalyst.

Suitable halogen carriers include:

- iron
- aluminium halides, e.g. $AlCl_3$ for chlorination; $AlBr_3$ for bromination.

The bromination of benzene is shown below.

> **KEY POINT**
>
> Bromination of alkenes and arenes are different types of reaction:
> alkenes: electrophilic **addition**
> arenes: electrophilic **substitution**

Mechanism (not Salters)

- Iron first reacts with bromine forming iron(III) bromide, $FeBr_3$.
- $FeBr_3$ acts as a halogen carrier, polarising the Br—Br bond.

$$Br_2 + FeBr_3 \longrightarrow Br^{\delta+}—Br^{\delta-} \, FeBr_3$$

- This electrophile reacts with benzene.

This is a similar principle to the nitration of the benzene ring.

attack of electrophile   proton loss

- The H^+ formed generates $FeBr_3$.

$$H^+ + FeBr_4^- \longrightarrow FeBr_3 + HBr$$

The $FeBr_3$ therefore acts as a **catalyst**.

- $FeBr_3$ can now polarise more bromine molecules.

Alkylation of arenes

EDEXCEL M5 SALTERS M5
WJEC M4

Alkylation reactions of arenes are commonly known as *Friedel–Crafts* reactions. These are very important reactions industrially as they provide a means of introducing an alkyl group onto the benzene ring.

Alkylation of benzene

> This is a similar principle to the halogenation of the benzene ring.

As with halogenation, a halogen carrier is required to generate a more reactive electrophile. With chloroethane, ethylbenzene is formed.

Mechanism (Edexcel only)

Using a tertiary halogenoalkane, RCl, in the presence of $AlCl_3$ as a halogen carrier, a **carbocation** is generated.

$$RCl + AlCl_3 \longrightarrow R^+ + AlCl_4^-$$

> By using different halogenoalkanes, different alkyl groups can be substituted onto the benzene ring.

- This carbocation acts as a powerful electrophile, which reacts with benzene.

attack of R^+ electrophile   proton loss

- The H^+ formed generates more $AlCl_3$.

$$H^+ + AlCl_4^- \longrightarrow AlCl_3 + HCl$$

- The $AlCl_3$ reacts with more of the tertiary halogenoalkane RCl to generate more carbonium ions. The $AlCl_3$ acts as a **catalyst**.

Acylation of arenes

AQA M4 SALTERS M5
EDEXCEL M5

Acylation introduces an acyl group such as $CH_3C=O$ onto the benzene ring. An acyl chloride is used in the presence of a halogen carrier.

> The mechanism for acylation is similar to that of alkylation.

acylium ion

The acylium ion is then able to react with the benzene ring, introducing an acyl group onto the ring.

Acylation of benzene

> The acylation of benzene is another example of a *Friedel–Crafts* reaction and is also important industrially.

Using ethanoyl chloride, CH_3COCl, the ethanoyl group $CH_3C=O$ can be introduced onto the benzene ring.

This reaction takes place by a similar mechanism to the alkylation reaction above (Edexcel only).

Sulfonation of arenes

EDEXCEL M5 SALTERS M5

Sulfonation of arenes produces sulfonic acids. Sodium salts of sulfonic acids are used for detergents and fabric conditioners.

Sulfonation of benzene

Benzene reacts with fuming sulfuric acid (concentrated sulfuric acid saturated with sulfur trioxide) forming a sulfonic acid.

The reaction takes place between benzene and sulfur trioxide.

$$\text{benzene} + SO_3 \xrightarrow{\ 80°C\ } \text{benzenesulfonic acid (SO}_3\text{H)}$$

benzenesulfonic acid

Oxidation of substituted arenes

WJEC ▶ M4

The side chains of substituted arenes can be readily oxidised by prolonged reflux with a strong oxidising agent.

Oxidation of methylbenzene

Using alkaline potassium manganate(VII), followed by addition of dilute aqueous acid, methylbenzene is oxidised to benzenecarboxylic acid (**benzoic acid**).

$$\text{CH}_3\text{-ring} + 3[O] \xrightarrow{\ \text{reflux}\ } \text{COOH-ring} + H_2O$$

benzenecarboxylic acid

Comparing hydrolysis of chloroarenes and chloroalkanes

Chloroalkanes, such as chloroethane, are hydrolysed by heating with aqueous alkali.

$$CH_3CH_2Cl + OH^- \longrightarrow CH_3CH_2OH + Cl^-$$

Using the same conditions, chloroarenes, such as chlorobenzene, are **not** hydrolysed.

* The aryl ring interacts with a p-orbital on the attached chlorine atom, drawing electron density towards the delocalised ring structure.

C–Cl bond
strengthened

* This results in the strengthening of the C–Cl bond, increasing the stability of chloroarenes compared with chloroalkanes.

Progress check

1 What is the common type of reaction of arenes?

2 Benzene reacts with bromine, nitric acid and chloroethane.
   (a) Using C_6H_6 to represent benzene and C_6H_5 to represent the phenyl group, write balanced equations for each of these reactions.
   (b) State the essential conditions that are needed for each of these reactions.

4.8 Phenols and alcohols

After studying this section you should be able to:

- *state the uses of phenols in antiseptics and disinfectants*
- *describe the reactions of phenol with sodium and bases*
- *explain the ease of bromination of phenol compared with benzene*

Phenols

General structure: ArOH (Ar is an aromatic ring)

| EDEXCEL | M5 | SALTERS | M4 |
| OCR | M4 | WJEC | M4 |

Phenols and alcohols both have a hydroxyl functional group. In alcohols, the hydroxyl group is bonded to a carbon chain but phenols have an aromatic ring bonded directly to a hydroxyl (–OH) group. Some phenols are shown below.

phenol, C_6H_5OH

2,4,6-trichlorophenol
(TCP)

4-hexyl-3-hydroxyphenol
(in cough drops)

thymol
(in thyme)

Uses

Dilute solutions of phenol are used as disinfectants and phenol was probably the first antiseptic. However, phenol is toxic and can cause burns to the skin. Less toxic phenols are used nowadays in antiseptics.

> With $FeCl_3$ solutions, phenols produce a violet colour. This colour change is often used as a test for the phenol group.

Phenols are also used in the production of plastics, such as the widely used phenol-formaldehyde resins. More complex phenols, such as thymol shown above, can be used as flavourings and aromas and these are obtained from essential oils of plants.

Properties

Like alcohols, a phenol has a **hydroxyl group** which is able to form intermolecular **hydrogen bonds**. The resulting properties include:

- higher melting and boiling points than hydrocarbons with similar relative molecular masses
- some solubility in water.

Reactions of phenol as an acid

| OCR | M4 | SALTERS | M4 |
| | | WJEC | M4 |

Unlike the neutrality shown by alcohols, phenols are very weak acids. The hydroxyl group donates a proton, H^+, by breaking the O–H bond.

$$C_6H_5OH \rightleftharpoons H^+ + C_6H_5O^-$$

Phenols take part in some typical acid reactions, reacting with sodium and bases to form ionic salts called **phenoxides**. However, the acidity is too weak to release carbon dioxide from carbonates and hydrogencarbonates (see carboxylic acids, page 119).

Key points from AS

- **Reaction with sodium**
  Revise AS page 138

Reaction with sodium

As with the hydroxyl groups in water and ethanol, phenol reacts with sodium, releasing hydrogen gas and forming a solution of sodium phenoxide, $C_6H_5O^-Na^+$.

$$2C_6H_5OH + 2Na \longrightarrow 2C_6H_5ONa + H_2$$

Compare these reactions with those of carboxylic acids page 119.

Reaction with an alkali

Phenol is a weak acid and is neutralised by aqueous alkalis. For example, aqueous sodium hydroxide forms the salt sodium phenoxide. Alcohols and water are not acidic enough to neutralise alkalis.

$$C_6H_5OH + NaOH \longrightarrow C_6H_5ONa + H_2O$$

Electrophilic substitution of the aryl ring of phenol

The aryl ring of phenol has a greater electron density than benzene because the adjacent oxygen reinforces the electron density in the ring. A p-orbital on the oxygen donates an electron pair to the benzene ring.

This results in:

- a greater electron density in the aryl ring, activating the ring
- greater reactivity of the ring towards electrophiles.

Bromination of phenol

- Phenol reacts directly with bromine. However, Benzene reacts with bromine only in the presence of a halogen carrier.
- Phenol undergoes multiple substitution with bromine. Benzene is monosubstituted only.

OH + 3Br$_2$ ⟶ (2,4,6-tribromophenol) + 3HBr

- The organic product 2,4,6-tribromophenol separates as a white solid.
- The bromine is decolourised.

Nitration of phenol (Edexcel only)

- Phenol reacts with dilute nitric acid in the cold to form a mixture of 2-nitrophenol and 4-nitrophenol.
- Benzene needs much stronger conditions – concentrated nitric acid and concentrated sulfuric acid at 55°C.
- This reaction again shows the increased reactivity of the aryl ring of phenol compared with benzene.

OH —dilute HNO$_3$(aq) / room temperature→ mixture: (2-nitrophenol with NO$_2$) + (4-nitrophenol with NO$_2$)

Reaction with iron(III) chloride, FeCl$_3$

Phenols form a violet coloration with FeCl$_3$ solution.

- This reaction is used as a test for a phenol.
- This allows phenols to be distinguished from alcohols.

Formation of esters

SALTERS ▶ M4 WJEC ▶ M4

Esters can be formed from an **alcohol** with a **carboxylic acid** in the presence of an acid catalyst (see page 120).

In phenols, the aryl ring reduces the electron density on the –OH group, reducing its effectiveness as a nucleophile. This means that phenols do **not** form esters in the same way as alcohols.

To form an ester from a phenol:

*   an acyl chloride is used rather than the less reactive carboxylic acid (see page 125)
*   alkaline conditions are used.

$$CH_3COCl + C_6H_5OH + NaOH \longrightarrow CH_3COOC_6H_5 + NaCl + H_2O$$

Reactions of the –OH group in alcohols

WJEC ▶ M4

Substitution reactions of alcohols with hydrogen bromide

Alcohols react with hydrogen bromide by **nucleophilic substitution**.

The alcohol is mixed with NaBr and H_2SO_4. The reaction mixture generates hydrogen bromide as H^+ and Br^- ions.

> You should also be aware of the use of ethanol as a biofuel.

$$C_2H_5OH + H^+ + Br^- \longrightarrow C_2H_5Br + H_2O$$

*   The polarity of the C–OH bond allows a reaction with nucleophiles such as Br^-, which attack the electron-deficient carbon atom.

Dehydration of alcohols

When an alcohol is refluxed with a concentrated acid catalyst such as sulfuric acid H_2SO_4, or phosphoric acid H_3PO_4, an elimination reaction takes place: water is eliminated with formation of an alkene.

$$C_2H_5OH \longrightarrow C_2H_4 + H_2O$$

Progress check

1 Phenols are easily nitrated with nitric acid in the cold. With concentrated HNO_3, multiple substitution takes place.
Suggest an equation for the reaction that takes place.

4.9 Amines

After studying this section you should be able to:

- explain the relative basicities of ethylamine and phenylamine
- describe the reactions of primary amines with acids to form salts
- describe the formation of phenylamine by reduction of nitrobenzene
- describe the synthesis of an azo dye from phenylamine
- understand the origin of colour in azo dyes
- describe the reactions of amines with halogenoalkanes and acyl chlorides
- describe the preparation and reaction of amides

Aliphatic and aromatic amines

AQA	M4	SALTERS	M4
EDEXCEL	M5	WJEC	M4
OCR	M4	CCEA	M5

Amines are organic compounds containing nitrogen derived from ammonia, NH_3. Amines are classified as primary, secondary or tertiary amines depending on how many of the hydrogen atoms in ammonia have been replaced by organic groups. The diagram below shows examples of aliphatic and aromatic amines.

Aliphatic amines			Aromatic amine
	1 hydrogen replaced	2 hydrogens replaced	3 hydrogens replaced	
	primary amine	*secondary amine*	*tertiary amine*	
NH_3	H_3C-NH_2	$\begin{array}{c}H_3C\\ \diagdown\\ NH\\ \diagup\\ H_3C\end{array}$	$\begin{array}{c}H_3C\\ \diagdown\\ H_3C-N\\ \diagup\\ H_3C\end{array}$	⬡—NH_2
ammonia	methylamine	dimethylamine	trimethylamine	phenylamine

Amines in nature

Amines are found commonly in nature. They are weak bases and the shortest chain amines, e.g. ethylamine $C_2H_5NH_2$, smell of fish. Some diamines, such as putrescine $H_2N(CH_2)_4NH_2$, and cadaverine $H_2N(CH_2)_5NH_2$, are found in decaying flesh.

Polarity

> Notice the similarity with ammonia.

The presence of an electronegative nitrogen atom in amines results in polar molecules. The diagram shows the polarity of the primary amine methylamine.

$$H_3C \overset{\overset{\displaystyle \cdot\cdot\, \delta-}{N}}{\underset{\underset{\delta+}{H}}{}} H\,\delta+$$

Physical properties of amines

> As with other polar functional groups, the solubility of amines in water decreases with increasing carbon chain length as the non-polar contribution to the molecule becomes more important.

The amino group dominates the physical properties of short-chain amines.

Hydrogen bonding takes place between amine molecules, resulting in:

- higher melting and boiling points than alkanes of comparable relative molecular mass
- solubility in water – amines with fewer than six carbons mix with water in all proportions.

Amines as bases

AQA	M4	SALTERS	M4
EDEXCEL	M5	WJEC	M4
OCR	M4	CCEA	M5

Amines are weak bases because they only partially associate with protons:

$$RNH_2 + H^+ \rightleftharpoons RNH_3^+$$

The basic strength of an amine measures its ability to **accept** a proton, H^+. This depends upon:

- the size of the $\delta-$ charge on the amino nitrogen atom
- the availability of the nitrogen lone pair.

> Amines are the organic bases.

The basicity of aliphatic and aromatic amines

Aliphatic amines are stronger bases than ammonia; aromatic amines are substantially weaker.

> Amines can also act as ligands with transition metal ions forming complex ions.

KEY POINT

- Electron-donating groups, e.g. alkyl groups, **increase** the basic strength.
- Electron-withdrawing groups, e.g. C_6H_5, **decrease** the basic strength.

inductive effect causes electron flow **away from** nitrogen

inductive effect causes electron flow **towards** nitrogen

decrease in electron density of nitrogen lone pair

increase in electron density of nitrogen lone pair

basicity increases

Organic ammonium salts

> Amines react by the usual 'base reactions' producing organic ammonium salts.

Amines are **neutralised by acids** forming salts.

In the example below, methylamine is neutralised by hydrochloric acid forming a primary **ammonium salt**.

$$CH_3NH_2 + HCl \longrightarrow CH_3NH_3^+Cl^-$$
methylammonium chloride

> A proton, H^+, is added to the amino nitrogen atom.

On evaporation of water, the primary ammonium salt crystallises out as an ionic compound.

Preparation of amines

AQA	M4	WJEC	M4
EDEXCEL	M5	CCEA	M5
OCR	M4		

Preparation of aromatic amines from nitroarenes

> Other reducing agents can also be used:
> - H_2/Ni catalyst
> - $LiAlH_4$ in dry ether
>
> $LiAlH_4$ is an almost universal reducing agent and works in most examples of organic reduction.

Aromatic amines can be prepared by **reducing** a nitroarene. For example, nitrobenzene is reduced by Sn in concentrated HCl to form phenylamine.

1. Sn / conc. HCl
reflux
2. NaOH(aq)

phenylamine

- Using tin and hydrochloric acid, the salt $C_6H_5NH_3^+Cl^-$ is formed.
- The amine is obtained from this salt by adding aqueous alkali.

Preparation of aliphatic amines from nitriles (not OCR)

Aliphatic amines can be prepared by **reducing** a nitrile with a suitable reducing agent (e.g. Na in ethanol; $LiAlH_4$ in dry ether).

$$CH_3CH_2C\equiv N + 4[H] \longrightarrow CH_3CH_2CH_2NH_2$$

This process is often called the *Hofmann degradation* and can be used to move down a homologous series.

See also: Increasing the carbon chain length pages 115–116.

Preparation of amines from amides (Edexcel only)

Primary amines can be prepared by heating a primary amide with bromine in alkali. The amine formed has **one less carbon** atom than the starting amide.

$$RCONH_2 + Br_2 + 4NaOH \longrightarrow RNH_2 + Na_2CO_3 + 2NaBr + 2H_2O$$

The preparation of dyes from aromatic amines

EDEXCEL	M5	WJEC	M4
OCR	M4	CCEA	M5
SALTERS	M5		

Aromatic amines, such as phenylamine, are important industrially for the production of dyes. Modern dyes are formed in a two-stage synthesis:

- the aromatic amine is converted into a **diazonium salt**
- the diazonium salt is **coupled** with an aromatic compound such as phenol, forming an **azo dye**.

Formation of diazonium salts

An aromatic amine, such as phenylamine, forms a diazonium salt in the presence of nitrous acid, HNO_2, and hydrochloric acid.

- HNO_2 is unstable and is prepared *in situ* from $NaNO_2$ and HCl(aq).
$$NaNO_2 + HCl \longrightarrow HNO_2 + NaCl$$

- This mixture is then reacted with phenylamine. It is important to keep the temperature **below 10°C** because diazonium salts decompose above this temperature.

benzenediazonium chloride
(diazonium salt)

$$C_6H_5NH_2 + HNO_2 + HCl \longrightarrow C_6H_5N_2^+Cl^- + 2H_2O$$

Formation of azo dyes by coupling

The diazonium salt is coupled with a suitable aromatic compound **below 10°C** in **aqueous alkali** to produce an azo dye.

E.g. coupling of benzenediazonium chloride with phenol:

azo dye

- The azo dye is coloured.
- Coupling of a diazonium salt with different aromatic compounds forms dyes with different colours.

Using benzene for the synthesis of dyes

Benzene is used as the raw material for the synthesis of dyes.
A four-stage synthesis is shown below:

- benzene is nitrated to nitrobenzene (see page 131)
- nitrobenzene is reduced to phenylamine (see above)
- phenylamine is converted into a **diazonium salt**
- the diazonium salt is **coupled** with an aromatic compound such as phenol, forming an **azo dye**.

Diazonium salts in synthesis (CCEA only)

In addition to azo dyes, diazonium salts are useful for the synthesis of a variety of aromatic organic compounds.

- The diazonium group, $-N_2^+$, can be replaced by nucleophilic reagents.
- The N_2^+ group is lost as N_2 gas.

Preparation of phenol

The solution of the diazonium salt is simply warmed. Diazonium salts are unstable above 10°C, and hydrolysis with water takes place.

$$C_6H_5-N^+\equiv N\ Cl^- + H_2O \longrightarrow C_6H_5-OH + N_2 + HCl$$

Preparation of iodobenzene

The solution of the diazonium salt is warmed with aqueous potassium iodide.

$$C_6H_5-N^+\equiv N\ Cl^- + KI \longrightarrow C_6H_5-I + N_2 + KCl$$

Colour in azo dyes

SALTERS	M5	WJEC	M4	
		CCEA	M5	

On pages 90–91, the origin of colour in transition elements is discussed. For organic compounds, the principles are the same.

When visible light strikes an organic compound that is coloured:

- an electron is promoted from a lower to a higher energy level
- **energy** of certain wavelengths is **absorbed**
- part of the visible spectrum has been removed and the **remaining wavelengths** are **reflected as colour**.

> When energy is absorbed, the electron moves between electronic energy levels.
> $\Delta E = hf$
> Where ΔE = energy gap, h = the Planck constant
> f = frequency
> (See page 90 for more details)

> **KEY POINT**
> A **chromophore** is part of an organic molecule responsible for its colour.

- Common chromophores include C=C, C=O, N=N, an aromatic ring, and features with lone pairs such as OH, NH_2.
- Colour is produced when the energy gap between energy levels matches the energy from part of the visible spectrum.
- For many organic molecules containing chromophores, this energy gap is large and matches energies in the ultraviolet region of the spectrum.

> The ultraviolet region of the spectrum has more energy than the visible region – the gaps between its energy levels are greater.

- Delocalisation reduces this energy gap. When the delocalisation is such that the energy gap matches energies in the visible part of the spectrum, the organic compound is coloured.

> The colour of an organic compound results from the **transfer** of an **electron** between energy levels in a delocalised system.

Colourless

Kekulé structure of benzene
Some delocalisation but electron energy gap is large and matches ultraviolet region of spectrum

ultraviolet

energy levels

Coloured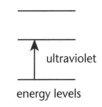

visible

energy levels

Azo dye has more delocalisation
(note the alternating double and single bonds)
Energy gap is smaller and matches visible part of spectrum

The key to colour in organic compounds is a delocalised arrangement of alternating double and single bonds, such as that in an azo dye.

Attaching dyes to fibres (Salters only)

Dyes attach themselves to fibres by:

- intermolecular bonds
- ionic attractions
- covalent bonding.

Modifying dyes (Salters only)

Chemists modify dyes by introducing different functional groups.

These may:

- modify the chromophore
- affect the solubility of the dye
- allow the dye to bond to fibres.

Complex ion formation with aqueous copper(II) ions

EDEXCEL M5

This reaction is similar to that of ammonia, NH_3 with transition metal ions.

However, the number of amine ligands that substitute may be different from NH_3.

An aqueous solution of copper(II) sulfate contains $[Cu(H_2O)_6]^{2+}$ complex ions.

- The lone pair of the amino group is able to form a coordinate bond to the Cu^{2+} ion.
- A ligand substitution reaction takes place (see page 93–94).
- This shows as a change in colour.

$$[Cu(H_2O)_6]^{2+} + 2C_6H_5NH_2 \longrightarrow [Cu(C_6H_5NH_2)_2(H_2O)_4]^{2+} + 2H_2O$$

Reactions of amines with halogenoalkanes

AQA M4   WJEC M4
EDEXCEL M5   CCEA M5
OCR M4

Key points from AS

- Nucleophilic substitution reactions of halogenoalkanes
  Revise AS pages 139–141

Formation of a primary amine by nucleophilic substitution

Amines act as **nucleophiles** with organic compounds such as halogenoalkanes.

Halogenoalkanes react with **excess ammonia** in hot ethanol, forming a primary amine. The reaction with bromomethane is shown below:

$$CH_3Br + 2NH_3 \longrightarrow CH_3NH_2 + NH_4^+Br^-$$

The reaction takes place in two steps:

- Nucleophilic substitution with ammonia forms an alkylammonium ion:

$$CH_3Br + NH_3 \longrightarrow CH_3NH_3^+ + Br^-$$

- Proton transfer with ammonia forms a primary amine:

$$CH_3NH_3^+Br^- + NH_3 \rightleftharpoons CH_3NH_2 + NH_4^+Br^-$$

Mechanism and further substitution (AQA only)

The mechanism for the formation of a primary amine from bromoethane is shown below.

With an **excess** of **ammonia**, the reaction essentially stops at this stage.

With an **excess** of the **halogenoalkane**, further substitution takes place, which continues until a quaternary ammonium salt is obtained.

$$RNH_2 \xrightarrow{RX} R_2NH \xrightarrow{RX} R_3N \xrightarrow{RX} R_4N^+X^-$$

primary   secondary   tertiary   quaternary
amine   amine   amine   ammonium salt

> Quaternary ammonium salts are used as cationic surfactants in fabric softeners.

Each reaction stage proceeds by **nucleophilic substitution**.

The mechanism for the final stage in the formation of the quaternary salt tetramethylammonium bromide is shown below.

- This mechanism stops at the quaternary salt as there are no further protons to be exchanged.

Amides

AQA	M4	WJEC	M4
EDEXCEL	M5	CCEA	M5
SALTERS	M4		

Amides

Primary amides have the general formula $RCONH_2$ – R is an alkyl group.

The first six members of the **amides** homologous series are shown below.

structural formula	molecular formula	name
$HCONH_2$	CH_3NO	methanamide
CH_3CONH_2	C_2H_5NO	ethanamide
$CH_3CH_2CONH_2$	C_3H_7NO	propanamide
$CH_3CH_2CH_2CONH_2$	C_4H_9NO	butanamide
$CH_3CH_2CH_2CH_2CONH_2$	$C_5H_{11}NO$	pentanamide
$CH_3CH_2CH_2CH_2CH_2CONH_2$	$C_6H_{13}NO$	hexanamide

Types of amide

primary amide   secondary amide   tertiary amide

Preparation of amides

The amide group is stable and relatively unreactive. Preparation directly from a carboxylic acid is difficult (although this type of reaction is essentially what happens when peptides form from amino acids – see pages 150 and 157).

Amides are generally prepared by the reaction of ammonia and amines with **acyl chlorides** or with acid anhydrides – these are much more reactive than carboxylic acids (see pages 124–125).

- Reaction with ammonia produces a **primary amide**.

$$CH_3COCl + NH_3 \longrightarrow + CH_3CONH_2 + HCl$$

(Then $NH_3 + HCl \longrightarrow NH_4Cl$)

> The acyl chloride is often prepared initially from a carboxylic acid. The acyl chloride can then be reacted with ammonia or amines to form amides.

- Reaction with a primary amine produces a **secondary amide**.

$$CH_3COCl + CH_3NH_2 \longrightarrow + CH_3CONHCH_3 + HCl$$

$$(Then\ NH_3 + HCl \longrightarrow NH_4Cl)$$

An amide can be prepared from a carboxylic acid by first converting the carboxylic acid into an acyl chloride (see pages 124–125 for more details).

Hydrolysis of amides (Salters and CCEA only)

Amides are stable organic compounds. They can be hydrolysed but they require much stronger conditions than esters. Alkaline hydrolysis requires prolonged refluxing with 6 mol dm^{-3} NaOH(aq).

Acid hydrolysis

Acid hydrolysis of amides form a carboxylic acid and an ammonium salt:

$$CH_3CONH_2 + H_2O + HCl \longrightarrow CH_3COOH + NH_4^+Cl^-$$

Alkaline hydrolysis

Alkaline hydrolysis of amides form an acid salt and ammonia:

$$CH_3CONH_2 + NaOH \longrightarrow CH_3COO^-Na^+ + NH_3$$

Dehydration of amides (CCEA only)

Amides are **dehydrated** by phosphorus pentoxide, P_2O_5, to form nitriles:

$$CH_3CONH_2 \longrightarrow CH_3C{\equiv}N + H_2O$$

Basicity of amides (CCEA only)

Compared to amines, amides are very weak bases. This lack of basicity is explained by delocalisation of the lone pair of electrons on the nitrogen atom by resonance.

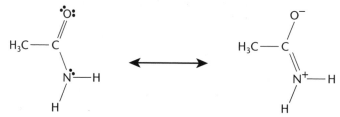

lone pair on nitrogen atom is delocalised

bond angles around N are close to 120°
the molecule has a near planar shape about C–N

The delocalisation reduces the electron density on the nitrogen lone pair, reducing its ability to donate its electron pair.

Progress check

1 Explain why ethylamine is a stronger base than phenylamine.

2 (a) Write equations for the conversion of:
   (i) benzene to nitrobenzene
   (ii) nitrobenzene to phenylamine
   (iii) phenylamine to benzenediazonium chloride.

3 (a) Write down the formula of the organic product formed between:
   (i) bromoethane and excess ammonia
   (ii) ammonia and excess bromoethane.

3 (a) (i) $C_2H_5NH_2$ (ii) $(C_2H_5)_4N^+Br^-$

(iii) $C_6H_5NH_2 + HNO_2 + HCl \longrightarrow C_6H_5N_2^+Cl^- + 2H_2O$

2 (a) (i) $C_6H_6 + HNO_3 \longrightarrow C_6H_5NO_2 + H_2O$ (ii) $C_6H_5NO_2 + 6[H] \longrightarrow C_6H_5NH_2 + 2H_2O$

the amine. This lone pair on the nitrogen will attract protons less strongly.

The phenyl group has a negative inductive effect which reduces the electron density on the nitrogen atom of

amine. This lone pair on the nitrogen will attract protons more strongly.

1 The ethyl group has a positive inductive effect which reinforces the electron density of the nitrogen atom of the

Sample question and model answer

This question looks at the structure and reactions of benzene.

(a) The average enthalpy of hydrogenation of a single C–C bond is –120 kJ mol^{-1}.

  (i) Assuming that benzene consists of a ring with three separate double bonds, predict the enthalpy change for the hydrogenation of benzene to form cyclohexane.

This is an easy mark. Don't forget to include the sign!

3×-120 kJ mol^{-1} = -360 kJ mol^{-1} ✓

  (ii) The actual enthalpy of hydrogenation of benzene is –205 kJ mol^{-1}. Using this information and your answer to (i), what conclusion can be drawn about the stability of the benzene ring? Use an enthalpy level diagram to illustrate your answer.

An enthalpy diagram is a good way of showing the delocalisation energy of delocalised benzene.

1 mark here is awarded for the relative positions of the delocalised and Kekulé structures of benzene.

Benzene has extra stability arising from delocalisation of π-electrons ✓

[3]

(b) Benzene can be nitrated to form nitrobenzene. Give the reagents, the equation and the conditions for this reaction.

This is standard bookwork that must be learnt.

Other reactions could have been chosen (e.g. bromination).

Remember that 'reagents' are the chemicals 'out of the bottle' that are reacted with the organic compound.

You must give the full name or formula for any 'reagent'.

Reagent(s):   concentrated HNO_3/H_2SO_4 ✓

Equation: $C_6H_6 + HNO_3 \longrightarrow C_6H_5NO_2 + H_2O$ ✓

Conditions: warm to 55°C ✓   [3]

(c) For the nitration of benzene:

  (i) write the formula of the electrophile

  NO_2^+ ✓

  (ii) write the equation to show the formation of the electrophile

More standard bookwork.

An alternative response here would be:

$HNO_3 + 2H_2SO_4 \rightarrow NO_2^+ + 2HSO_4^-$

  $HNO_3 + H_2SO_4 \longrightarrow NO_2^+ + HSO_4^-$ ✓

  (iii) state the type of mechanism

  electrophilic substitution ✓

  (iv) outline the mechanism.

Notice how precise you need to be to score all three marks:

• arrow to electrophile ✓
• correct intermediate ✓
• arrow on C–H for loss of H$^+$ ✓.

The sulfuric acid catalyst is then regenerated:

$H^+ + HSO_4^- \longrightarrow H_2SO_4$ ✓   [7]

[Total:13]

Practice examination questions

1 Compounds **A**, **B** and **C** are structural isomers, each containing a carbonyl group. The compounds have a relative molecular mass of 72 and the following percentage composition by mass: C, 66.7%; H, 11.1%; O, 22.2%.

(a) Calculate the molecular formula of the isomers. [2]

(b) What are the structural formulae of **A**, **B** and **C**? [3]

(c) Name a reagent that reacts with **A**, **B** and **C**. State the observation. [2]

(d) Name a reagent that reacts with only two of the isomers **A**, **B** and **C**. Identify which isomers react and state the observation. [3]

(e) One of the isomers **A**, **B** and **C** is reacted with $NaBH_4$ to form a product that has optical isomers. Identify this product and the isomer that has been reacted with $NaBH_4$. [2]

[Total: 12]

2 (a) Compound **D**, $CH_3CH_2COOCH_2CH_3$, is an ester.

(i) Name compound **D**.

(ii) Compound **D** was hydrolysed by heating with aqueous sodium hydroxide. An alcohol **E** was formed, together with another organic product, **F**. Give the structural formulae of compounds **E** and **F**. [4]

(b) Compound **G** is a di-ester formed by the reaction of ethane-1,2-diol and methanoic acid.

(i) Draw the structural formula of compound **G**.

(ii) Identify a substance that could catalyse this reaction. [2]

(c) Compound **H** is a tri-ester. Complete and balance the equation below for the formation of the tri-ester **H** by esterification.

$$\longrightarrow \quad \begin{array}{l} CH_3COO-CH_2 \\ CH_3COO-CH \\ CH_3COO-CH_2 \end{array}$$

tri-ester H

[3]

[Total: 9]

3 An aromatic hydrocarbon has a relative molecular mass of 106 and has the following composition by mass: C, 90.56%; H, 9.44%.

(a) (i) Deduce the molecular formula of the aromatic hydrocarbon.

(ii) Draw structures for all the structural isomers of this aromatic hydrocarbon. [7]

(b) In the presence of a sulfuric acid, one of these isomers, **I**, reacts with nitric acid to give only one mononitro product **J**.

(i) Deduce which of the isomers in (a)(ii) is isomer **I**.

(ii) Draw the structure of **J**. [2]

[Total: 9]

Practice examination questions (continued)

4 Methylbenzene can be converted into an azo dye using the reaction scheme below.

(a) For Step 1:

   (i) name the mechanism

   (ii) state the reagents required. [2]

(b) For the reduction in Step 2:

   (i) state the reagents required

   (ii) write a balanced equation (use [H] to represent the reducing agent). [3]

(c) For Step 3:

   (i) state the reagents required and the essential conditions

   (ii) show the structure of the diazonium salt formed (the functional group should be displayed with charges clearly shown). [3]

(d) For Step 4:

   (i) give the name and formula of a suitable organic compound for coupling with the diazonium salt

   (ii) show the structure of the azo dye formed. [2]

[Total: 10]

5 Compound **C**, $CH_3CH_2CH_2COOCH(CH_3)_2$, can be prepared using the reaction scheme below.

$$CH_3CH_2CH_2CHO \xrightarrow{\text{Step 1}} A \quad + \quad B \xleftarrow{\text{Step 2}} CH_3COCH_3$$

$$\downarrow \text{Step 3}$$

$$CH_3CH_2CH_2COOCH(CH_3)_2$$
$$C$$

(a) Show the structural formulae of compounds **A** and **B**. [2]

(b) For each of the three steps, give the reagents and conditions and name the type of reaction. [9]

[Total: 11]

Chapter 5

Polymers, analysis and synthesis

The following topics are covered in this chapter:

- Amino acids
- Polymers, proteins and nucleic acids
- Chromatography

- Analysis
- NMR spectroscopy
- Organic synthetic routes

5.1 Amino acids

After studying this section you should be able to:

- describe the acid–base properties of amino acids and the formation of zwitterions
- explain the formation of polypeptides and proteins as condensation polymers of amino acids
- describe the acid hydrolysis of proteins and peptides

LEARNING SUMMARY

Amino acids

AQA	M4	SALTERS	M4
EDEXCEL	M5	WJEC	M4
OCR	M4	CCEA	M5

There are 22 naturally occurring amino acids.

A typical amino acid has organic molecules with both acidic and basic properties comprising:

- a basic amino group, $-NH_2$
- an acidic carboxyl group, $-COOH$.

Each amino acid has a unique organic R group or side chain. The formula of a typical amino acid is shown below.

$$H_2N-\underset{\underset{H}{|}}{\overset{\overset{R}{|}}{C}}-COOH$$

Examples of some amino acids are shown below:

$$H_2N-\underset{\underset{H}{|}}{\overset{\overset{H}{|}}{C}}-COOH$$
R = H
glycine

$$H_2N-\underset{\underset{H}{|}}{\overset{\overset{CH_3}{|}}{C}}-COOH$$
R = CH$_3$
alanine

$$H_2N-\underset{\underset{H}{|}}{\overset{\overset{CH(CH_3)_2}{|}}{C}}-COOH$$
R = CH(CH$_3$)$_2$
valine

Acid–base properties of amino acids

AQA	M4	SALTERS	M4
EDEXCEL	M5	WJEC	M4
OCR	M4	CCEA	M5

Isoelectric points and zwitterions

Each amino acid has a particular pH called the **isoelectric point** at which the overall charge on an amino acid molecule is zero.

Examples of isoelectric points

amino acid	aspartic acid	glycine	histidine	arginine
isoelectric point	3.0	6.1	7.6	10.8

At the isoelectric point, the amino acid exists in equilibrium with its zwitterion form.

At the isoelectric point, an amino acid exists as a zwitterion:

- the **carboxyl** group **has donated** a proton to the **amino** group, which form a positive NH_3^+ ion.

A **zwitterion** is a dipolar ion with both positive and negative charges in different parts of the molecule.

$$H_3\overset{+}{N}-\underset{\underset{H}{|}}{\overset{\overset{R}{|}}{C}}-C\overset{\nearrow O}{\searrow_{O^-}}$$

zwitterion – two ions
in one molecule

Amino acids as bases

In strongly **acidic** conditions a **positive ion** forms:

- an amino acid behaves as a **base**
- the COO^- ion gains a proton.

$$H_3\overset{+}{N}-\underset{\underset{H}{|}}{\overset{\overset{R}{|}}{C}}-C\overset{\nearrow O}{\searrow_{O^-}} + H^+ \longrightarrow H_3\overset{+}{N}-\underset{\underset{H}{|}}{\overset{\overset{R}{|}}{C}}-C\overset{\nearrow O}{\searrow_{OH}}$$

positive ion

Amino acids as acids

> Because of their reactions with strong acids and strong bases, amino acids act as buffers and help to stabilise the pH of living systems.

In strongly **alkaline** conditions a **negative ion** forms:

- an amino acid behaves as an **acid**
- the NH_3^+ ion loses a proton.

$$H_3\overset{+}{N}-\underset{\underset{H}{|}}{\overset{\overset{R}{|}}{C}}-C\overset{\nearrow O}{\searrow_{O^-}} + OH^- \longrightarrow H_2N-\underset{\underset{H}{|}}{\overset{\overset{R}{|}}{C}}-C\overset{\nearrow O}{\searrow_{O^-}} + H_2O$$

negative ion

> **KEY POINT**
> - At the **isoelectric point**, the amino acid is **neutral**.
> - At a pH more **acidic** than the isoelectric point, the amino acid forms a **positive ion**.
> - At a pH more **alkaline** than the isoelectric point, the amino acid forms a **negative ion**.

Physical properties of amino acids

AQA	M4	SALTERS	M4
EDEXCEL	M5	WJEC	M4
OCR	M4	CCEA	M5

Solid amino acids

Solid amino acids have higher melting points than expected from their molecular masses and structure. This suggests that amino acids crystallise in a giant lattice with strong electrostatic forces between the **zwitterions**.

Optical isomers

With the exception of aminoethanoic acid (*glycine*), H_2NCH_2COOH, all amino acids have a chiral centre and are optically active.

Other reactions of amino acids (CCEA only)

An amino acid has both amino and carboxyl groups. Each functional group can take part in their typical reactions.

Reaction with carbonates

With carbonates, $CO_2(g)$ is evolved and a salt is produced. The reaction of sodium carbonate with the amino acid glycine is shown below.

$$Na_2CO_3 + 2H_2NCH_2COOH \longrightarrow 2H_2NCH_2COO^-Na^+ + CO_2 + H_2O$$

This reaction is similar to that of ammonia, NH_3 with transition metal ions.

It is difficult to predict how many amino acid molecules have exchanged with water molecules.

Reaction with copper(II) sulfate

An aqueous solution of copper(II) sulfate contains $[Cu(H_2O)_6]^{2+}$ complex ions.

- The lone pair of the NH_2 part of the amino acid molecule is able to form a coordinate bond to the Cu^{2+} ion.
- A ligand substitution reaction takes place (see pages 93–94).
- This shows as a change in colour.

$$[Cu(H_2O)_6]^{2+} + x\ H_2NCH_2COOH \longrightarrow [Cu(H_2NCH_2COOH)_x(H_2O)_{6-x}]^{2+} + x\ H_2O$$

Reaction with nitrous acid

With nitrous acid, HNO_2, the amino part of the amino acid molecule reacts, producing a hydroxyl group and nitrogen gas:

$$HNO_2 + H_2NCH_2COOH \longrightarrow HOCH_2COOH + N_2 + H_2O$$

Polypeptides and proteins

A protein is formed by condensation polymerisation of amino acids. See page 157.

In nature, individual amino acids are linked together in chains as **polypeptides** and **proteins** (see page 157).

The diagram below shows the condensation of the amino acids glycine and alanine to form a **dipeptide**. The amino acids are bonded together by a **peptide link**.

$$H_2N-\underset{\underset{H}{|}}{\overset{\overset{H}{|}}{C}}-C\overset{O}{\underset{OH}{\diagup}} + H_2N-\underset{\underset{H}{|}}{\overset{\overset{CH_3}{|}}{C}}-C\overset{O}{\underset{OH}{\diagup}} \longrightarrow H_2N-\underset{\underset{H}{|}}{\overset{\overset{H}{|}}{C}}-\overset{\overset{O}{||}}{C}-\underset{\underset{H}{|}}{\overset{\overset{H}{|}}{N}}-\underset{\underset{H}{|}}{\overset{\overset{CH_3}{|}}{C}}-C\overset{O}{\underset{OH}{\diagup}} + H_2O$$

glycine　　　　*alanine*　　　　　　　*peptide link*

Each peptide link forms:

- between the **carboxyl group** of glycine and the **amino group** of alanine
- with loss of a water molecule in a **condensation reaction**.

Further condensation reactions between amino acids build up a **polypeptide** or **protein**.

A polypeptide is the name given to a short chain of amino acids linked by peptide bonds.

A protein is simply the name given to a long-chain polypeptide.

- For each amino acid added to a protein chain, one water molecule is lost.
- Most common proteins contain more than 100 amino acids.
- Each protein has a unique sequence of amino acids and a complex three-dimensional shape, held together by intermolecular bonds, including hydrogen bonds.

Hydrolysis of proteins

Hydrolysis breaks down a protein into its separate amino acids.

- The protein is refluxed with 6 mol dm^{-3} HCl(aq) for 24 hours.
- The resulting solution is neutralised.

The equation below shows the hydrolysis of a dipeptide.

Proteins can also be hydrolysed with hot aqueous alkali.

$$H_2N-\underset{\underset{H}{|}}{\overset{\overset{H}{|}}{C}}-\overset{\overset{O}{||}}{C}-\underset{\underset{H}{|}}{\overset{\overset{H}{|}}{N}}-\underset{\underset{H}{|}}{\overset{\overset{CH_3}{|}}{C}}-C\overset{O}{\underset{OH}{\diagup}} + H_2O \xrightarrow[\text{2 neutralise}]{\text{1 6M HCl, reflux}} H_2N-\underset{\underset{H}{|}}{\overset{\overset{H}{|}}{C}}-C\overset{O}{\underset{OH}{\diagup}} + H_2N-\underset{\underset{H}{|}}{\overset{\overset{CH_3}{|}}{C}}-C\overset{O}{\underset{OH}{\diagup}}$$

peptide link　　　　　　　　　*glycine*　　　*alanine*

- Hydrolysis of a protein is the reverse process to the condensation polymerisation that forms proteins.
- Biological systems use enzymes to catalyse this hydrolysis, which takes place at body temperature without the need for acid or alkali.

Identifying the amino acids in a protein

To determine the amino acids present in a protein, the protein is first boiled with 6 mol dm^{-3} hydrochloric acid. The amino acids formed are separated using paper chromatography and made visible by spraying the paper with ninhydrin.

Each amino acid moves a different distance on the chromatography paper, making for easy identification of the amino acids in the protein.

Progress check

1 The isoelectric point of serine (R = –CH$_2$OH) is 5.7. Draw the form of the molecule in aqueous solutions of pH 3.0, pH 5.7 and pH 10.0.

2 Draw the structure of the tripeptide with the sequence alanine–serine–aspartic acid (alanine: R = –CH$_3$; aspartic acid: R = –CH$_2$COOH).

(Answers, shown inverted at the foot of the page)

2 Tripeptide structure:

$$H_2N-\overset{\displaystyle CH_3}{\underset{H}{\overset{|}{\underset{|}{C}}}}-\overset{O}{\overset{\|}{C}}-N-\overset{CH_2}{\underset{OH}{\overset{|}{\underset{|}{C}}}}-\overset{O}{\overset{\|}{C}}-N-\overset{CH_2COOH}{\underset{H}{\overset{|}{\underset{|}{C}}}}-COOH$$

1

pH = 3.0
$$H_3\overset{+}{N}-\overset{\displaystyle CH_2OH}{\underset{H}{\overset{|}{\underset{|}{C}}}}-COOH$$

pH = 5.7
$$H_3\overset{+}{N}-\overset{\displaystyle CH_2OH}{\underset{H}{\overset{|}{\underset{|}{C}}}}-COO^-$$

pH = 10.0
$$H_2N-\overset{\displaystyle CH_2OH}{\underset{H}{\overset{|}{\underset{|}{C}}}}-COO^-$$

151

5.2 Polymers, proteins and nucleic acids

After studying this section you should be able to:

- *describe the characteristics of addition polymerisation*
- *describe the characteristics of condensation polymerisation in polypeptides, proteins, polyamides and polyesters*
- *discuss the disposal of polymers*
- *describe primary, secondary and tertiary structures of protein*
- *describe the characteristics of enzyme catalysis*
- *describe the structure and functions of DNA and its importance in directing protein synthesis*

During the study of alkenes in AS Chemistry, you learnt about addition polymers. For A2 Chemistry, addition polymerisation is reviewed and compared with condensation polymerisation.

Monomers and polymers

AQA	M4	SALTERS	M4
EDEXCEL	M4, M5	WJEC	M4
OCR	M4	CCEA	M5

A **polymer** is a compound comprising very large molecules that are multiples of simpler chemical units called **monomers**.

Monomers are small molecules that can combine together to form a single large molecule, called a **polymer**.

Two processes lead to formation of a polymer.

- **Addition polymerisation** – monomers react together forming the polymer **only**. There are no by-products.
- **Condensation polymerisation** – monomers react together forming the polymer **and** a simple compound, usually water.

Addition polymerisation

AQA	M4	SALTERS	M4
EDEXCEL	M5	WJEC	M5
OCR	M4	CCEA	M5

In addition polymerisation:

- the monomer is an **unsaturated** molecule with a double C=C bond
- the double bond is **lost** as the **saturated** polymer forms.

Many different addition polymers can be formed using different monomer units based upon alkenes.

Key points from AS

- **Addition polymerisation of alkenes**
  Revise AS pages 132–133

Make sure that you can show a repeat unit of a polymer from the monomer (and a monomer from a repeat unit).

Poly(propenamide) and poly(ethenol) are highly water-absorbent polymers because of the ability of the polar –OH and –CONH$_2$ groups to hydrogen bond with water.

phenylethene → poly(phenylethene) *polystyrene* — packaging as expanded foam

ethenol → poly(ethenol) — soluble laundry bags and liquid detergent capsules

propenamide → poly(propenamide) — water treatment to remove suspended matter, soft contact lenses

Properties of monomers and addition polymers

The monomers are volatile liquids or gases. Polymers are solids.
This difference can be explained in terms of van der Waals' forces.

- The van der Waals' forces acting between the large polymer molecules are much stronger than those acting between the much smaller monomer molecules.

Addition polymers of hydrocarbon monomers and of halogenated monomers are very stable and inert, e.g. poly(ethene), poly(propene) and poly(phenylethene) (polystyrene), poly(chloroethene) (PVC) and poly(tetrafluoroethene) (PTFE). These polymers are insoluble in solvents and are non-biodegradable.

Low density poly(ethene) (LDPE) and high density poly(ethene) (HDPE) (CCEA only)

Production

	LD poly(ethene)	HD poly(ethene)
Temperature	150–300 °C	40–90 °C
Pressure	(High) 1000–3000 atm	(Low) 1–50 atm
Catalyst/Initiator	O_2 initiator (>0.1%)	Ziegler-Natta catalysts
Branching	branched chains	straight chains
Crystallinity	50 – 75%	95%

- LDPE is relatively soft and flexible. It is used for plastic bags and flexible sheeting.
- HDPE is relatively hard and rigid. It is used to make bottles, washing up bowls and plastic pipes.

Branching, crystallinity and properties (Salters and CCEA only)

The flexibility and softening of polymers such as LDPE and HDPE depend upon temperature, branching and crystallinity.

Crystallinity

HDPE is more crystalline than LDPE.

The polymer chains in HDPE can align with one another more easily.

Crystallinity is the regular packing of the chains, due to the regular structure of the polymer. The lower the temperature, the more effective the intermolecular bonds.
- A polymer softens and loses its crystallinity above its 'crystalline melting temperature', T_m
- A polymer becomes brittle below its glass transition temperature, T_g.

Chain length and branching

HDPE has non-branched chains.
LDPE has branched chains.
HDPE has stronger intermolecular forces and has more strength than LDPE.

LDPE is flexible.
HDPE is rigid.

- As chain length increases, there are more intermolecular bonds, leading to greater strength.
- With branched chains, the polymer chains cannot get as close together as in non-branched chains and intermolecular bonds will be weaker.
- Flexibility depends on the ability of the polymer chains to slide over each other and this is more evident in polymers with branched chains.

Modifying properties

The properties of all materials depend on their structure and bonding.

Chemists can modify the properties of a polymer to meet particular needs by:
- cold-drawing, to make the structure more crystalline
- copolymerisation – producing mixed polymers by using more than one monomer
- use of plasticisers, which change T_g and increase flexibility.

Condensation polymerisation

In condensation polymerisation, the formation of a bond between monomer units also produces a small molecule such as H_2O or HCl.

Condensation polymers can be divided into natural polymers and man-made (synthetic) polymers.

- Natural polymers in living organisms include proteins, cellulose, rayon and DNA.
- Man-made polymers include synthetic fibres such as polyamides (e.g. *nylon*) and polyesters (e.g. *terylene*).

Polyamides

> Nylon, proteins and polypeptides are all polyamides.

Proteins and polypeptides are natural condensation polymers. The link between the amino acid monomer units is usually described as a **peptide link** but chemically this is identical to an **amide** group. Hence polypeptides and proteins are **natural polyamides**.

Nylon-6,6 was the first man-made condensation polymer and was synthesised as an artificial alternative to natural protein fibres such as wool and silk.

> Compare the use of two monomers in the production of synthetic nylon-6,6 with the natural condensation polymerisation using amino acids only.

The principle used was to mimic the natural polymerisation process above but, instead of using an amino acid monomer with two different functional groups, **two chemically different monomers are usually used**:

- a dicarboxylic acid **A** $HO-\overset{O}{\overset{\|}{C}}-\square-\overset{O}{\overset{\|}{C}}-OH$ $\square$ } carbon chain or
- a diamine **B** $H_2N-\bigcirc-NH_2$ $\bigcirc$ } ring structure

Each diamine molecule bonds to a dicarboxylic acid molecule with loss of water molecule.

> Many different polyamides can be made using different carbon chains or rings which bridge the double functional group.

- the two monomers **A** and **B** join alternately: –A–B–A–B–A–B–A–B–

$$-\overset{O}{\overset{\|}{C}}-\square-\overset{O}{\overset{\|}{C}}-\underset{H}{N}-\bigcirc-\underset{H}{N}-\overset{O}{\overset{\|}{C}}-\square-\overset{O}{\overset{\|}{C}}-\underset{H}{N}-\bigcirc-\underset{H}{N}-$$

Polyamides can also be made using a diacyl chloride instead of a dicarboxylic acid.

- The greater reactivity of an acyl chloride results in easier polymerisation.
- Hydrogen chloride is lost instead of water.

Formation of nylon-6,6 from its monomers

> Nylon-6,6 gets its name from the number of carbon atoms in each monomer (diamine first).
> The diamine has 6 carbon atoms.
> The dicarboxylic acid has 6 carbon atoms.
> Hence: nylon-6,6.

hexane-1,6-dioic acid

$$\underset{HO}{\overset{O}{\diagdown}}C-(CH_2)_4-C\underset{OH}{\overset{O}{\diagup}}$$

1,6-diaminohexane

$$H_2N-(CH_2)_6-NH_2$$

> The diacyl chloride for preparing nylon-6,6 would be ClOC(CH$_2$)$_4$COCl.

n molecules of a **dicarboxylic acid**   *n* molecules of a **diamine**

$$HO-\overset{O}{\overset{\|}{C}}-(CH_2)_4-\overset{O}{\overset{\|}{C}}-\boxed{OH \quad H}-\underset{H}{N}-(CH_2)_6-\underset{H}{N}-H$$

polymerisation

amide link

$$\left[\overset{O}{\overset{\|}{C}}-(CH_2)_4-\overset{O}{\overset{\|}{C}}-\underset{H}{N}-(CH_2)_6-\underset{H}{N}\right]_n + n\,H_2O$$

repeat unit

nylon-6,6

One water molecule forms for each amide bond formed

Formation of Kevlar from its monomers

Polyesters

Polyesters are polymers made by a condensation reaction between monomers with formation of an ester group as the linkage between the molecules.

The first man-made polyester produced was *Terylene*. As with polyamides, polyesters are used as fibres for clothing.

As with artificial polyamides, man-made polyesters are usually made from **two** different monomers:

- a dicarboxylic acid
- a diol

Each diol molecule bonds to a dicarboxylic acid molecule with loss of a water molecule.

Many different polyesters can be made by using different carbon chains or rings bridging the double functional group.

Formation of Terylene from its monomers

Disposal of polymers

Solid domestic and industrial waste contains a high percentage of polymers.

Disposal requires waste management strategies such as:

- incineration – to reduce waste bulk and to generate energy
- recycling – to preserve natural oil-produced finite resources produced from oil.

Problems with addition polymers (polyalkenes)

Addition polymers are non-polar and chemically inert.
This creates potential environmental problems during disposal of polymers.
Disposal by landfill causes long-term problems.

- Addition polymers are non-biodegradable and take many years to break down.

Disposal by burning can produce toxic fumes.

- Depolymerisation produces poisonous monomers.
- Disposal of poly(chloroethene) (*pvc*) by incineration can lead to the formation of very toxic dioxins if the temperature is too low.

Condensation polymers

Condensation polymers are polar.

- Condensation polymers are broken down naturally by acid and alkaline hydrolysis into their monomer units. They are therefore biodegradable and easier to dispose of than addition polymers.

- They may be photodegradable as the C=O bond absorbs radiation.

Chemists are minimising environmental waste by developing degradable polymers, similar in structure to poly(lactic acid).

lactic acid   repeat unit   poly(lactic acid)

Poly(lactic acid) is used for waste sacks, packaging, disposable eating utensils and medical applications such as internal dissolvable stitches.

'Green polymers' (Salters only)

The principles of green chemistry are important in the manufacture, use, recycling and eventual disposal of polymers. They involve:

- minimising any hazardous waste during the production of raw materials and their resulting polymers to reduce any negative impact on the environment
- reducing carbon emissions resulting from the 'life cycle' of a polymer
- recycling to produce energy and chemical feedstocks.

Progress check

1 (a) Draw the structure of the monomer needed to make poly(tetrafluoroethene).
(b) Draw the repeat unit of the polymer perspex, made from the monomer methyl 2-methylpropenoate, shown below.

2 (a) Show the structures of the two monomers needed to make nylon-4,6.
(b) Draw a short section of nylon 4,6 and show its repeat unit.

3 Draw the structures of the two monomers needed to make the polyester shown below.

3 HO—◯—OH   HOOC—◯—COOH

2 (a) $H_2N-(CH_2)_4-NH_2$ and $HOOC-(CH_2)_4-COOH$

(b) repeat unit of nylon-4,6

1 (a) F₂C=CF₂ monomer   (b) perspex repeat unit

Proteins and polypeptides

AQA	M4	SALTERS	M4
EDEXCEL	M5	WJEC	M4
OCR	M4	CCEA	M5

Proteins and polypeptides

A protein is a chain of many amino acids linked together with 'peptide bonds' formed by **condensation polymerisation**.

Each amino acid molecule has both **amino** and **carboxyl** groups.
A **peptide** bond forms, with loss of a water molecule, between:

- the **amino** group of one amino acid molecule and
- the **carboxyl** group of another amino acid molecule.

The diagram below shows how amino acid molecules are linked together during condensation polymerisation.

Although a 'repeat unit' is shown on the diagram, the R group may be different in each unit. There are over 20 different amino acids, each having a different R group.

- Most common proteins contain more than 100 amino acids.
- Each protein has a unique sequence of amino acids and a complex three-dimensional shape, held together by intermolecular bonds including hydrogen bonds.

Primary structure (Salters and CCEA only)

The **primary** structure of a protein is the actual **sequence** of **amino acids** joined by **peptide** links.

e.g.   ....ala–gly–lys–cys–asn–arg–gly–leu–try–val–............

- There are countless possible sequences, with over 20 different amino acids and sequences of 50–2000 amino acids in different proteins. Each amino acid has its own shorthand code (e.g. ala). You do not need to know these.
- The amino acid sequence determines the properties of proteins and accounts for the diversity of proteins in living things. But each protein has its own unique primary structure.

> Just think of how many 100 letter words you could make out of 20 letters of the alphabet!

> For CCEA, you should know the R– groups in 2 amino acids:
> glycine (gly): R = H
> alanine (ala): R = CH₃
> All other R– groups would be provided.

Secondary structure (Salters and CCEA only)

The **secondary** structure of a protein is a region in which there are regular structures.

There are two types, an α-**helix** and a β-**sheet**, each held together by **hydrogen bonds** between C=O and N–H:

$$C{=}O \cdots H{-}N$$

α-**helix**   β-**sheet**

Tertiary structure (Salters and CCEA only)

The **tertiary** structure of a protein is the **three-dimensional** shape. The tertiary structure will contain regions of secondary structures and will always have the sequence of amino acids in the primary structure.

The tertiary structure is held together by intermolecular bonds that act between R– groups of different amino acids.

Possible R– group interactions are:

- **hydrogen bonding** – between polar side chains such as CH_2OH and CH_2CONH_2
- **covalent bonding** caused by SH groups forming $-S-S-$ linkages
- **ionic attractions** – between ions on side chains such as $-CH_2COO^-$ and NH_3^+
- **instantaneous dipole–induced dipole attractive forces** (van der Waals' forces) – between non-polar hydrocarbon chains.

> The tertiary structure determines the properties of proteins.

Enzyme catalysis

Specificity (Salters and CCEA only)

An **enzyme** is:

- a **biological catalyst**
- a protein with a definite **three-dimensional** tertiary structure.

An enzyme is **specific** about the reactions that can be catalysed. Within the tertiary structure, there is an **active site**.

The substrate has to have the correct shape but the intermolecular bonds must also fit. Otherwise there will be nothing to hold the substrate to the active site.

- The active site has a definite shape that will only accept a molecule if it is the correct shape – the 'Lock and Key' analogy.
- The molecule that fits the active site is called the substrate.
- The substrate bonds to the active site by intermolecular bonds.

By bonding to the active site, a reaction is able to take place with a pathway of lower activation energy.

The effect of pH on enzyme activity (Salters and CCEA only)

Enzymes work at a particular optimum pH. Changes in pH will affect the ability of the substrate to bond by intermolecular bonds to the active site.

Extremes of pH will interfere with the intermolecular bonds within the tertiary structure. This can change the shape of the active site so that the substrate no longer fits.

The effect of temperature on enzyme activity (Salters and CCEA only)

Higher temperatures increase the rate of enzyme-catalysed reactions at the active site. However, if the temperature is too high,

- the intermolecular bonds within the tertiary structure may start to break,
- the shape of the active site is changed and the substrate no longer fits.

This change is irreversible and the enzyme will no longer function – it is denatured.

Inhibition (Salters only)

If you study Biology, you may have also come across non-competitive inhibition in which an inhibitor binds to another site on the enzyme, changing the shape of the active site.

An inhibitor is a molecule with a similar shape and with a similar arrangement of binding sites as the substrate.

- The inhibitor competes with the substrate for the active site and may block the site for access to a substrate molecule.
- The process is reversible as the inhibitor will also leave the active site.
- The rate of the enzyme-catalysed reaction slows down.

This is known as competitive inhibition.

Rates of enzyme-catalysed reactions (Salters only)

The graph below shows how the rate of an enzyme-catalysed reaction changes with increasing substrate concentration.

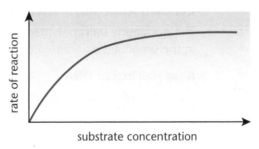

At low substrate concentrations:

See page 21 for shapes of rate/concentration graphs for different orders of reaction.

- the rate of reaction is proportional to the substrate concentration – the order with respect to substrate molecules is one
- active sites are available for any increase in substrate molecules.

As substrate concentration increases:

- there is progressively less effect until the rate levels off.
- the active sites become progressively occupied
- eventually all active sites are occupied and increasing the substrate concentration makes no difference to the rate – the order with respect to substrate molecules is zero.

Nucleic acids: DNA and RNA

SALTERS   M4

DNA is a condensation polymer formed from monomer units called **nucleotides**, having three components: **phosphate**, **sugar** and **base**.
- The sugar is deoxribose in **DNA** (deoxyribonucleic acid).
- The sugar is ribose in **RNA** (ribonucleic acid).

Phosphate and sugars

> Various models for DNA were devised before the currently accepted version was formulated.

phosphate   ribose   deoxyribose

Bases

> DNA has thymine.
> RNA has uracil.
> The other three bases are the same in DNA and RNA.

Each **nucleotide** can have one of **four** possible bases:
- DNA has: adenine;   **thymine**;   cytosine;   guanine.
- RNA has: adenine;   **uracil**;   cytosine;   guanine.

uracil   cytosine   adenine   guanine

(thymine has a –CH₃ at position *)

The nucleotides

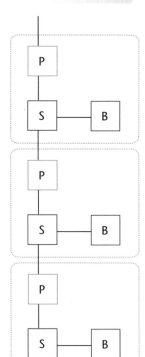

Simplified section of a DNA strand
- P = phosphate
- S = sugar
- B = base

Each nucleotide has this sequence: phosphate–deoxyribose–base.
The phosphate unit and base are joined by condensation with deoxyribose, as shown below.

phosphate   base (cytosine)

condensation

deoxyribose

Condensation polymerisation of nucleotides

The nucleotide units polymerise through the sugar–phosphate backbone as shown in the simplified diagram in the margin.

Base pairing in DNA

Two separate **strands** are linked together in the **double helix** structure of DNA. In DNA,
- Adenine and Thymine pair up with **two** hydrogen bonds.
- Cytosine and Guanine pair up with **three** hydrogen bonds.

The geometry of each base ensures that the correct bases pair up.

> DNA analysis can be used for genetic fingerprinting. There are discussions about developing a national DNA database of every person in the UK but this carries with it ethical issues and concern about storage of personal information.

• A and T 2 H bonds	• C and G 3 H bonds
Adenine Thymine	Guanine Cytosine

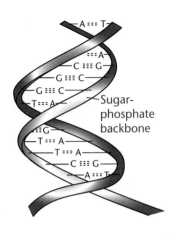

Sugar-phosphate backbone

Each strand of DNA contains a sequence of bases in a definite order. The **complimentary strand** must contain only the correct sequence of the complimentary bases (see the margin diagram).

DNA can **replicate** by first 'unzipping' each strand:

• Each separate strand attracts nucleotides.
• By base pairing, the nucleotides are attached in the correct order.
• The result is **two** double helices of DNA, made from one original double helix.
• Each new double helix is identical to the original.

Every person's DNA is unique but sections of DNA are identifiable as **genes**. Some genes are inherited and are handed down through generations. These genes give family characteristics. There are also other genes that are common to every person's DNA and these carry the necessary information for the body to create proteins.

DNA and proteins

DNA encodes for an amino acid sequence in a protein by using a base sequence within a '**protein gene**' section of DNA.

The DNA double helix can make a strand of RNA by base pairing.

RNA has some important differences:

• A strand contains four bases but with the base **uracil** instead of **thymine**.
• **Ribose** is the sugar instead of deoxyribose.
• The strand is formed from just a section of the DNA double helix; it is much shorter than a DNA strand.
• RNA exists as a single strand.

The protein code

The strand of RNA formed is called **messenger RNA, m-RNA**.

• The sequence of bases in m-RNA contains **triplet codes**, each with **three** bases.
• Each amino acid can bond to another type of RNA strand called **transfer RNA, t-RNA** within the ribosome region of a cell.
• Each **amino acid** has its own **special t-RNA** with a special sequence of bases that have triplet codes – these are **complimentary** to the code in m-RNA.
• The m-RNA strand **attracts t-RNA** molecules in sequence, each carrying an amino acid. The triplet codes ensure that the correct t-RNA molecule is attached.

The diagram below shows a section of the m-RNA strand with 12 bases: **four triplet codes**.

Diagram to illustrate protein synthesis

The amino acids join together in the correct sequence for a protein. As soon as two amino acid molecules join by a peptide link, the t-RNA molecule leaves to collect another amino acid molecule.

In the left-hand side of the diagram above, the t-RNA molecule that codes for Leu (leucine) is leaving. Note the correct base pairing within each matching of triplets.

Ala (alanine) is the next amino acid that needs to be added and you can see this on the right-hand side of the 'conveyor belt'.

5.3 Chromatography

After studying this section you should be able to:

- *understand what is meant by chromatography*
- *know that components are separated by absorption and partition*
- *understand what is meant by R_f value and retention time*
- *know that chromatography can be combined with mass spectrometry*

LEARNING SUMMARY

Types of chromatography

Chromatography is an analytical technique that separates components in a mixture between a **mobile phase** and a **stationary phase**. The technique is especially useful for the purification of an organic substance.

- The **mobile phase** moves in a definite direction and may be a liquid (as in thin-layer chromatography, TLC) or a gas (as in gas chromatography, GC).
- The **stationary phase** is the substance that is fixed in place during the chromatography. It may be a solid (as in TLC) or either a liquid or solid on a solid support (as in GC).
- A solid stationary phase separates by **adsorption** of the components in the mixture on the surface.
- A liquid stationary phase separates by **partition** between the liquid and the mobile phase.

Thin-layer and paper chromatography

Thin-layer chromatography (TLC) uses a stationary phase in the form of a thin layer of an adsorbent such as silica gel or alumina on a flat, inert support.

Paper chromatography and TLC use a similar technique.

- A small dot of sample solution is placed on the TLC plate or paper.
- The paper or plate is placed in a jar containing a shallow layer of solvent and sealed.
- As the solvent rises, it meets the sample of the mixture. Different compounds in the mixture travel different distances depending on how strongly they interact with the paper and their solubility in the solvent.

This allows the calculation of a **Retardation factor**, R_f for each component (see below).

$$R_f = \frac{\text{distance moved by component}}{\text{distance moved by solvent front}}$$

KEY POINT

The R_f value can be compared to standard compounds to aid in the identification of an unknown substance. The diagram below shows some R_f values.

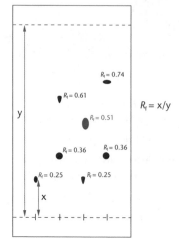

$R_f = x/y$

Using TLC, the separated components can be located as spots using iodine or ultraviolet radiation. Components can be identified by comparing the R_f values with known compounds.

The amino acids in a mixture can be separated and identified by paper chromatography and located using ninhydrin.

Two-way chromatography (CCEA only)

Sometimes more than one component in a mixture may have the same R_f value in a particular solvent. The chromatogram can be run a second time, at right-angles using a second solvent. This can result in separation of the components with the same R_f value in the first solvent. This is called **two-way chromatography**.

This is a useful technique for separating the components in complex mixtures of similar compounds, such as amino acids. The diagram below shows the result of carrying out two-way chromatography on a mixture of amino acids.

For amino acids, the spots are usually developed as purple spots using ninhydrin.

You can see which amino acids have been separated by each solvent by comparing the R_f values vertically and horizontally.

In this chromatogram:

- some amino acids have been separated by butan-1-ol/ethanoic acid and some by aqueous phenol
- 15 out of 17 amino acids have been separated, with only isoleucine and leucine unseparated.

Liquid chromatography

AQA   M4
EDEXCEL   M5
WJEC   M4

Liquid chromatography uses a stationary phase within a column. The liquid mobile phase is passed through the column and components are separated depending on their solubility in the mobile phase and retention in the stationary phase. Liquid chromatography can be run under pressure using very small packing particles. This is referred to as **high pressure liquid chromatography (HPLC)**.

Gas Chromatography GC

AQA   M4   SALTERS   M5
EDEXCEL   M4   WJEC   M4
OCR   M4   CCEA   M5

Gas chromatography (GC) or Gas-Liquid chromatography (GLC) is a separation technique in which the mobile phase is a gas. Gas chromatography is always carried out in a column. The column contains the stationary phase, which is either a high-boiling liquid or a solid on a solid, porous support.

- The sample is injected into the column, which is heated to vaporise the components in the mixture.
- The gas mobile phase flushes the mixture along the column.
- As the mixture moves through the column, components are slowed down as they interact with the stationary phase. Different components are slowed down by different amounts, which causes them to separate.
- Each component leaves the column at a different time.

This allows the calculation of the retention time for each component.

Retention time is the time it takes for a component to pass from the column inlet to the detector.

The retention time can be compared to standard compounds to aid in the identification of an unknown substance. The peak area also gives the approximate percentage composition of a mixture. The diagram below shows a GC chromatogram with some retention times.

Limitations

Analysis by gas chromatography has limitations:

- Similar compounds often have similar retention times.
- Unknown compounds have no reference retention times for comparison.

OCR	M4
SALTERS	M5
CCEA	M5

Combining mass spectrometry with chromatography

Mass spectrometry can be combined with chromatography to provide a far more powerful analytical tool than chromatography alone. For example, mass spectrometry is used with GC as GC-MS and with high pressure liquid chromatography as HPLC-MS.

In GC-MS:

- the components in a mixture are first separated using GC
- the separated components are directed into the mass spectrometer
- the generated mass spectra can be analysed or compared with a spectral database by computer for positive identification of each component.

GC-MS is extensively used in modern analysis, e.g. in forensics, environmental analysis and airport security.

Progress check

1 What is meant by the following terms?
(a) R_f value
(b) retention time

2 How does GC-MS enable components in a mixture to be identified?

2 GC separates the components. Each component then passes into a mass spectrometer. The resulting mass spectrum is analysed against a spectral database to identify the component.

(b) The time it takes for a component to pass from the column inlet to the detector.

1 (a) $R_f = \dfrac{\text{distance moved by component}}{\text{distance moved by solvent front}}$

5.4 Analysis

> **After studying this section you should be able to:**
> - *review from AS Chemistry the use of infra-red spectroscopy and mass spectrometry in organic analysis*

Infra-red spectroscopy and mass spectrometry in organic analysis

AQA	M4	SALTERS	M4, M5
EDEXCEL	M4, M5	WJEC	M4
OCR	M4		

Key points from AS

- **Analysis**
  Revise AS pages 143–146

In AS Chemistry, you were introduced to the use of two important instrumentation techniques in organic analysis:

- Infra-red spectroscopy.
- Mass spectrometry.

For A2 chemistry, you study a further important instrumentation technique called nuclear magnetic resonance, NMR. Analytical chemists often combine the best features of each spectral technique to identify an unknown compound. This section starts with a review of the key features of IR and MS. For full details, you will need to refer to *Revise AS Chemistry*, Chapter 4.7.

Using infra-red (IR) spectroscopy in organic analysis

IR spectroscopy is useful for identifying the functional groups in a molecule.

An infra-red spectrum is particularly useful for identifying:

> IR spectroscopy is most useful for identifying C=O and O–H bonds.
> Look for the distinctive patterns.

- an alcohol from absorption of the O–H bond (3230–3550 cm^{-1})
- a carbonyl compound from absorption of the C=O bond (1680–1750 cm^{-1})
- a carboxylic acid from absorption of the C=O bond (1680–1750 cm^{-1}) and broad absorption of the O–H bond (2500–3300 cm^{-1} (broad)).

Fingerprint region

- Between 1000 and 1550 cm^{-1}

> The fingerprint region is unique for a particular compound.

Many spectra show a complex pattern of absorption in this range.

- This pattern can allow the compound to be identified by comparing with spectra of known compounds.

Using mass spectrometry in organic analysis

Mass spectrometry of organic compounds is useful for identifying:

- the relative molecular mass from the molecular ion peak, *M*
- parts of the skeletal formula by the fragmentation pattern.

The fragmentation pattern provides clues about the molecular structure of the compound. The table below shows the identity of the main peaks in the mass spectrum of butanone, $CH_3COCH_2CH_3$.

> Note that only ions are detected in the mass spectrum.
> Uncharged species such as the radical cannot be deflected within the mass spectrometer.

m/z	ion	fragment lost
72	$CH_3COCH_2CH_3^+$	–
57	$CH_3CH_2CO^+$	$CH_3\bullet$
43	CH_3CO^+	$CH_3CH_2\bullet$
29	$CH_3CH_2^+$	$CH_3CO\bullet$
15	CH_3^+	$CH_3CH_2CO\bullet$

> The skill in interpreting a mass spectrum is in searching for known patterns, evaluating all the evidence and reassembling all the information into a molecular structure.

5.5 NMR spectroscopy

After studying this section you should be able to:

* *understand that NMR spectroscopy is carried out with ^1H and ^{13}C*
* *predict the different types of proton and carbon present in a molecule from chemical shift values*
* *predict the relative numbers of each type of proton present from an integration trace*
* *predict the number of protons adjacent to a given proton from the spin-spin coupling pattern*
* *predict possible structures for a molecule from ^1H and ^{13}C spectra*
* *predict the chemical shifts and splitting patterns of the protons in a given molecule*
* *describe the use of D_2O in NMR spectroscopy*

LEARNING SUMMARY

Nuclear magnetic resonance

AQA	M4	SALTERS	M5
EDEXCEL	M4, M5	WJEC	M4
OCR	M4	CCEA	M5

Nuclear Magnetic Resonance (NMR) spectroscopy is an extremely important modern method of analysis. It is used extensively in the pharmaceutical industry and in universities for identification and purity checking of organic compounds.

Key principles

The nucleus of an atom of hydrogen (i.e. a proton) has a magnetic spin.
When placed in a strong electromagnetic field:

> Only nuclei with an odd number of nucleons (neutrons + protons) possess a magnetic spin: e.g. ^1H, ^{13}C. Proton NMR spectroscopy is the most useful general purpose technique.

* the nucleus can absorb energy from the low energy **radio-frequency** region of the spectrum to move to a higher energy state
* **nuclear magnetic resonance** occurs as protons resonate between their spin energy states.

The different nuclear spin states in an applied magnetic field

> The energy gap is equal to that provided by radio waves.

An NMR spectrum shows **absorption peaks** corresponding to the radio-frequency absorbed.

Chemical shift, δ

Electrons around the nucleus **shield** the nucleus from the applied field.

* The magnetic field at the nucleus of a particular proton is different from the applied magnetic field.

> NMR spectroscopy is the same technology as used in MRI (magnetic resonance imaging) in medical body scanners. It is a non-invasive technique.

* Different radio-frequencies are absorbed, depending on the **environment** of the proton.

> Protons in different environments absorb at different chemical shifts.

* **Chemical shift** is a measure of the magnetic field experienced by protons in different environments resulting from nuclear shielding.

KEY POINT

> Chemical shift, δ, is measured relative to a standard: tetramethylsilane (TMS), Si(CH$_3$)$_4$.
> • The chemical shift of TMS is defined as δ = 0 ppm.

Carbon-13 NMR spectroscopy

AQA — M4
OCR — M4

Carbon-13 NMR spectroscopy allows the identification of carbon atoms in an organic molecule and is an important tool in the determination of structure in organic chemistry.

Typical chemical shifts

Chemical shifts indicate the chemical environment of the **carbon atoms** present. The table below shows typical chemical shift values for different types of carbon atom.

type of carbon		chemical shift, δ/ppm
C–C		5–55
C–Cl or C–Br		30–70
C–N (amines)		35–60
C–O		50–70
C=C (alkenes)		115–140
aromatic		110–165
carbonyl (ester, carboxylic acid, amide)		160–185
carbonyl (aldehyde, ketone)		190–220

> You don't need to learn these chemical shifts - the data is provided on exam papers.

> The presence of an electronegative atom or group causes chemical shift 'downfield'. This is called 'deshielding'.
> Notice the chemical shift caused by the carbonyl group, oxygen, halogens and a benzene ring.

• The actual chemical shift may be slightly different depending upon the actual environment of the carbon.

In a carbon–13 NMR spectrum, the size of the peak tells us nothing about the number of carbon atoms responsible. This is in contrast to proton NMR spectroscopy. However, carbon-13 spectrum is far more sensitive with a much larger range of chemical shift values. Unless there are carbon atoms present in an identical environment, each carbon atom is likely to show as a separate single signal.

Interpreting a carbon-13 NMR spectrum

A carbon-13 NMR spectrum of ethyl ethanoate, CH$_3$COOCH$_2$CH$_3$ shows absorptions at **four** chemical shifts showing carbon atoms in **four different environments**:

- The four chemical shifts can be matched to the table of chemical shifts on page 167 so that the carbon atom responsible for each absorption can be identified.

chemical shift/ppm	environment
171	
60	
21	
14	

> Carbon-13 NMR spectroscopy is useful for identifying the **type** of environment of each carbon – the chemical shift.
>
> KEY POINT

Progress check

1 For each structure, predict the chemical shift of each carbon atom.
   (a) CH_3CH_2OH; (b) CH_3CH_2CHO; (c) CH_3COCH_3.

Proton NMR spectroscopy

AQA	M4	SALTERS	M5
EDEXCEL	M5	WJEC	M4
OCR	M4	CCEA	M5

Proton NMR spectroscopy allows the identification of hydrogen atoms in an organic molecule and is an important tool in the determination of structure in organic chemistry.

Typical chemical shifts

Chemical shifts indicate the **types of protons** and **functional groups** present. The table below shows typical chemical shift values for protons in different chemical environments.

> The presence of an electronegative atom or group causes chemical shift 'downfield'. This is called 'deshielding'.
>
> Notice the chemical shift caused by the carbonyl group, oxygen, halogens and a benzene ring.

> You don't need to learn these chemical shifts – the data is provided on exam papers.

type of proton	chemical shift, δ/ppm
$R\text{-}CH_3$	0.7–1.6
$R\text{-}CH_2\text{-}R$	1.2–1.4
$H_3C-C\overset{O}{\diagdown}$ $R-CH_2-C\overset{O}{\diagdown}$	2.0–2.9
⬡$-CH_3$ ⬡$-CH_2-R$	2.3–2.7
$X\text{–}CH_3$ $X\text{–}CH_2\text{–}R$ (X = halogen)	3.2–3.7
$-O\text{–}CH_3$ $-O\text{–}CH_2\text{–}R$	3.3–4.3
$R\text{–}O\text{–}H$	3.5–5.5
⬡$-H$	7
$H_3C-C\overset{O}{\underset{H}{\diagdown}}$	9.5–10
$H_3C-C\overset{O}{\underset{OH}{\diagdown}}$	11.0–11.7

> The only reliable means of identifying O–H in NMR is to use D_2O: see Identifying O–H protons, page 171.

- The actual chemical shift may be slightly different depending upon the actual environment of the proton.
- The chemical shift for O–**H** can vary considerably and depends upon concentration, solvent and other factors.

Interpreting low resolution NMR spectra

AQA	M4	SALTERS	M5
EDEXCEL	M4, M5	WJEC	M4
OCR	M4	CCEA	M5

Low resolution NMR spectrum of ethanol

A low resolution NMR spectrum of ethanol shows absorptions at **three** chemical shifts, showing the **three different types of proton:**

> The relative areas of each peak are usually measured by running a second NMR spectrum as an *integration trace*.

> An NMR spectrum is obtained in solution. The solvent must be proton-free, usually CCl_4 or $CDCl_3$ is used.

169

- The **area** under each peak is in direct proportion to the **number of protons** responsible for the absorption.
- The three chemical shifts can be matched to the table of chemical shifts on page 169 so that the protons responsible for each absorption can be identified.

chemical shift/ppm	no. of protons	environment	type of proton
$\delta = 1.0$	3H	CH_3CH_2OH	CH_3 adjacent to a carbon chain
$\delta = 3.5$	2H	CH_3CH_2OH	CH_2 adjacent to –O
$\delta = 4.9$	1H	CH_3CH_2OH	OH

> **KEY POINT**
>
> A low resolution NMR spectrum is useful for identifying:
> - the **number** of different types of proton from the number of peaks
> - the **type** of environment of each proton from the chemical shift
> - **how many** protons of each type from the integration trace.

Interpreting high resolution NMR spectra

AQA	M4	WJEC	M4
OCR	M4	CCEA	M5
EDEXCEL	M4, M5	SALTERS	M5

Different types of proton have different chemical shifts.

A high resolution NMR spectrum shows splitting of peaks into a pattern of sub-peaks.

Spin-spin coupling patterns:
- arise from interactions between protons on **adjacent** carbon atoms which have **different chemical shifts**
- indicate the number of **adjacent** protons.

Equivalent protons (i.e. protons with the same chemical shift) will **not** couple with one another.

The **spin-spin coupling** pattern shows as a **multiplet** – a doublet, triplet, quartet, etc.

A singlet is next to C.
A doublet is next to CH.
A triplet is next to CH_2.
A quadruplet is next to CH_3.

> **KEY POINT**
>
> We can interpret the spin-spin coupling pattern using the **n+1 rule**.
> For **n adjacent protons**, the number of peaks in a multiplet = **n+1**.

The high resolution NMR spectrum of ethanol

The high resolution NMR spectrum of ethanol shows spin-spin coupling patterns – some of the signals have been split into multiplets:

The multiplicity (doublet, triplet, quartet) does not indicate the number of protons on that carbon. The number of protons is given by the integration trace.

Notice the different sizes of each sub-peak within the splitting pattern:
- doublet 1:1
- triplet 1:2:1
- quartet 1:3:3:1.

- The **chemical shift** identifies the **type of protons** responsible for each peak.
- The n+1 rule can be used to identify the **number of adjacent protons**.

chemical shift /ppm	environment	number of adjacent protons (n)	splitting pattern (n+1)
$\delta = 1.2$	**CH$_3$**CH$_2$OH	2H	2+1 = 3: triplet
$\delta = 3.6$	CH$_3$**CH$_2$**OH	3H	3+1 = 4: quartet
$\delta = 4.5$	CH$_3$CH$_2$O**H**	–	singlet

- Note that O–**H** splitting is not normally seen owing to H-bonding or exchange with the solvent used.

Equivalent protons do not interact with each other.

- The three equivalent CH$_3$ protons in ethanol cause splitting of the adjacent CH$_2$ protons, but not amongst themselves.

> **KEY POINT**
>
> A high resolution NMR spectrum is useful for identifying the **number** of **adjacent** protons from the spin-spin coupling pattern.

Identifying O–H protons

The OH absorption peak at 4.5 δ is absent in D$_2$O.

O–H protons can absorb at different chemical shifts depending on the solvent used and the concentration. The signals are often broad and usually show no splitting pattern.

These factors can make it difficult to identify O–H protons. However, they can be identified by using deuterium oxide, D$_2$O.

- A second NMR spectrum is run with a small quantity of D$_2$O added to the solvent.
- The D$_2$O exchanges with O–H protons and any such peak will disappear.

Solvents

Deuterated solvents such as CDCl$_3$ are used in NMR spectroscopy. Any protons in a solvent such as CHCl$_3$ would produce a large proton absorption peak. By using CDCl$_3$, this absorption is absent and the spectrum is that of the organic compound alone.

Progress check

1 For each structure, predict the number of peaks in its low resolution NMR spectrum corresponding to the different types of proton and also the number of each different type of proton
(e.g. CH$_3$CH$_2$OH has 3 peaks in the ratio 3:2:1).
(a) CH$_3$OH (b) CH$_3$CH$_2$CHO (c) CH$_3$COCH$_3$ (d) (CH$_3$)$_2$CHOH.

2 The NMR spectrum of compound **X** (C$_2$H$_4$O) has a doublet at δ 2.1 and a quartet at δ 9.8.
(a) Identify compound **X**. (Use the table of chemical shifts on page 169).
(b) How many protons are responsible for each multiplet?

1 (a) 2 peaks in the ratio 3:1 (b) 3 peaks in the ratio 3:2:1 (c) 1 peak
(d) 3 peaks in the ratio 6:1:1
2 (a) ethanal, CH$_3$CHO.
(b) doublet at δ 2.1, 3H; quartet at δ 9.8, 1H.

5.6 Organic synthetic routes

There are many variations possible and the schemes below could not include all reactions without appearing more complicated.

Organic chemists are frequently required to synthesise an organic compound in a multistage process. This is fundamental to the design of new organic compounds such as those needed for modern drugs to combat disease, a new dye or a new fibre. With so many reactions to consider, it is essential to see how different functional groups can be interconverted and summary charts are useful for showing these links. The flow-charts on the next pages show reactions drawn from both the AS and A2 parts of A Level Chemistry.

Construct a scheme of your own using only those reactions in your course.

In revision it is useful to draw your own schemes from memory.

Aliphatic synthetic routes

AQA	M4	SALTERS	M4, M5
EDEXCEL	M5	WJEC	M4
OCR	M4	CCEA	M4, M5

The scheme below is based upon two main sets of reactions:
- a set based around bromoalkanes
- a set based around carboxylic acids and their derivatives.

The two sets of reactions are linked via the oxidation of primary alcohols.
- A reaction scheme based upon a secondary alcohol would result in oxidation to a ketone only.

Radiation is usually linked with analysis but it is also used in some synthetic methods.

Microwaves are used for heating organic reagents in organic research. As with cooking, a reaction can take place in a fraction of the time using less vigorous conditions.

Ultraviolet radiation is used to initiate some reactions.

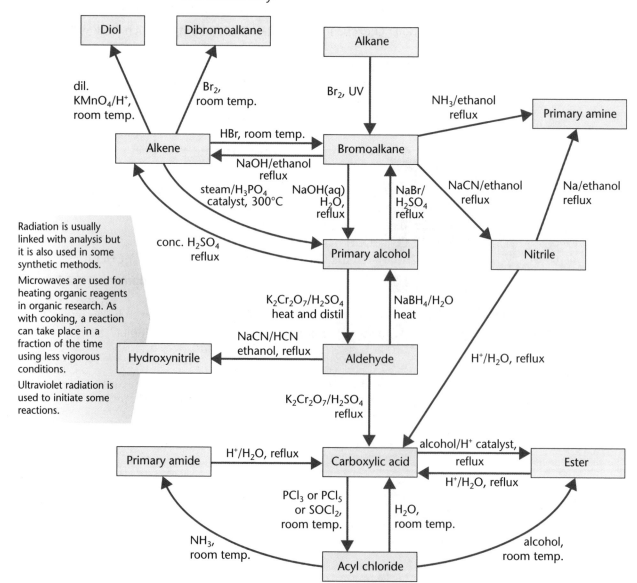

Aromatic synthetic routes

AQA	M4	SALTERS	M5
EDEXCEL	M5	WJEC	M4
OCR	M4	CCEA	M5

Compared with aliphatic organic chemistry at A Level, there are comparatively few aromatic reactions.

Benzene

- Reactions involving the benzene ring are mainly electrophilic substitution.

It is essential, if you are to answer such questions, that you thoroughly learn suitable reagents and conditions for all the reactions in your syllabus.

- Questions are often set in exams asking for reagents, conditions or products.
- More searching problems may expect a synthetic route from a starting material to a final product. The synthetic route may include several stages.

Synthesis of medicines

Synthesis of chiral drugs (OCR and Edexcel only)

The structures of many drugs include a chiral carbon atom. Often the drug is **stereo-specific** with only one of the optical isomers having the desired effect.

Modern synthesis of a pharmaceutical is often carried out to produce a **single optical isomer**. This **reduces** any **risks** on the body from **side effects** of the 'other' optical isomer.

It is difficult to separate optical isomers produced by chemical synthesis and this increases costs. Various strategies have been developed to synthesise just the required optical isomer.

- **Enzymes** or bacteria could be used for any synthetic steps that introduce a chiral centre. Enzymes promote stereo-selectivity.

In the synthesis of stereo-specific drugs, it is important to understand the mechanism of the reaction and how this can help to plan the synthesis.

- Methods of chemical synthesis have been devised that use '**chiral catalysts**'.
- Natural chiral molecules, such as L-amino acids or D-sugars, can be used as starting materials for the synthesis. This makes use of the natural '**chiral pool**'.

Combinatorial chemistry (Edexcel and Salters only)

More effective medicines can be obtained by modifying the structure of existing medicines. **Combinatorial chemistry** is a modern technique that has been adopted by the pharmaceutical industry in drug research.

> This process often includes passing reactants over reagents on polymer supports.

In combinatorial chemistry a **large number** of related compounds are made together so that their potential effectiveness as medicines can be assessed by **large-scale screening**.

Testing and identifying a new medicine (Salters only)

Testing a medicine involves clinical trials to assess a potential new drug:

- Step I – Is it safe?
- Step II – Does it work?
- Step III – Is it better than the standard treatment?

Chemists have a role in:

- designing and making new compounds for use as pharmaceuticals
- ethical testing
- using computer modelling in the design of medicines.

Pharmacologically active compounds (Salters only)

Many medicines and drugs are **pharmacologically active** – they induce a biological interaction of a living organism.

The structure and action of a pharmacologically active compound depends upon:

> The pharmacophore is the part of a molecular structure that is responsible for a particular biological or pharmacological interaction.

- the **pharmacophore** and groups that modify it
- its **interaction** with receptor sites
- the ways that species interact in three dimensions (size, shape, bond formation, orientation).

Identification of the pharmacophore is a key step in devising a synthesis for a new drug.

Retrosynthesis

SALTERS M5

Retrosynthesis is a modern method for devising an organic synthesis.

Conventional synthetic routes are developed by working forwards from starting materials to a target molecule.

- In retrosynthesis an **alternative synthesis** is worked out, **backwards** from a target molecule into simpler structures.
- This procedure is repeated until simple or commercially available starting materials are reached.

Retrosynthesis is useful for identifying **potential synthetic routes** in a logical and straightforward fashion.

The chemist will then **reverse** this process to develop a synthetic route towards the required target molecule.

Sample question and model answer

The structures of the four esters with the molecular formula $C_4H_8O_2$ are shown below.

$$CH_3CH_2COOCH_3 \quad CH_3COOCH_2CH_3 \quad HCOOCH_2CH_2CH_3 \quad HCOOCH(CH_3)_2$$
$$\quad\ \ \textbf{A} \qquad\qquad\qquad \textbf{B} \qquad\qquad\qquad\quad \textbf{C} \qquad\qquad\qquad \textbf{D}$$

(a) For each structure predict the number of peaks in its NMR spectrum and the ratio of the number of protons responsible for each peak.

When we are predicting the number of peaks, we are identifying the number of different types of proton.

In compound **D**, $HCOOCH(CH_3)_2$, both the methyl groups (6H) are equivalent and will have the same chemical shift.

Ester **A**, $CH_3CH_2COOCH_3$, has 3 peaks ✓ in the ratio 3:2:3 ✓

Ester **B**, $CH_3COOCH_2CH_3$, has 3 peaks ✓ in the ratio 3:2:3 ✓

Ester **C**, $HCOOCH_2CH_2CH_3$, has 4 peaks ✓ in the ratio 1:2:2:3 ✓

Ester **D**, $HCOOCH(CH_3)_2$, has 3 peaks ✓ in the ratio 1:1:6 ✓ [8]

(b) The NMR spectrum of one of the four esters is shown below. Integration data is shown by each peak. Analyse the spectrum to find out which ester has produced it. Include all the supporting evidence from the spectrum.

Notice how the answer is methodical, going through each piece of evidence separately.

The combination of a triplet and quartet is a giveaway for a CH_3CH_2 combination.

The integration data and splitting patterns point to either structure **A** or **B**.

The chemical shifts are conclusive though.

The integration data supports either structure A or B:

  There are three types of proton in the ratio 3:2:3 ✓

The splitting pattern supports either structure A or B:

  The CH_3 group at δ = 1.14 ppm has been split into a triplet ✓ by 2 protons on an adjacent carbon atom. ✓

  The CH_2 group at δ = 2.29 ppm has been split into a quartet ✓ by 3 protons on an adjacent carbon atom. ✓

  The CH_3 group at δ = 3.68 ppm is a singlet ✓ so there can be no protons on an adjacent carbon. ✓

From chemical shifts,

  the CH_3 group at δ = 3.68 ppm must be adjacent to an O atom ✓

  the CH_2 group at δ = 2.29 ppm must be adjacent to a C=O group. ✓

Taking all the evidence together:

  the ester must be A, $CH_3CH_2COOCH_3$. ✓ [10]

(c) The IR and mass spectra can also be used to help confirm structures. What key IR absorptions and m/z values would you expect to see in the mass and IR spectra of ester A?

There are 4 marks here. The first is for the key information: the C=O absorption in the IR and the molecular ion peak in the mass spectrum. The second mark is for identification of another key feature.

IR: A C=O absorption at about 1700 cm^{-1}. ✓ A C–O absorption at 1000–1300 cm^{-1}. There should be no absorption above 3000 cm^{-1} as there is no –OH group present. ✓

Other fragment ions could have been chosen.

Mass spectrum: A molecular ion peak at m/z = 88 confirming the molecular mass. ✓ Fragments ions at m/z = 57 from $CH_3CH_2CO^+$; also at m/z = 31 for CH_3O^+. ✓ [4]

[Total: 22]

Practice examination questions

1 Valine, $(CH_3)_2CH(NH_2)COOH$, is an amino acid.

(a) What is the 'R' group in valine? [1]

(b) Valine reacts with an amino acid, **A**, to form the dipeptide below.

(i) Draw a circle around the peptide linkage.

(ii) Draw the structure of the amino acid, **A**.

(iii) Valine can react with the amino acid, **A**, to form a different dipeptide from that shown above. Draw the structural formula of this other dipeptide. [3]

(c) Valine has a chiral centre and can exist as two optical isomers.

(i) State what is meant by a *chiral centre* and explain how a chiral centre gives rise to optical isomerism.

(ii) Draw diagrams to show the two optical isomers of valine. State the bond angle around the chiral centre. [5]

(d) In aqueous solution, valine exists as different ions at different pH values. The zwitterion exists in the pH range 3–10. Draw the displayed formula of the ion of valine present at pH values of 2.0, 7.0 and 12.0. [3]

(e) Compound **B** is an amino acid with the molecular formula $C_3H_7NO_3$.

Draw the structure of amino acid **B**. [1]

[Total: 13]

2 Lactic acid has the structural formula $CH_3CH(OH)COOH$.

(a) What is the systematic name for lactic acid? [1]

(b) Lactic acid has optical isomers.

(i) What structural feature in lactic acid results in optical isomerism?

(ii) How does optical isomerism arise?

(iii) Draw a three-dimensional diagram to show the optical isomers of lactic acid. [4]

(c) Lactic acid can polymerise to form poly(lactic acid)

(i) What type of polymer is poly(lactic acid)?

(ii) Draw a short section of poly(lactic acid) showing two repeat units. [3]

[Total: 8]

3 The repeat units of two polymers **C** and **D** are shown below.

C   **D**

    (a) (i) Draw the structure of the monomer of polymer **C**.

       (ii) Name the type of polymerisation. [2]

    (b) (i) Draw the structure of the two monomers of polymer **D**.

       (ii) Name the type of polymerisation. [3]

    (c) Suggest why polymer **D** would be more likely to be hydrolysed than polymer **C**. [2]

[Total: 7]

4 Compounds **E** and **F** are both diols with the molecular formula $C_4H_{10}O_2$.

    (a) The proton NMR spectrum of a diol **E**, $C_4H_{10}O_2$, is shown below. The numbers by each peak represent the integration trace. The peak at $\delta = 3.65$ ppm disappears when the spectrum is run a second time with D_2O added.

      (i) How many different types of proton are present in the diol?

      (ii) The peaks at $\delta = 1.63$ ppm and $\delta = 0.90$ ppm result from a single alkyl group. Identify this group and explain the splitting pattern.

      (iii) What can be deduced from the single peak at $\delta = 1.32$ ppm?

      (iv) What can be concluded about the peak at $\delta = 3.65$ ppm?

      (v) Show the structure of the diol **E**. [9]

    (b) The proton NMR spectrum diol **F**, run in D_2O, is shown below.

      (i) What can be concluded about the two peaks?

      (ii) Show the structure of the diol **F**. [5]

[Total: 14]

Chapter 6

Synoptic assessment

What is synoptic assessment?

Synoptic assessment emphasises your understanding and your application of the principles included in your chemistry course.

Part of your chemistry course is assessed using **synoptic questions**. These are written so that you can **draw together** knowledge, understanding and skills learned in **different parts** of AS and A2 Chemistry.

Synoptic assessment takes place mainly in **module exams** but part may be assessed in coursework.

What type of questions will be asked?

You will need to answer **two** main types of synoptic question.

You make the links between different areas of chemistry yourself. You choose and use the context for your answer.

1 **You make links** and **use connections** between different areas of chemistry. Some examples are given below.

Using examples drawn from different parts of your chemistry course:
- discuss the role of a lone pair in chemistry...
- discuss the chemistry of water...
- compare the common types of chemical bonding...

The context has been made for you. Often this will be a situation or will involve data that you will not have seen before.

2 **You use ideas and skills** which **permeate chemistry**.
This type of question will be more structured and you are unlikely to have as much choice in how you construct your answer.

Your task is to interpret any information using the 'big ideas' of chemistry.

Examples of themes that permeate chemistry are shown below:
- formulae, moles, equations and oxidation states
- chemical bonding and structure
- periodicity
- reaction rates, chemical equilibrium and enthalpy changes.

How will you gain synoptic skills?

A synoptic question may present you with a new piece of information.

You may be expected to calculate formulae from data, write correct formulae, balance equations and perform quantitative calculations using the mole concept, use knowledge of the Periodic Table to predict reactions of unfamiliar elements or compounds, etc.

Luckily chemistry is very much a synoptic subject. Throughout your study of chemistry, you apply many of the ideas and skills learnt during AS Chemistry or your GCSE course.

In studying A2 Chemistry, you will have been using synoptic skills naturally, probably without realising it. You certainly can make little real progress in chemistry without a sound grasp of concepts such as equations, the mole, structure and bonding!

Worked synoptic question

Here, some of the big ideas of chemistry are being tested: formulae, bonding, redox, moles, equations. These will always appear on an exam paper with synoptic questions.

You have nothing to fear from this type of question provided that your chemistry is sound.

Structured type question

In its reactions, sulfuric acid, H_2SO_4, can behave as an acid, an oxidising agent and as a dehydrating agent.

The displayed formula of pure sulfuric acid is shown below.

$$H-O \diagdown \diagup O \\ S \\ H-O \diagup \diagdown O$$

(a) The boiling point of pure sulfuric acid, at 270°C, is higher than might be expected.

Suggest why the boiling point of sulfuric acid is higher than might be expected. Explain your reasoning. Show a diagram in your answer.

Sulfuric acid molecules form hydrogen bonds ✓

$$H-O \diagdown \diagup O \text{---------} H-O \diagdown \diagup O \\ S \qquad S \\ H-O \diagup \diagdown O \text{---------} H-O \diagup \diagdown O ✓$$

hydrogen bonds break (on boiling) ✓

[3]

Nice clues in the question.

You are given the structure of sulfuric acid for a reason. You are being tested on whether you can apply hydrogen bonding to a new situation.

This is not much different from water's H-bonding!

(b) Dilute sulfuric acid takes part in the typical acid reactions, reacting with metals, carbonates and bases.

Write balanced equations for reactions of sulfuric acid with

(i) a metal $\qquad Mg + H_2SO_4 \longrightarrow MgSO_4 + H_2$

(ii) a carbonate $\quad MgCO_3 + H_2SO_4 \longrightarrow MgSO_4 + CO_2 + H_2O$

(iii) a base $\qquad 2NaOH + H_2SO_4 \longrightarrow Na_2SO_4 + 2H_2O$ [3]

Just keep your nerve when writing equations. You can choose any reasonable examples.

Do think about ionic charges. Many students blindly assume that a sulfate ion has a 1– charge but how can this be so if we have H_2SO_4 with $2H^+$ ions?

(c) Concentrated sulfuric acid will readily oxidise halide ions to the halogen.

Equation 5.1 represents the unbalanced equation for the oxidation of iodide ions by sulfuric acid.

$$H^+ + SO_4^{2-} + I^- \longrightarrow I_2 + H_2S + H_2O \qquad \text{Equation 5.1}$$

(i) Determine the oxidation numbers of sulfur and iodine on either side of the equation.

$$SO_4^{2-} : +6 \longrightarrow H_2S: -2 ✓$$

$$I^-:-1 \longrightarrow I_2: 0 ✓$$ [2]

(ii) Balance Equation 5.1

$$10H^+ + SO_4^{2-} + 8I^- \longrightarrow 4I_2 + H_2S + 4H_2O ✓$$ [1]

In (i), you are just using oxidation number rules.

– this should be 2 easy marks.

(ii) is far harder.

You have to make sure that there is the same oxidation number change up and down.

Here, each S goes down by 8 from +6 to – 2.

Each I goes up by 1 from –1 to 0 ... so we need 8 x I

Finally balance the H_2O and finally the H^+.

Worked synoptic question *(continued)*

Here you are provided with information and you must use your chemical knowledge and understanding to solve the problem.

Use the information – the whole question is about **dehydration** (loss of water) caused by sulfuric acid.

Good advice is to look for the obvious. If your answer looks like some chemistry that you have never seen before, then you have probably made a mistake!

Key points here:

A must be made out of H, C, or O.

B is black. What do you know that is black?

C is hard but is still based on dehydration.

(d) Concentrated sulfuric acid reacts with many organic compounds, forming water as one of the products.

For example, sulfuric acid dehydrates ethanol by eliminating water to form ethane.

$$C_2H_5OH \longrightarrow C_2H_4 + H_2O$$

Three other examples are shown below.

- Sulfuric acid dehydrates methanoic acid to form a gas, **A**, with the same molar mass as ethene.
- Sulfuric acid dehydrates sucrose, $C_{12}H_{22}O_{11}$, to form a black solid, **B**.
- Sulfuric acid dehydrates ethane-1,2-diol to form a compound **C** with a molar mass of 88 g mol^{-1}.

Suggest the identity of **A**, **B** and **C**. Write equations for each reaction and deduce the structural formula of compound **C**.

A: CO ✓ $HCOOH \longrightarrow CO + H_2O$ ✓

B: C ✓ $C_{12}H_{22}O_{11} \longrightarrow 12C + 11H_2O$ ✓

C: $C_4H_8O_2$ ✓ $2C_2H_6O_2 \longrightarrow C_4H_8O_2 + 2H_2O$ ✓

Structure:

 ✓

[7]

[Total: 16]

OCR Unifying concepts Q5 Jan 2007

Practice examination questions

1 Organic acids occur widely in nature.

(a) Butanoic acid, $CH_3(CH_2)_2COOH$, is a straight-chain organic acid, largely responsible for the odour of rancid butter.

Caprylic acid is a straight-chain organic acid. It is produced in the body in small amounts as an antifungal agent in human sweat.

(i) Some caprylic acid was isolated from human sweat and analysed. The sample of caprylic acid had the percentage composition by mass:

C, 66.7%; H, 11.1%; O, 22.2%. $M_r = 144$.

Calculate the molecular formula of caprylic acid and suggest its structural formula.

(ii) Tracking dogs are trained to follow odours such as the characteristic blend of organic acids in the sweat from a person's feet. A dog is able to detect extremely small quantities of these acids.

Sweat containing equal amounts of butanoic and caprylic acids produces more butanoic acid vapour than caprylic acid vapour.

Suggest a reason for this. Explain your answer. [6]

(b) Compound **A** is a straight chain organic acid. A chemist analysed a sample of acid **A** by the procedure below.

The chemist first prepared a 250 cm³ solution of **A** by dissolving 10.8 g of **A** in water.

In a titration, 25.00 cm³ 0.500 mol dm⁻³ NaOH were neutralised by exactly 21.40 cm³ of solution **A**.

(i) Calculate the pH of the NaOH(aq) used in the titration.
$K_w = 1.00 \times 10^{-14}$ mol² dm⁻⁶.

(ii) Use the results to calculate the molar mass of acid **A** and suggest its identity. [8]

[Total: 14]

OCR Unifying concepts Q4 Jan 2003

2 *Refer to data on Page 169 for this question.*

Compounds **A** to **G** are all isomers with the molecular formula $C_6H_{12}O_2$.

(a) Isomer **A**, $C_6H_{12}O_2$, is a neutral compound and is formed by the reaction between compounds **X** and **Y** in the presence of a small amount of concentrated sulfuric acid.

X and **Y** can both be formed from propanal by different redox reactions.

X has an absorption in its infra-red spectrum at 1750 cm⁻¹.

Deduce the structural formulae of **A**, **X** and **Y**. Give suitable reagents, in each case, for the formation of **X** and **Y** from propanal and state the role of concentrated sulfuric acid in the formation of **A**. [8]

(b) Isomers **B**, **C**, **D** and **E** all react with aqueous sodium carbonate to produce carbon dioxide.

Deduce the structural formulae of the three isomers that contain an asymmetric carbon atom.

The fourth isomer has only three singlet peaks in its proton NMR spectrum. Deduce the structural formula of this isomer and label it **E**. [4]

(c) Isomer **F**, $C_6H_{12}O_2$, has the structural formula shown below, on which some of the protons have been labelled.

$$H_3C - \overset{a}{C}H_2 - O - CH_2 - \overset{b}{C}H_2 - \overset{\overset{\displaystyle O}{\|}}{C} - CH_3$$

A proton NMR spectrum is obtained for **F**. Predict a value of δ for the protons labelled *a* and also for those labelled *b*. State and account for the splitting patterns of the peaks assigned to the protons *a* and *b*. [6]

(d) Isomer **G**, $C_6H_{12}O_2$, contains six carbon atoms in a ring. It has an absorption in its infra-red spectrum at 3270 cm⁻¹ and shows only three different proton environments in its proton NMR spectrum. Deduce a structural formula for **G**. [2]

[Total: 20]

AQA Further Physical and Organic Chemistry Q6 Jun 2003

Practice examination answers

Chapter 1 Rates and equilibria

1 (a) (i) 1st order with respect to H_2O_2 ✓
Double concentration of H_2O_2, rate doubles ✓
1st order with respect to I^- ✓
7 times concentration of I^-, rate x 7 ✓
Zero order with respect to H^+ ✓
Double concentration of H^+, rate stays constant ✓

(ii) Rate = $k[H_2O_2][I^-]$ ✓
2.8×10^{-2} dm^3 mol^{-1} s^{-1} ✓✓ [9]

(b) (i) The slowest step of a multi-step process ✓

(ii) $H_2O_2 + I^- \longrightarrow H_2O + IO^-$ ✓ [2]

[Total: 11]

2 (a) (i) Rate = $k[A]^2[B]$ ✓

(ii) 3 ✓

(iii) 27 ✓

(iv) $k = 3.14 \times 10^{-3}$ dm^6 mol^{-2} s^{-1} ✓✓ [5]

(b) (i) H^+ is a catalyst ✓
H^+ appears in the rate equation but not the overall equation ✓

(ii) $CH_3COCH_3(aq) + H^+(aq) \longrightarrow [CH_3COHCH_3(aq)]^+$ ✓ [3]

[Total: 8]

3 (a) $K_c = \dfrac{[CH_3COOH]\,[CH_3CH_2OH]}{[CH_3COOCH_2CH_3]\,[H_2O]}$ ✓

$K_c = 0.26$ ✓; No units ✓ [3]

(b) (i) Equilibrium would move to the left ✓ to counteract the added CH_3CH_2OH ✓

(ii) No effect ✓ K_c only changes with temperature ✓ [4]

[Total: 7]

4 (a) (i) $[H_2(g)]$, 0.44 mol dm^{-3}; ✓ $[I_2(g)]$, 0.02 mol dm^{-3}; ✓
$[HI(g)]$, 0.32 mol dm^{-3} ✓

(ii) $K_c = \dfrac{[HI(g)]^2}{[H_2(g)]\,[I_2(g)]}$ ✓ $= \dfrac{0.32^2}{0.44 \times 0.02} = 11.6$ ✓ no units ✓ [6]

(b) Equilibrium moves to left ✓; Forward reaction is exothermic ✓ [2]

[Total: 8]

5 (a) Proton donor ✓ [1]

(b) $HCOOH + HNO_3 \rightleftharpoons HCOOH_2^+ + NO_3^-(aq)$ ✓
HCOOH is a base because it accepts a proton ✓ [2]

(c) (i) pH = 0.75 ✓

(ii) $K_w = [H^+(aq)][OH^-(aq)]$ ✓
$[H^+(aq)] = 1.0 \times 10^{-14}/0.372 = 2.69 \times 10^{-14}$ mol dm^{-3} ✓ pH = 13.57 ✓

(iii) $K_a = \dfrac{[H^+(aq)][HCOO^-(aq)]}{[HCOOH(aq)]} = \dfrac{[H^+(aq)]^2}{[HCOOH(aq)]}$ ✓

$[H^+(aq)] = \sqrt{(1.6 \times 10^{-4} \times 0.263)} = 6.49 \times 10^{-3}$ mol dm^{-3} ✓ pH = 2.19 ✓

(iv) $[H^+(aq)] = K_a \times [HCOOH(aq)]/[HCOO^-(aq)]$ ✓
$[H^+(aq)] = 1.6 \times 10^{-4} \times 0.255/0.325 = 1.26 \times 10^{-4}$ mol dm^{-3} ✓
pH = 3.90 ✓ [10]

[Total: 13]

6 (a) (i) A strong acid completely dissociates to donate protons.
A weak acid partially dissociates to donate protons. ✓
(ii) Proton acceptor ✓ [2]

(b) (i) $[OH^-(aq)] = 1.50 \times 10^{-3} \times 1000/25 = 0.060$ mol dm^{-3} ✓
$K_w = [H^+(aq)][OH^-(aq)]$ ✓
$[H^+(aq)] = 1.0 \times 10^{-14}/0.060 = 1.67 \times 10^{-13}$ mol dm^{-3} ✓ pH = 12.78 ✓

(ii) Amount of HCl added = 0.0125 mol ✓
Amount of HCl remaining = 0.0125 − 1.50 × 10^{-3} = 0.011 mol ✓
[HCl] = 0.011 × 1000/75 = 0.147 mol dm^{-3} ✓ pH = 0.83 ✓ [8]

(c) $[H^+(aq)] = 10^{-pH} = 0.0302$ mol dm^{-3} ✓
amount of HCl = 0.0302 × 25/1000 = 7.55 × 10^{-4} mol ✓
$[H^+(aq)]$ in diluted solution = 7.55 × 10^{-4} × 1000/40 = 0.0189 mol dm^{-3} ✓
pH = 1.72 ✓ [4]

[Total: 14]

Chapter 2 Energy changes in chemistry

1 (a) (i)

definition	letter
1st ionisation energy of potassium	B
1st electron affinity of bromine	F ✓
the enthalpy of atomisation of potassium	C
the enthalpy of atomisation of bromine	A ✓
the lattice enthalpy of potassium bromide	E
the enthalpy of formation of potassium bromide	D ✓

(ii) −394 − (89 + 419 + 112 −325) ✓ = −689 kJ mol^{-1} ✓ [5]

(b) (i) KI is less exothermic because I$^-$ has a smaller charge density ✓ and
attraction between K$^+$ and I$^-$ ions is weaker ✓

(ii) CaBr$_2$ is more exothermic because Ca^{2+} has a greater charge density ✓ and
attraction between Ca^{2+} and Br$^-$ ions is stronger ✓ [4]

[Total: 9]

2 (a) (i) Mg^{2+}(g) + 2Cl$^-$(g) $\longrightarrow$ MgCl$_2$(s) ✓
(ii) Mg^{2+}(g) + aq $\longrightarrow$ Mg^{2+}(aq) ✓
(iii) MgCl$_2$(s) + aq $\longrightarrow$ Mg^{2+}(aq) + 2Cl$^-$(aq) ✓ [3]

(b) ΔH(solution) = −(lattice enthalpy) + Σ(enthalpy changes of hydration) ✓
= −(−2526) + (−1891 + 2 × −384) ✓ = −133 kJ mol^{-1} ✓ [3]

[Total: 6]

3 $\Delta H_r = \Sigma \Delta H_f(\text{products}) - \Sigma \Delta H_f(\text{reactants})$
  $= (-1676) - (-602)$ ✓
  $= -1074 \text{ kJ mol}^{-1}$ ✓
  $\Delta S_r = \Sigma S (\text{products}) - \Sigma S (\text{reactants})$
  $= [(2 \times 81) + 51] - [27 + (2 \times 28)]$ ✓
  $= 130 \text{ J K mol}^{-1}$ ✓ $= 0.13 \text{ kJ mol}^{-1}$ ✓
  $\Delta G = \Delta H - T\Delta S$ ✓
  $\Delta G = -1074 - 298 \times 0.13 = -1113 \text{ kJ mol}^{-1}$ ✓
  Reaction is feasible at 298 K because $\Delta G < 0$ ✓

[Total: 8]

4 (a) 298 K; $[Ni^{2+}(aq)]$ 1 mol dm^{-3} ✓; $[Fe^{2+}(aq)]$ $[Fe^{3+}(aq)]$ are the same ✓ [2]

  (b) It allows ions to flow between half-cells ✓ [1]

  (c) (i) 1.02 V ✓

   (ii) Electrons flow along wire from nickel half-cell ✓

   (iii) Ni is − electrode; Pt is + electrode ✓ [3]

  (d) (i) $Ni \longrightarrow Ni^{2+} + 2e^-$ ✓
    $Fe^{3+} + e^- \longrightarrow Fe^{2+}$ ✓

   (ii) $2Fe^{3+} + Ni \longrightarrow 2Fe^{2+} + Ni^{2+}$ ✓ [3]

  (e) In Ni redox equilibrium, increase in $[Ni^{2+}(aq)]$ shifts equilibrium to the right.
  Electrons are less available and electrode potential becomes less negative. ✓
  Difference in cell potentials becomes less and cell potential will decrease. ✓ [2]

[Total: 11]

5 (a) (i) $Mn^{3+}(aq)$ ✓

   (ii) $Mn^{3+}(aq)$ ✓ I$^-$ must provide electrons and have the more negative $E^{\ominus}$
    (+0.54). ✓ The more positive $E^{\ominus}$ system (+1.49 V) will gain electrons. ✓ [4]

  (b) 0.66 V ✓
    $4V^{2+}(aq) + O_2(g) + 2H_2O(l) \longrightarrow 4OH^-(aq) + 4V^{3+}(aq)$ ✓✓ [3]

[Total: 7]

Chapter 3 The Periodic Table

1 (a) MgO, Al_2O_3, SiO_2; ✓ P_4O_{10}, SO_3 ✓ [2]

  (b) The oxidation number matches the number of outer shell electrons involved in
  bonding to oxygen. ✓ [1]

  (c) $MgO(s) + H_2O(l) \longrightarrow Mg(OH)_2(aq)$ ✓
    Al_2O_3 and SiO_2 are insoluble ✓
    $P_4O_{10}(s) + 6H_2O(l) \longrightarrow 4H_3PO_4(aq)$ ✓
    $SO_3(l) + H_2O(l) \longrightarrow H_2SO_4(aq)$ ✓ [4]

  (d) Giant ionic oxides form alkaline solutions ✓
  Giant covalent oxides are insoluble ✓
  Simple molecular oxides form acidic solutions ✓ [3]

[Total: 10]

2 (a) Ni: $1s^2 2s^2 2s^6 3s^2 3p^6 3d^8 4s^2$ ✓; Ni^{2+}: $1s^2 2s^2 2s^6 3s^2 3p^6 3d^8$ ✓ [2]

  (b) A d-block element has its highest energy electron in a d sub-shell. ✓
  A transition element has at least one ion with a partially filled d sub-shell. ✓ [2]

(c) (i) Lone pair of electrons on oxygen atom ✓

(ii) Ion $[Ni(H_2O)_6]^{2+}$ ✓

(iii) Covalent bonding in H_2O ✓ and coordinate bonding from water ligands to the Ni^{2+} ion. ✓

(iv) Octahedral ✓ ; 109.5° ✓   [6]

(d) (i) $Ni(OH)_2$ or $Ni(OH)_2(H_2O)_4$ ✓
$Ni^{2+}(aq) + 2OH^-(aq) \longrightarrow Ni(OH)_2(s)$ ✓
or $[Ni(H_2O)_6]^{2+}(aq) + 2OH^-(aq) \longrightarrow Ni(OH)_2(H_2O)_4(s) + 2H_2O(l)$

(ii) $[NiCl_4]^{2-}$ ✓

(iii) $[Ni(H_2O)_6]^{2+}(aq) + 6NH_3(aq) \longrightarrow [Ni(NH_3)_6]^{2+}(aq) + 6H_2O(l)$ ✓
ligand substitution ✓   [5]

[Total: 15]

3 (a) (i) +6 ✓

(ii) +1 ✓

(iii) +4 ✓   [3]

(b) $2Cr^{3+} + 10OH^- + 3H_2O_2 \longrightarrow 2CrO_4^{2-} + 8H_2O$ ✓   [1]

(c) Vanadium as V_2O_5 in the contact process for the manufacture SO_3 for H_2SO_4 ✓
Iron in the Haber process for the manufacture of NH_3 ✓   [2]

[Total: 6]

4 (a) (i) +7 ✓

(ii) $5H_2O_2 + 2MnO_4^- + 6H^+ \longrightarrow 5O_2 + 8H_2O + 2Mn^{2+}$ ✓   [2]

(b) Reducing agent ✓   [1]

(c) Amount of $KMnO_4 = 0.0150 \times \dfrac{23.80}{1000} = 3.57 \times 10^{-4}$ mol ✓

Amount of H_2O_2 that reacted $= 2.5 \times 3.57 \times 10^{-4} = 8.925 \times 10^{-4}$ mol ✓

Concentration of $H_2O_2 = \dfrac{1000}{25.0} \times 8.925 \times 10^{-4} = 0.0357$ mol ✓   [3]

[Total: 6]

5 (a) (i) A coordinate (dative covalent bond) forms ✓ between a lone pair on a ligand and the central metal ion. ✓

(ii) Bidentate ligand ✓   [3]

(b) (i) +3 ✓

(ii) $1s^2 2s^2 2s^6 3s^2 3p^6 3d^7$ ✓   [2]

(c) (i) 6 ✓

(ii) Octahedral ✓

(iii) Add an excess of 1,2-diaminoethane or $NH_2CH_2CH_2NH_2$ ✓
$[Ni(H_2O)_6]^{2+} + 3NH_2CH_2CH_2NH_2 \rightarrow [Ni(NH_2CH_2CH_2NH_2)_3]^{2+} + 6H_2O$ ✓   [4]

[Total: 9]

Chapter 4 Chemistry of organic functional groups

1. (a) C : H : O = 66.7/12 : 11.1/1 : 22.2/16 ✓
   Molecular formula = C_4H_8O ✓ [2]
   (b) $CH_3CH_2COCH_3$ ✓; $CH_3CH_2CH_2CHO$ ✓; $(CH_3)_2CHCHO$ ✓ [3]
   (c) 2,4-dinitrophenylhydrazine ✓ orange precipitate ✓ [2]
   (d) Tollens' reagent ✓. Reacts with butanal and methylpropanal ✓
   Silver mirror forms ✓ (or $H_2SO_4/K_2Cr_2O_7$; from orange to green) [3]
   (e) Product: $CH_3CH_2CH(OH)CH_3$ ✓ formed from $CH_3CH_2COCH_3$ ✓ [2]

   [Total: 12]

2. (a) (i) Ethyl propanoate ✓
       (ii) E: CH_3CH_2OH ✓
            F: $CH_3CH_2COO^-Na^+$ ✓✓ (1 mark if CH_3CH_2COOH) [4]
   (b) (i) HCOO—CH_2
           | ✓
           HCOO—CH_2
       (ii) Concentrated H_2SO_4 ✓ [2]
   (c)

   [3]

   [Total: 9]

3. (a) (i) Molar ratio C:H = 90.56/12 : 9.44/1 ✓
            Empirical formula = C_4H_5 ✓
            Molecular formula = C_8H_{10} ✓
       (ii)

   [7]
   (b) (i) 1,4-dimethylbenzene ✓
       (ii)

   [2]

   [Total: 9]

4. (a) (i) Electrophilic substitution ✓
       (ii) Concentrated HNO_3 and concentrated H_2SO_4 ✓ [2]
   (b) (i) Tin and concentrated HCl ✓
       (ii)

   [3]

(c) (i) Reagents $NaNO_2$/HCl(aq) ✓ Conditions: <10°C ✓

(ii)

[3]

(d) (i) Phenol, C_6H_5OH ✓

(ii)

[2]

[Total: 10]

5 (a) Compound **A**: $CH_3CH_2CH_2COOH$ ✓
Compound **B**: $(CH_3)_2CHOH$ ✓ [2]

(b) Step 1: H_2SO_4/$K_2Cr_2O_7$ ✓ reflux ✓ oxidation ✓
Step 2: $NaBH_4$ ✓ with H_2O or ethanol ✓ reduction ✓
Step 3: Conc. H_2SO_4 catalyst ✓ reflux ✓ esterification ✓ [9]

[Total: 11]

Chapter 5 Polymers, analysis and synthesis

1 (a) $(CH_3)_2CH$ ✓ [1]

(b) (i)

(ii)

(iii)

[3]

(c) (i) A chiral carbon atom has **four** different groups attached to it. ✓ It provides two possible forms that are non-superimposable mirror images of one another. ✓

(ii)

Bond angle = 109.5° ✓ [5]

(d)

$H_3N^+ - C - C$ (with H above C, O double bond, OH) $(CH_3)_2CH$ pH = 2

$H_3N^+ - C - C$ (with H above C, O double bond, O$^-$) $(CH_3)_2CH$ pH = 7

$H_2N - C - C$ (with H above C, O double bond, O$^-$) $(CH_3)_2CH$ pH = 12 ✓✓✓ [3]

(e)

$H_2N - C - C$ (with H above C, O double bond, OH) CH_2OH ✓

[1]

[Total: 13]

2 (a) 2-hydroxypropanoic acid ✓   [1]

(b) (i) A chiral carbon with four different groups attached ✓

(ii) Optical isomers are non-superimposable mirror images ✓

(iii)

COOH C H H_3C OH   COOH C H   HO CH_3 ✓✓   [4]

(c) (i) Polyester or a condensation polymer ✓

(ii)

$-O - C - C - O - C - C -$ (with H and O double bonds above, CH_3 below each)   ester link ✓ structure ✓   [3]

[Total: 8]

3 (a) (i)

$C=C$ (H, H above; H_3C, H below) ✓

(ii) Addition ✓   [2]

(b) (i)

$H_2N - C - C - NH_2$ (with H, H above; CH_3, CH_3 below) $HO - C - \bigcirc - C - OH$ (with O double bonds) ✓✓

(ii) Condensation ✓   [3]

(c) Polymer **D** has a polar CONH group. Polymer **C** is non-polar. ✓
Polar group in polymer **D** will attract water or hydroxide ions. ✓   [2]

[Total: 7]

4 (a) (i) 4 ✓

(ii) C_2H_5 ✓
The CH_2 group at δ = 1.63 ppm is split into a quartet ✓ by 3 protons on an adjacent carbon. ✓
The CH_3 group at δ = 0.90 ppm is split into a triplet ✓ by 2 protons on an adjacent carbon. ✓

(iii) A CH_3 group with no protons on an adjacent carbon. ✓

(iv) Two equivalent OH protons as the absorption disappears with D_2O. ✓

(v) $CH_3CH_2C(OH)_2CH_3$ ✓   [9]

(b) (i) There are 8H atoms with a peak ratio of 1:3. The peak at $\delta = 3.64$ ppm is from a CH_2-O ✓ with no protons on an adjacent carbon atom ✓
The peak at $\delta = 1.24$ ppm is from two equivalent CH_3 groups ✓ with no protons on an adjacent carbon atom. ✓

(ii) $(CH_3)_2C(OH)CH_2OH$ ✓ [5]

[Total: 14]

Chapter 6 Synoptic assessment

1 (a) (i) $C : H : O = \dfrac{66.7}{12} / : \dfrac{11.1}{1} : \dfrac{22.2}{16}$ ✓

$= 5.56 : 11.1 : 1.39 = 4 : 8 : 1$
empirical formula $= C_4H_8O$ ✓
$48 + 8 + 16 = 72$ which is half of M_r
Therefore molecular formula $= C_8H_{16}O_2$ ✓
Structural formula $= CH_3(CH_2)_6COOH$ ✓

(ii) caprylic acid has a longer carbon chain and contains more electrons ✓
caprylic acid has more van der Waals' forces ✓ [6]

(b) (i) $[H^+(aq)] = \dfrac{K_w}{[OH^-(aq)]}$ ✓ $= \dfrac{1.00 \times 10^{-14}}{0.500}$

$= 2.00 \times 10^{-14}$ mol dm^{-3} ✓
$pH = -\log[H^+(aq)] = -\log(2.00 \times 10^{-14}) = 13.70$ ✓

(ii) moles NaOH in 25.00 cm^3 = moles NaOH = 0.0125 mol ✓
moles **A** in 21.40 cm^3 = moles NaOH = 0.0125 mol ✓
moles **A** in 250 cm^3 = $\dfrac{0.0125 \times 250}{21.40}$ = 0.146 mol ✓

molar mass of **A** = $\dfrac{10.8}{0.146}$ = 74 g mol^{-1} ✓

Therefore **A** is propanoic acid / CH_3CH_2COOH ✓ [8]

[Total: 14]

2 (a) **A** = $CH_3CH_2COOCH_2CH_2CH_3$ ✓
X = CH_3CH_2COOH ✓
Y = $CH_3CH_2CH_2OH$ ✓
For propanal $\longrightarrow$ **X**, H_2SO_4 ✓ and $K_2Cr_2O_7$ ✓
For propanal $\longrightarrow$ **Y**, $NaBH_4$ ✓ in ethanol or water ✓
Concentrated H_2SO_4 is a catalyst ✓ [8]

(b) 3 isomers with asymmetric carbon atom: **B**, **C** and **D**
$CH_3CH_2CH_2CH(CH_3)COOH$ ✓
$CH_3CH_2CH(CH_3)CH_2COOH$ ✓
$(CH_3)_2CHCH(CH_3)COOH$ ✓
E: $(CH_3)_3CCH_2COOH$ ✓ [4]

(c) a: $\delta = 3.3-4.3$ ppm ✓; b: $\delta = 2.0-2.9$ ppm ✓
a: splitting will be a quartet ✓ as there is an adjacent CH_3 ✓
b: splitting will be a triplet ✓ as there is an adjacent CH_2 ✓ [6]

(d)

✓ (structure) ✓ (2 x OH groups at correct positions) [2]

[Total: 20]

Periodic Table

The Periodic Table

Key:
- relative atomic mass — 1.0
- atomic symbol — H
- atomic number — 1
- name — Hydrogen

1	2												3	4	5	6	7	0
																		4.0 **He** 2 Helium
6.9 **Li** 3 Lithium	9.0 **Be** 4 Beryllium												10.8 **B** 5 Boron	12.0 **C** 6 Carbon	14.0 **N** 7 Nitrogen	16.0 **O** 8 Oxygen	19.0 **F** 9 Fluorine	20.2 **Ne** 10 Neon
23.0 **Na** 11 Sodium	24.3 **Mg** 12 Magnesium												27.0 **Al** 13 Aluminium	28.1 **Si** 14 Silicon	31.0 **P** 15 Phosphorus	32.1 **S** 16 Sulfur	35.5 **Cl** 17 Chlorine	39.9 **Ar** 18 Argon
39.1 **K** 19 Potassium	40.1 **Ca** 20 Calcium	45.0 **Sc** 21 Scandium	47.9 **Ti** 22 Titanium	50.9 **V** 23 Vanadium	52.0 **Cr** 24 Chromium	54.9 **Mn** 25 Manganese	55.8 **Fe** 26 Iron	58.9 **Co** 27 Cobalt	58.7 **Ni** 28 Nickel	63.5 **Cu** 29 Copper	65.4 **Zn** 30 Zinc		69.7 **Ga** 31 Gallium	72.6 **Ge** 32 Germanium	74.9 **As** 33 Arsenic	79.0 **Se** 34 Selenium	79.9 **Br** 35 Bromine	83.8 **Kr** 36 Krypton
85.5 **Rb** 37 Rubidium	87.6 **Sr** 38 Strontium	88.9 **Y** 39 Yttrium	91.2 **Zr** 40 Zirconium	92.9 **Nb** 41 Niobium	95.9 **Mo** 42 Molybdenum	[98] **Tc** 43 Technetium	101.1 **Ru** 44 Ruthenium	102.9 **Rh** 45 Rhodium	106.4 **Pd** 46 Palladium	107.9 **Ag** 47 Silver	112.4 **Cd** 48 Cadmium		114.8 **In** 49 Indium	118.7 **Sn** 50 Tin	121.8 **Sb** 51 Antimony	127.6 **Te** 52 Tellurium	126.9 **I** 53 Iodine	131.3 **Xe** 54 Xenon
132.9 **Cs** 55 Caesium	137.3 **Ba** 56 Barium	138.9 **La*** 57 Lanthanum	178.5 **Hf** 72 Hafnium	180.9 **Ta** 73 Tantalum	183.8 **W** 74 Tungsten	186.2 **Re** 75 Rhenium	190.2 **Os** 76 Osmium	192.2 **Ir** 77 Iridium	195.1 **Pt** 78 Platinum	197.0 **Au** 79 Gold	200.6 **Hg** 80 Mercury		204.4 **Tl** 81 Thallium	207.2 **Pb** 82 Lead	209.0 **Bi** 83 Bismuth	[209] **Po** 84 Polonium	[210] **At** 85 Astatine	[222] **Rn** 86 Radon
[223] **Fr** 87 Francium	[226] **Ra** 88 Radium	[227] **Ac*** 89 Actinium	[261] **Rf** 104 Rutherfordium	[262] **Db** 105 Dubnium	[266] **Sg** 106 Seaborgium	[264] **Bh** 107 Bohrium	[277] **Hs** 108 Hassium	[268] **Mt** 109 Meitnerium	[271] **Ds** 110 Darmstadtium	[272] **Rg** 111 Roentgenium								

Elements with atomic numbers 112–116 have been reported but not fully authenticated

lanthanides

140.1 **Ce** 58 Cerium	140.9 **Pr** 59 Praseodymium	144.2 **Nd** 60 Neodymium	144.9 **Pm** 61 Promethium	150.4 **Sm** 62 Samarium	152.0 **Eu** 63 Europium	157.2 **Gd** 64 Gadolinium	158.9 **Tb** 65 Terbium	162.5 **Dy** 66 Dysprosium	164.9 **Ho** 67 Holmium	167.3 **Er** 68 Erbium	168.9 **Tm** 69 Thulium	173.0 **Yb** 70 Ytterbium	175.0 **Lu** 71 Lutetium

actinides

232.0 **Th** 90 Thorium	[231] **Pa** 91 Protactinium	238.1 **U** 92 Uranium	[237] **Np** 93 Neptunium	[242] **Pu** 94 Plutonium	[243] **Am** 95 Americium	[247] **Cm** 96 Curium	[245] **Bk** 97 Berkelium	[251] **Cf** 98 Californium	[254] **Es** 99 Einsteinium	[253] **Fm** 100 Fermium	[256] **Md** 101 Mendelevium	[254] **No** 102 Nobelium	[257] **Lr** 103 Lawrencium

Index